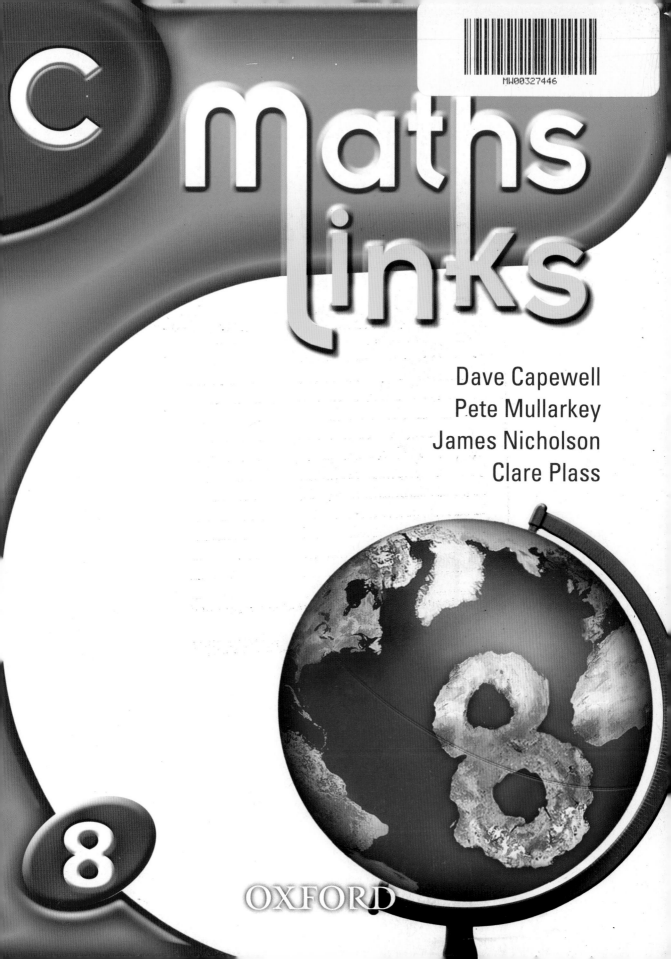

C maths links

Dave Capewell
Pete Mullarkey
James Nicholson
Clare Plass

8

OXFORD

OXFORD
UNIVERSITY PRESS

Great Clarendon Street, Oxford OX2 6DP

Oxford University Press is a department of the University of Oxford.
It furthers the University's objective of excellence in research, scholarship, and education by
publishing worldwide in

Oxford   New York

Auckland   Cape Town   Dar es Salaam   Hong Kong   Karachi
Kuala Lumpur   Madrid   Melbourne   Mexico City   Nairobi
New Delhi   Shanghai   Taipei   Toronto

With offices in

Argentina   Austria   Brazil   Chile   Czech Republic   France   Greece
Guatemala   Hungary   Italy   Japan   Poland   Portugal   Singapore
South Korea   Switzerland   Thailand   Turkey   Ukraine   Vietnam

British Library Cataloguing in Publication Data

Data available

ISBN: 9780-19-915293-3

10 9 8 7 6 5 4 3 2 1

Printed in China by Print Plus

Paper used in the production of this book is a natural, recyclable product made
from wood grown in sustainable forests. The manufacturing process conforms to
the environmental regulations to the country of origin.

Acknowledgments
The editors would like to thank Pete Crawford for his work in creating the case studies;
Stefanie Sullivan, Nottingham Shell Centre, for her advice with the case studies.

p1 guscott/ NASA; NAIC - Arecibo Observatory **p8** Derek Ingram/ Gonville & Caius College; **p21**
Hulton-Deutsch Collection/CORBIS; **p33** rafost; **p41** The National Archives; **p43**
jasminam; **p46** Joe_Potato/iStockphoto; Najin/Shutterstock; Pablo Caridad/Dreamstime;
cloudyaz/iStockphoto; Vladislav Gansovsky/Dreamstime; Svetoslav Iliev/Dreamstime
Soniak/Dreamstime; duckpondstudios/123RF.com; Paulpaladin/Dreamstime; Christopher
King/Dreamstime; Kitsen/Dreamstime; gollykim/iStockphoto; pixhook/iStockphoto; Maksym
Bondarchuk/Dreamstime; **p75** Deutsche Bundesbank; **p76** Ollirg; **p93** Lawrence Lawry/
Science photo library; **p97** Leslie Garland Picture Library/Alamy; **p113** Martin Wall; **p115**
The Print Collector / Alamy; **p125** British Columbia Dept of Mathematics; **p126** Rob Walls/
Alamy; **p129** Gilbert Iundt/TempSport/Corbis; **p139** Joan Kerrigan; **p141** Holmes Garden
Photos / Alamy;**p142** Richard Leeney/Dorling Kindersley; **p145** Ridgway **p146** Jostein Hauge/
Dreamstime; John Teate/Shutterstock; Fiona Dix/www.lovefibre.com; meo Photo/iStockphoto;
rusm/iStockphoto; Tihis/Dreamstime; Jenny/Dreamstime; webphotographeer/iStockphoto;
sedmak/iStockphoto; Ann Creswell; istihza/iStockphoto; **p149** Richard Bowden/Alamy; **p167**
Kruchankova May; Porsche; **p196** Scott Liddell/Morguefile; George M. Bosela/Morguefile;
Wojtek Kryczka/iStockphoto; Jacob Rodriguez Call/Dreamstime; **p199** Pixelbrat; **p212** Steve
Weaver; **p219** prism; **p226** Best Web; **p239** Crown copyright 2004; **p260** Giles Bracher / Alamy;
p245 Anja Niedringhaus/ Associated Press;**p247** G. Baden/zefa/Corbis**p254** Mark Turner @
Beehive Illustration; **p257** Visions of America, LLC/Alamy

Figurative artworks are by
p268-75 Matt Latchford;
All other figurative artworks are by Peter Donnelly

Contents

1 Number

Integers

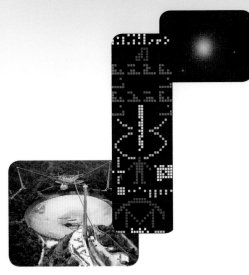

On 16th November 1974 the Arecibo radio telescope sent a message into space directed at the globular cluster Messier 13. Its interpretation relied on factorising 1679 as 23×73.

Astronomers reasoned that the prime numbers are so fundamental that any alien civilisation would know all about them!

What's the point? The prime numbers are like the chemical elements. Every integer can be uniquely factorised into primes. Knowing this can make many calculations much faster.

✓ Check in

Level 5

1 Calculate
   a $5 + \text{-}11$ **b** $\text{-}16 + \text{-}9$ **c** $\text{-}7 - \text{-}12$ **d** $\text{-}13 - \text{-}5$

2 Calculate
   a $5 \times \text{-}4$ **b** $\text{-}3 \times \text{-}5$ **c** $\text{-}4 \times \text{-}6$
   d $\text{-}25 \div 5$ **e** $\text{-}36 \div \text{-}6$ **f** $32 \div \text{-}8$

3 Write all the factors of
   a 60   **b** 132   **c** 225

4 Find the HCF and LCM of
   a 8 and 12   **b** 15 and 20   **c** 18 and 27

Highest Common Factor	HCF
Lowest Common Multiple	LCM

5 Work out the value of
   a $2 \times 3 \times 5$ **b** $2^2 \times 3^2$ **c** $2 \times 5^2 \times 7$

6 Write each of these numbers as the product of its prime factors.
   a 24   **b** 40   **c** 84

7 Work out these using a calculator where appropriate.
   a 9^2 **b** 13^2 **c** 35^2 **d** 5^3 **e** 15^3

- Order negative decimals
- Add and subtract with negative integers
- Multiply and divide with negative integers

Keywords
Integer
Negative

To calculate with **negative integers** make sure that both the size and the sign of the answer are correct.

- When you add or subtract negative integers, re-write the calculation according to these rules.

  Adding a negative integer is the same as subtracting a positive integer.

  Subtracting a negative integer is the same as adding a positive integer.

example

Calculate

a -27 + -31 **b** -18 − -14

a -27 + -31 = -27 − 31
  = -58

Add -31 is the same as subtract 31

b -18 − -14 = -18 + 14
  = -4

Subtract -14 is the same as add 14

- When you are multiplying or dividing a pair of numbers a good rule to remember for the sign of the answer is:

Multiply or divide	Positive	Negative
Positive	+ Answer	− Answer
Negative	− Answer	+Answer

If the signs are the same, the answer will be positive.

If the signs are different, the answer will be negative.

example

Calculate

a -8 × 6 **b** -48 ÷ -8 **c** -48 ÷ 6 **d** -8 × -6 **e** 48 ÷ -6

a -8 × 6	**b** -48 ÷ -8	**c** -48 ÷ 6	**d** -8 × -6	**e** 48 ÷ -6
= -48	= 6	= -8	= 48	= -8
negative answer	positive answer	negative answer	positive answer	negative answer

Exercise 1a

1 Place $<$ 'less than' or $>$ 'greater than' between these pairs of numbers to show which number is the larger.

Hint: to compare the size of negative decimals compare their digits starting with the highest place value digit.

   a -8 and -6   b -3.5 and -5   c -5.8 and -6
   d -3.2 and -3.19   e -0.05 and -0.489 f -1.271 and -1.268

2 Put these numbers in order from smallest to largest.

   a -1.8   -2   5   1.5   -3
   b -2.7   -3.4   -3.8   -3.2   -3
   c -5.2   -5.28   -5.3   5.4   -5.25

Did you know?

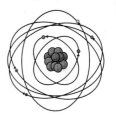

In Coulomb's law, the force between two electric charges is attractive or repulsive depending on the sign of their product.

3 Calculate

   a 7 + -11   b -12 + -9   c -8 − -15
   d -6 − -15   e -19 + -15   f -5 + 7 − -4
   g -6 − -8 + -7   h -12 + 32 + -27   i 33 + -16 − 24

4 Calculate

   a 9 × -4   b -12 × 15   c -14 × -6   d -15 × -7
   e -250 ÷ -5   f -306 ÷ 6   g -184 ÷ -8   h 288 ÷ -9

5 Copy and complete these calculations.

   a ☐ + -8 = 0   b 5 × ☐ = -10   c 8 − ☐ = -7
   d ☐ ÷ 7 = -13   e 7 + ☐ = -9   f ☐ × -6 = 84
   g ☐ − -23 = -7   h -72 ÷ ☐ = 12   i ☐ ÷ -3 = -8

6 Here are six calculations

   a ☐ ÷ ☐ = -4   b ☐ − ☐ = -10   c ☐ + ☐ = 12
   d ☐ × ☐ = 36   e ☐ × ☐ = 0   f ☐ + ☐ = 0

   Suggest, with reasons, what the missing numbers could be in each question.

7 Find three consecutive integers with a product of -504.

   a Copy and complete this multiplication grid.
      Try to find two different ways to complete it.
   b Design your own multiplication grid problem.
      What is the least amount of information that you need to include to obtain a unique solution?

×			2	-7	
			-12	42	
-5			-10		
		32			-12
					27

- Recognise and use factors and primes
- Use divisibility tests
- Investigate primes

Keywords
Divisibility   Factor
test   Prime

Divisibility tests can be used to find larger **factors** of a number.

example

Is 15 a factor of 255?

Use simple divisibility tests
to check if 3 and 5 are factors
of 255.

Factor	Is it a factor of 255?
3	Yes: 2 + 5 + 5 = 12
5	Yes: 255 ends in a 5

3 and 5 are both factors of 255.
This means that 15 is also a factor
of 255.

Check: $255 \div 15 = 17$

Divisibility Tests
÷2   the number ends in a 0, 2, 4, 6 or 8
÷3   the sum of the digits is divisible by 3
÷4   half the last two digits are divisible by 2
÷5   the number ends in a 0 or a 5
÷6   the number is divisible by both 2 and 3
÷7   there is no simple check for divisibility by 7
÷8   half of the number is divisible by 4
÷9   the sum of the digits is a multiple of 9
÷10   the number ends in a 0
÷11   the alternating sum of the digits is a multiple of 11
÷12   the number is divisible by both 3 and 4

- A **prime** number has exactly two factors: the number itself and 1.

The factors of a number are those numbers that divide into the number exactly.

To check if a number is prime use the divisibility tests for prime factors.

Here 'exactly' means leaving no remainder.

example

Is 139 a prime number?

Factor   Is it a factor of 139?

2	No: 139 ends in a 9
3	No: 1 + 3 + 9 = 13
5	No: 139 ends in a 9
7	No: $139 \div 7 = 19 \text{ r } 6$
11	No: 1 + 9 − 3 = 7

$13^2 = 169$ so you do not need to divide
by any higher prime numbers.

139 is a prime number.

149

150

151

152

Exercise 1b

1 Use the divisibility tests, where possible, to answer each of these questions. In each case, explain your answer and then check your answer by division.

    a Is 5 a factor of 385?   **b** Is 3 a factor of 746?

    c Is 7 a factor of 164?   **d** Is 11 a factor of 3234?

    e Is 12 a factor of 458?   **f** Is 15 a factor of 2010?

    g Is 18 a factor of 1926?   **h** Is 24 a factor of 2712?

> Remember factors always come in pairs:
> $16 = 1 \times 16, 2 \times 8$
> and 4×4

2 Write all the factors of

    a 460   **b** 864   **c** 625

    d 924   **e** 1024   **f** 1225

3 Use the divisibility tests to find which of these numbers are prime. In each case explain your answer.

    a 199   **b** 161   **c** 221

    d 239   **e** 301   **f** 379

4 Use your calculator to find all the prime numbers between 10 000 and 10 050.

> **Did you know?**
>
> Searching for primes is very competitive. At the start of 2009 the largest known prime number is
>
>
>
> That is one less than 2 multiplied by itself a lot of times! The number has 12 978 189 digits!

5 Siobhan makes a sequence out of hexagons.

    a How many hexagons are there in each diagram?

    b How many hexagons will there be in each of the next two diagrams in this sequence?

    c What do you notice about the types of numbers in your sequence?

    d Investigate bigger numbers in this sequence.

Investigation

Siobhan reads an article that says that all prime numbers can be described by mathematical formulae such as $6n + 1$.

For example   when $n = 1$, $6n + 1 = 7$ (a prime number)

                  when $n = 2$, $6n + 1 = 13$ (a prime number)

                  when $n = 3$, $6n + 1 = \dots$

Investigate these formulae, to see which of them generate prime numbers.

    a $6n + 1$ **b** $6n - 1$ **c** $n^2 - n + 41$ **d** $2^n - 1$

Write a report about what you have found out.

• Find the prime factor decomposition of an integer
• Find the factors of an integer

Keywords
Decompose
Factor tree
Prime factor

• Every whole number can be **decomposed** as the product of its **prime factors**.

example

What number is represented by $2^3 \times 3 \times 5^2$?

. . . .

$2^3 \times 3 \times 5^2 = 2 \times 2 \times 2 \times 3 \times 5 \times 5$
$= 600$

To write two numbers as the product of their prime factors you can use a **factor tree** or another method based on repeated division.

example

Write each number as the product of its prime factors.
a 2100   **b** 1800

. . . .

a

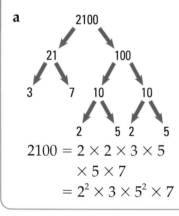

$2100 = 2 \times 2 \times 3 \times 5$
$\qquad \times 5 \times 7$
$\qquad = 2^2 \times 3 \times 5^2 \times 7$

b

2)	1800
2)	900
2)	450
3)	225
3)	75
5)	25
	5 STOP

$1800 = 2 \times 2 \times 2 \times 3 \times 3$
$\qquad \times 5 \times 5$
$\qquad = 2^3 \times 3^2 \times 5^2$

A factor tree can start with any pair of factors. It will always stop with the same prime factors.

In repeated division, it is easiest to divide by the smallest prime you can. Stop when you reach a prime number.

The prime factors of a number can be used to list all of its factors.

example

Write the factors of 140.

. . . .

$140 = 2 \times 2 \times 5 \times 7$
In addition to 1, 2, 5 and 7 the factors of 140 are
$2 \times 2 = 4$ $2 \times 2 \times 5 = 20$ $2 \times 5 \times 7 = 70$
$2 \times 5 = 10$ $2 \times 2 \times 7 = 28$ $2 \times 2 \times 5 \times 7 = 140$
$2 \times 7 = 14$ $5 \times 7 = 35$
The factors of 140 = {1, 2, 4, 5, 7, 10, 14, 20, 28, 35, 70 and 140}

Exercise 1c

1 Work out the value of

a $2^2 \times 3 \times 5$ **b** $2^2 \times 7$ **c** $2 \times 3^2 \times 5$ **d** $2^2 \times 5^2 \times 7$

e $2^2 \times 5 \times 11$ **f** $2^2 \times 3^2 \times 7$ **g** $2^3 \times 13$ **h** $2^2 \times 3^2 \times 7$

i $2^3 \times 3 \times 5^2 \times 7$ **j** $2^4 \times 5 \times 11$

2 Write each of these numbers as the products of its prime factors.

a 18   **b** 42   **c** 80   **d** 54   **e** 128

f 420   **g** 200   **h** 175   **i** 360   **j** 480

k 576   **l** 1080   **m** 2520   **n** 1296   **o** 2025

3 Gina has used the factor tree method to find all the prime factors of 12 600 and 26 460. Here is her working out.

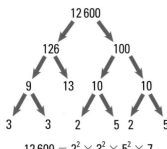

$12\,600 = 2^2 \times 3^2 \times 5^2 \times 7$

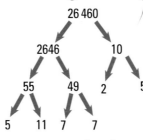

$26\,460 = 2 \times 5^2 \times 7^2 \times 11$

a Can you spot her mistakes?

b Copy and correct Gina's work.

c Write down any strategies you used to find Gina's mistakes.

4 List all the factors of these numbers.

a 80   **b** 180   **c** 450   **d** 330   **e** 1470   **f** 1000

5 a A number has prime factors of 2, 3 and 5.
   What are the smallest five values it could take?

b Find the smallest number greater than 200 with exactly four prime factors.

c Find the smallest number greater than 200 with four different prime factors.

Verity has to make 12 different numbers between 100 and 600. She is allowed to multiply any of the numbers 3, 5 and 7 together as many times as she likes. Copy and complete Verity's table.

$3^2 \times 5^2 = 225$	$3 \times 5^2 \times 7 = 525$				
$3 \times 7^2 = 147$					

How many more examples can you find?

- Find the lowest common multiple and highest common factor of two numbers using prime factors
- Use the LCM to add two fractions
- Use the HCF to write a fraction in its simplest form

Keywords
Highest common factor (HCF)
Lowest common denominator
Lowest common multiple (LCM)

The **highest common factor (HCF)** and the **lowest common multiple (LCM)** of two numbers can be found using prime factors.

- The HCF is the largest number that will divide into the two numbers exactly.

- The LCM is the smallest number that both numbers will divide into exactly.

example

Find the HCF and LCM of 240 and 540.

Write both numbers as the product of their prime factors.

```
2) 240          2) 540
2) 120          2) 270
2)  60          3) 135
2)  30          3)  45
3)  15          3)  15
     5  STOP         5  STOP
```

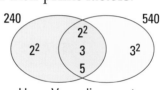

240 ⟨ 2^2 ⟩ 540

2^2 2^2 3 5 3^2

Use a Venn diagram to record your results.

$240 = 2^4 \times 3 \times 5$ $540 = 2^2 \times 3^3 \times 5$

Multiply the prime factors they have in common:
HCF of 240 and 540 $= 2^2 \times 3 \times 5 = 60$

Multiply the highest power of each of the prime factors:
LCM of 240 and 540 $= 2^4 \times 3^3 \times 5 = 2160$

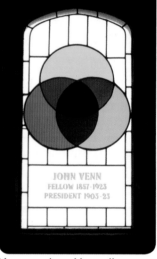

JOHN VENN
FELLOW 1857–1923
PRESIDENT 1905–23

You can draw Venn diagrams for more than two sets.

The LCM can be used to add or subtract fractions with different denominators, and the HCF used to simplify fractions.

example

a Simplify $\frac{96}{168}$ **b** Calculate $\frac{23}{28} + \frac{17}{40}$

280 is the **lowest common denominator** for the two fractions in part **b**.

a The HCF of 96 and 168 is 24

$\frac{96}{168} \overset{\div 24}{\underset{\div 24}{=}} \frac{4}{7}$

b The LCM of 28 and 40 $= 280$

$\frac{23}{28} \overset{\times 10}{\underset{\times 10}{=}} \frac{230}{280}$ $\frac{17}{40} \overset{\times 7}{\underset{\times 7}{=}} \frac{119}{280}$

Find equivalent fractions with denominator 280.

$\frac{23}{28} + \frac{17}{40} = \frac{230 + 119}{280} = \frac{349}{280} = 1\frac{69}{280}$

Add the numerators.

Exercise 1d

1 Find the HCF of
   a 10 and 15   b 35 and 50   c 72 and 96
   d 95 and 133   e 6, 15 and 21   f 24, 40 and 64

2 Find the LCM of
   a 10 and 15   b 35 and 50   c 68 and 85
   d 140 and 196   e 6, 15 and 21   f 10, 25 and 40

3 Find the missing numbers in these productogons.
   a   b

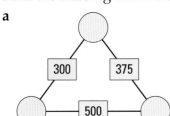

300   375   972   1620

500   1215

4 Find the HCF and LCM of
   a 108 and 144   b 280 and 360   c 385 and 660
   d 441 and 819   e 480 and 1080   f 720 and 1260
   g 35, 56 and 63   h 45, 75 and 90

5 Cancel down each of these fractions into their simplest form.
   a $\frac{24}{36}$ b $\frac{50}{90}$ c $\frac{72}{96}$ d $\frac{81}{135}$ e $\frac{120}{192}$

6 Work out these, leaving your answer as a fraction in its simplest form.
   a $\frac{7}{10} - \frac{7}{15}$ b $\frac{5}{12} + \frac{7}{15}$ c $\frac{7}{20} + \frac{3}{25}$ d $\frac{12}{25} + \frac{13}{40}$

7 In a faraway galaxy, three planets are lined up around a giant sun. They have orbits of 28, 42 and 49 weeks.
   a After how many weeks will the three planets be next in line?
   b How many orbits will each planet have completed before they are back in alignment?

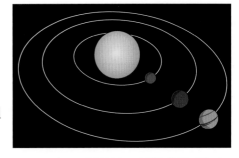

The number in a rectangle is the product of the numbers in the circles either side of it.

Write each number as the product of its prime factors.

You can use the HCF.

---

a The HCF of two numbers is 20. What could the two numbers be? Describe the answers you might expect as precisely as possible.

b The LCM of two numbers is 100. What could the two numbers be? Describe the answers you might expect as precisely as possible.

• Find square roots and cube roots

Keywords
Cube number
Cube root
Square number
Square root

You can use the and function keys on your calculator to find the **square root** of any positive number and the **cube root** of any number.

---

example

Work out the value of   **a** $\sqrt{1849}$ **b** $\sqrt[3]{1849}$ **c** $\sqrt[3]{-2197}$

a To find $\sqrt{1849}$ you type

$$\sqrt{1849} = 43$$

Check: $43^2 = 1849$

But $(-43)^2$ is also equal to 1849.

The square roots of 1849 = ±43

> Here ±43 means +43 and -43.

b To find $\sqrt[3]{1849}$ you type

$$\sqrt[3]{1849} = 12.273\ 797\ 97...$$
$$= 12.3\ (1\,dp)$$

When an answer is not a whole number, you need to round it to an appropriate degree of accuracy.

c $\sqrt[3]{-2197} = -13$

Check: $(-13)^3 = -13 \times -13 \times -13 = -2197$

> Not all calculators are the same, check the keys on yours.

MEMO

Things to remember
• There are two square roots for a positive number: one positive and one negative.
• You cannot have the square root of a negative number.
• The cube root of a positive number is positive.
• The cube root of a negative number is negative.

It is possible to find the square root of a **square number** and the cube root of a **cube number** by using prime factors.

---

example

Work out the value of   **a** $\sqrt{784}$ **b** $\sqrt[3]{-64}$

a Find the prime factors of 784.
$$784 = 2 \times 2 \times 2 \times 2 \times 7 \times 7$$
$$\sqrt{784} = \sqrt{(2 \times 2 \times 2 \times 2 \times 7 \times 7)}$$
$$= \sqrt{(2 \times 2 \times 7) \times (2 \times 2 \times 7)}$$
$$= 2 \times 2 \times 7$$
$$= 28$$

b Find the prime factors of 64.
$$64 = 2 \times 2 \times 2 \times 2 \times 2 \times 2$$
$$\sqrt[3]{-64} = \sqrt[3]{(-2 \times 2 \times -2 \times 2 \times -2 \times 2)}$$
$$= \sqrt[3]{(-2 \times 2) \times (-2 \times 2) \times (-2 \times 2)}$$
$$= -2 \times 2$$
$$= -4$$

Exercise 1e

1 Work out these using a calculator where appropriate.
   a 12^2 **b** 19^2 **c** 25^2 **d** 7^3 **e** 13^3 **f** $(-8)^2$
   g 10^3 **h** 3.5^2 **i** 20^3 **j** 4.2^3 **k** 12.1^3 **l** $(-5)^3$

2 Calculate these using a calculator where possible.
   Give your answer to 1 dp.

   > 1 dp means one decimal place.

   a $\sqrt{70}$ **b** $\sqrt{120}$ **c** $\sqrt[3]{70}$
   d $\sqrt{200}$ **e** $\sqrt{-40}$ **f** $\sqrt[3]{-90}$

3 Calculate these **without** a calculator.

   > Hint: write each number as the product of its prime factors.

   a $\sqrt{225}$ **b** $\sqrt{324}$ **c** $\sqrt{576}$
   d $\sqrt[3]{216}$ **e** $\sqrt[3]{512}$ **f** $\sqrt{1296}$

4 **a** Two consecutive numbers are multiplied together.
      The answer is 8930. What are the two numbers?
   b Three consecutive numbers are multiplied together.
      The answer is 185 136. What are the three numbers?
   c A digital camera screen is in the shape of a square. It has
      an area of 70.56 cm². What length is the side of the screen?

5 Hanif works out $\sqrt{10} = 3.162\,277\,66$
   He then calculates $3.162\,277\,66^2$ but the answer is not 10.
   Explain why the answer is not 10.

challenge

Hatti has a trial and improvement method for finding $\sqrt{40}$ without using
the $\boxed{\sqrt{}}$ key on her calculator. Here is her working.

Estimate	Check (square of estimate)	Answer	Result
6	6^2	36	Too small
7	7^2	49	Too big
6.5	6.5^2	42.25	Too big
6.3	6.3^2	39.69	Too small
6.4	6.4^2	40.96	Too big
6.35	6.35^2	40.3225	Too big

$$\sqrt{40} = 6.3 \ (1\,dp)$$

> Make sure you have both upper and lower bounds for your answer.

Use Hatti's method to estimate
   a $\sqrt{20}$, $\sqrt{95}$, $\sqrt{300}$
   b $\sqrt[3]{100}$, $\sqrt[3]{10}$, $\sqrt[3]{1600}$

> Give your answers to 1 decimal place.

1f Indices

- Evaluate numbers written using index notation
- Multiply and divide numbers in index form

- When you have the same number multiplied by itself several times you can use index notation:

The small number is called the **index** or **power**.

example

Work out the value of 15^4.

. . . .

$15^4 = 15 \times 15 \times 15 \times 15$

$= 50\,625$

You can use the y^x function key on your calculator to evaluate powers.

The y^x key may look different on your calculator or may not be there at all.

Any number raised to the power of zero is equal to 1.

- The decimal system is based upon powers of 10, and can be written using **index notation**.

1 thousand	= 1000	= $10 \times 10 \times 10$	= 10^3
1 ten	= 10	= 10	= 10^1
1 unit	= 1		= 10^0
1 tenth	= $\frac{1}{10}$	= $\frac{1}{10^1}$	= 10^{-1}

Negative powers mean 'one over', for example, $2^{-1} = \frac{1}{2}$

Scientists use some very big and very small powers.

10^{-15} m = 1 femtometre the size of an atomic nucleus

10^{21} m = 1 zettametre a typical distance between stars

You can multiply numbers written in **index form**.

example

Calculate   **a** $5^3 \times 5^2$ **b** $5^2 \times 5^1$

. . . .

a $5^3 \times 5^2 = (5 \times 5 \times 5) \times (5 \times 5) = 5^5$

$\qquad = 5^{3+2} \qquad\qquad\qquad = 5^5$

The indices are added when multiplying.

b $5^2 \times 5 = 5^{2+1}$

$\qquad = 5^3$

A number written to the power of 1 is equal to the number itself, for example, $5^1 = 5$

You can divide numbers written in index form.

example

Calculate   **a** $5^5 \div 5^2$ **b** $5^2 \div 5^4$

. . . .

a $5^5 \div 5^2 = \dfrac{5 \times 5 \times 5 \times \cancel{5} \times \cancel{5}}{\cancel{5} \times \cancel{5}} = 5 \times 5 \times 5 = 5^3$ **b** $5^2 \div 5^4 = 5^{2-4} = 5^{-2}$

$\qquad = 5^{5-2} \qquad\qquad\qquad = 5^3$

The indices are subtracted when dividing.

Exercise 1f

1 Calculate these.

   a 5^3 **b** 2^6 **c** 3^3 **d** 1^7 **e** 5^0

   f 10^5 **g** 2^1 **h** 7^0 **i** 10^{-2} **j** 11^3

2 Put these numbers in order from smallest to largest.

   2^8 3^5 4^4 11^3

3 Jasmine knows that $2^8 = 256$.

   Uri says that she can use this information to work out 2^{10}.

   Explain how Jasmine can use 2^8 to work out 2^{10}.

4 Use the fact that $4^6 = 4096$ to work out

   a 4^5 **b** 4^7

5 Use the $\boxed{y^x}$ function key on your calculator to find the power x in these questions.

   a $3^x = 81$ **b** $2^x = 32$

   c $10^x = 1\,000\,000$ **d** $7^x = 49$

   e $4^x = 1024$ **f** $6^x = 1296$

   g $2^x = 256$ **h** $10^x = 0.1$

6 Simplify each of these, leaving your answer as a single power of the number.

   a $4^2 \times 4^3$ **b** $3^4 \times 3^2$ **c** $5^3 \times 5^4$ **d** $4^5 \times 4^2$ **e** $2^6 \times 2^2$

   f $4^5 \div 4^2$ **g** $3^7 \div 3^3$ **h** $5^5 \div 5^3$ **i** $4^6 \div 4^4$ **j** $2^5 \div 2^4$

7 Calculate these, leaving your answer in index form where possible.

   a $5^2 \times 2^3$ **b** $3^3 + 3^2$ **c** $4^3 - 2^4$ **d** $3^5 \div 4^2$ **e** $2^4 \div 2^5$

8 Simplify each of these, leaving your answer as a single power of the number.

   a $3^2 \times 3^3 \times 3^2$ **b** $4^5 \times 4$ **c** $10^3 \times 10^4 \times 10^2$

   d $\dfrac{2^4 \times 2^5}{2^3}$ **e** $\dfrac{4^2 \times 4^4 \times 4^3}{4^6}$ **f** $10^3 \div 10^5$

a Guess $x = 5$,

   evaluate $3^5 = 243$

   too high,

   try a lower value,

   $x = 4$

   evaluate $3^4 = 81$

   $3^x = 81, x = 4$

Ali makes a cube using 125 smaller cubes.

He paints the outside of the cube with red paint.

  a How many of the smaller cubes have 1 face painted red?

  b How many of the smaller cubes have 0 faces painted red?

     2 faces painted red? 3 faces painted red?

  c Investigate different-sized starting cubes.

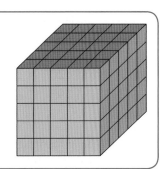

1 Put these numbers in order from smallest to largest.

a -0.5   -3   2   0.5   -2

b -2.5   -3.5   -4.5   -1.5   -0.5

c -4.5   -4.6   -5   -5.2   3

2 Calculate

a $5 + -10$ **b** $-11 + -13$ **c** $-6 - -18$ **d** $-5 - -12$

e $-17 + -13$ **f** $13 + -19$ **g** $-24 + -23$ **h** $-35 - -38$

i $48 - -52$ **j** $-37 + -35.5$ **k** $-7 - 8 - -9$ **l** $-7 - -8 - -9$

3 Calculate

a 7×-9 **b** -8×9 **c** -11×-7 **d** -13×-9

e -12×15 **f** 17×-15 **g** -18×13 **h** -19×-9

i -15×-23 **j** -21×19 **k** $-150 \div -6$ **l** $-231 \div 7$

m $-216 \div -8$ **n** $-306 \div -9$ **o** $372 \div -12$ **p** $-345 \div -15$

4 Write all the factors of

a 200   **b** 288   **c** 289   **d** 300   **e** 440   **f** 256

g 500   **h** 639   **i** 777   **j** 999   **k** 1000   **l** 2304

5 Use the divisibility tests to see which of these numbers are prime.
In each case explain your answer.

a 401   **b** 413   **c** 419   **d** 437   **e** 451   **f** 479

6 Write each of these numbers as the product of its prime factors.

a 22   **b** 46   **c** 84   **d** 58   **e** 132   **f** 104

g 185   **h** 425   **i** 205   **j** 181   **k** 366   **l** 309

m 489   **n** 585   **o** 1089   **p** 2529   **q** 1305   **r** 3025

7 Use prime factors to list all the factors of these numbers.

a 60   **b** 96   **c** 110   **d** 165   **e** 430   **f** 600

g 950   **h** 1225   **i** 2116   **j** 1764   **k** 3136   **l** 3969

8 Find the HCF and LCM of

a 100 and 120   **b** 144 and 192   **c** 210 and 240   **d** 336 and 378

e 315 and 495   **f** 616 and 728   **g** 40, 56 and 72   **h** 48, 80 and 176

9 Cancel down each of these fractions into its simplest form.

You can use the HCF.

a $\frac{35}{49}$ b $\frac{100}{120}$ c $\frac{144}{192}$ d $\frac{210}{240}$ e $\frac{105}{175}$

f $\frac{234}{273}$ g $\frac{210}{378}$ h $\frac{96}{528}$ i $\frac{477}{583}$ j $\frac{198}{858}$

10 Work out these, leaving your answer as a fraction in its simplest form.

a $\frac{6}{7} - \frac{3}{14}$ b $\frac{7}{16} + \frac{1}{4}$ c $\frac{3}{5} + \frac{1}{10}$ d $\frac{6}{13} + \frac{12}{39}$

e $\frac{13}{15} - \frac{5}{6}$ f $\frac{7}{24} + \frac{17}{30}$ g $\frac{8}{15} + \frac{7}{40}$ h $\frac{7}{30} + \frac{11}{25}$

11 Calculate these using a calculator. Give your answers to 1 dp.

a $\sqrt{11}$ b $\sqrt{111}$ c $\sqrt[3]{111}$ d $\sqrt[3]{-1111}$ e $\sqrt{-9}$ f $\sqrt[3]{91}$

12 a Three consecutive numbers are multiplied together. The result is -1716.
   What are the three numbers?

   b Two consecutive numbers are multiplied together. The result is 1806.
   Give the two possible pairs of consecutive numbers.

13 Calculate these without a calculator.

Try writing each number as the product of its prime factors.

a $\sqrt{256}$ b $\sqrt{441}$ c $\sqrt{729}$

d $\sqrt[3]{1728}$ e $\sqrt[3]{3375}$ f $\sqrt{2025}$

14 Use the $\boxed{y^x}$ function key on your calculator to find the power x in these questions.

a $3^x = 2187$ b $2^x = 512$ c $4^x = 65\,536$ d $5^x = 15\,625$

e $10^x = 1$ f $7^x = 16\,807$ g $4^x = 1$ h $6^x = 7776$

i $2^x = 16$ j $2^x = 0.5$

15 Simplify each of these, leaving your answer as a single power of the number.

a $2^3 \times 2^4$ b $7^4 \times 7^8$ c $4^3 \times 4^9$ d $3^5 \times 3^0$ e $6^5 \times 6^5$

f $2^5 \div 2^3$ g $2^7 \div 2^7$ h $4^5 \div 4^4$ i $3^6 \div 3$ j $10^5 \div 10^6$

16 Calculate these, leaving your answer in index form where possible.

a $3^4 \times 4^3$ b $2^3 + 4^2$ c $5^3 - 2^4$ d $4^5 \div 2^2$ e $3^2 \times 3^2$

17 Simplify each of these, leaving your answer as a single power of the number.

a $5^3 \times 5^3 \times 5^3$ b $3^5 \times 3^5 \times 3^5$ c $10^4 \times 10^4 \times 10^4$

d $(2^4)^3$ e $(5^3)^3$ f $8^9 \div 8^9$

g $\dfrac{3^4 \times 3^3}{3^2}$ h $\dfrac{2^2 \times 2^4 \times 2^6}{2^8}$ i $10^3 \div 10^3$

1 Summary

Assessment criteria
- Multiply and divide positive and negative whole numbers **Level 5**
- Use index notation **Level 5/Level 6**
- Write a number as the product of its prime factors **Level 6**

1 a Tony thinks that 2^5 is the same as 5^2.
  Explain why he is wrong.

b The value of 8^4 is 4096.
  Calculate 8^5.

Samima's answer ✔

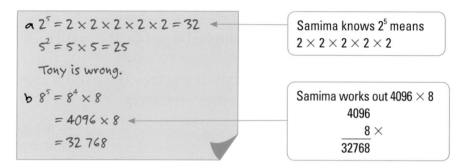

a $2^5 = 2 \times 2 \times 2 \times 2 \times 2 = 32$

$5^2 = 5 \times 5 = 25$

Tony is wrong.

b $8^5 = 8^4 \times 8$

$= 4096 \times 8$

$= 32\,768$

Samima knows 2^5 means
$2 \times 2 \times 2 \times 2 \times 2$

Samima works out 4096×8

```
  4096
     8 ×
 ─────
 32768
```

2 Write the missing numbers in the table.
  The first row is done for you.

First number	Second number	Sum of first and second numbers	Product of first and second numbers
3	6	9	18
5	-3		
-8		-5	

KS3 2004 4–6 Paper 1

Measures

The distances on the signpost are probably in miles, but `m` could mean metres.

Units of measurement are essential in everyday life. You should always give the correct units when you measure quantities and always give the units to the answers of your calculations.

What's the point? Without the units you don't know what the measurement is: $3\frac{1}{2}$ miles is 1609 times further than $3\frac{1}{2}$ metres.

Check in

1 Calculate

  a 7.4×10 **b** $3.9 \div 10$ **c** 0.6×100 **d** $250 \div 1000$

2 Calculate

  a 25×0.6 **b** 12×4.5 **c** 5.5×30 **d** 5.5×2.2

3 Calculate

  a $126 \div 4.5$ **b** $2 \div 2.5$ **c** $480 \div 1.6$ **d** $5.4 \div 0.6$

4 Calculate the perimeter and the area of these rectangles. State the units of your answers.

  a 8 m, 5 m

  b 4.5 cm, 6 cm

  c 25 mm, 12.5 mm

- Use appropriate metric units to measure length, mass, capacity, area and time

Keywords

Area   Length
Capacity   Mass
                    Metric

The **length** of an object is its linear extent.

You can measure length or distance using millimetres (mm), centimetres (cm), metres (m) and kilometres (km).

The **mass** of an object is how heavy it is.

You can measure mass using grams (g), kilograms (kg) and tonnes (t).

Capacity is the amount of liquid a container holds.

You can measure capacity using millilitres (ml), centilitres (cl) and litres (l).

Area is the amount of surface a shape covers.

You measure area in squares using square millimetres (mm²), square centimetres (cm²), square metres (m²) and square kilometres (km²).

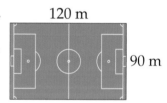

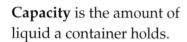

Common metric units

1 cm = 10 mm	1 kg = 1000 g	1 l = 1000 ml	1 hectare (ha) = 10 000 m²
1 m = 1000 mm	1 t = 1000 kg	1 l = 100 cl	
1 m = 100 cm			
1 km = 1000 m			

example

A rectangular football pitch measures 120 metres by 90 metres. Calculate the area of the pitch in hectares.

120 m

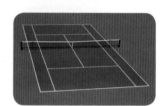

90 m

Area = 120 × 90
    = 10 800 m²
    = 1.08 hectares

×10 000

1 ha = 10 000 m²

÷10 000

example

Convert these measurements into the units indicated in brackets.
a 4.7 km (into m)   b 75 cl (into l)

a   4.7 km = 4.7 × 1000 m
        = 4700 m

×1000

1 km = 1000 m

÷1000

b 75 cl = 75 ÷ 100 l
      = 0.75 l

×100

1 l = 100 cl

÷100

Exercise 2a

1 Choose the most appropriate metric unit to measure each of these quantities and give a possible value in each case.
  a The amount of water in a swimming pool
  b The diagonal distance across a flat-screen television
  c The surface of the cover of this textbook
  d The amount of petrol in a car
  e The weight of a Year 8 pupil
  f The distance across an ocean
  g The height of a skyscraper
  h The weight of a box of drawing pins
  i The surface area of a DVD
  j The capacity of a cup.

2 A sunflower grows to 1.76 metres tall.
  Calculate the height in
  a centimetres   b millimetres.

3 What is the total of these weights in
  a grams   b kilograms?

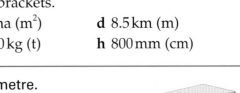
4.5 kg   825 g   3.05 kg

4 Shahid is running a 10 km road race.
  He has already run 5230 metres.
  How much further has he to run?

5 One teaspoon holds 5 millilitres.
  How many teaspoons of medicine can be poured from a 15 cl medicine bottle?

6 A square field has an area of exactly 1 hectare.
  Calculate the length and width of the field in metres.

7 Convert these measurements to the units in the brackets.
  a 40 cm (mm)   b 0.2 kg (g)   c 2.5 ha (m²)   d 8.5 km (m)
  e 6.5 l (cl)   f 500 ml (l)   g 6300 kg (t)   h 800 mm (cm)

---

problem

10 sheets of A4 paper stack to a height of 1 millimetre.
How many sheets of A4 paper would you need to stack to your height?

- Know rough metric equivalents of some imperial units
- Read and interpret scales on a range of measuring instruments

Keywords
Imperial   Metric
Instrument Scale

Measurements can use **metric** or **imperial** units.
Imperial units include for ...

length and distance   **mass**   **capacity**

inch, foot, yard and mile   ounce (oz), pound   pint and gallon.
                            (lb) and stone

1 foot = 12 inches 1 yard = 3 feet 1 mile = 1760 yards	1 pound = 16 ounces 1 stone = 14 pounds 1 ton = 160 stones	1 gallon = 8 pints

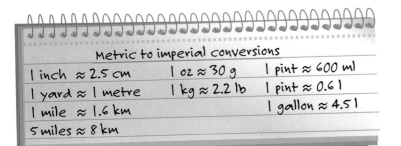

Metric to imperial conversions

1 inch ≈ 2.5 cm	1 oz ≈ 30 g	1 pint ≈ 600 ml
1 yard ≈ 1 metre	1 kg ≈ 2.2 lb	1 pint ≈ 0.6 l
1 mile ≈ 1.6 km		1 gallon ≈ 4.5 l
5 miles ≈ 8 km		

≈ means
approximately equal

example

a Convert 4.5 pints to litres.   **b** Convert 480 g to ounces.

. . . .

a 4.5 pints ≈ 4.5 × 0.6 litres   ×0.6   **b** 480 g ≈ 480 ÷ 30 ounces   ×30
        = 2.7 l   = 16 oz

1 pint ≈ 0.6 l

1 oz ≈ 30 g

÷0.6   ÷30

To use a measuring **instrument** to measure metric and imperial
quantities you will need to understand the **scale** to read them.

example

Write the reading on each of the scales.

a ⌐┬┬┬┬┬┐ kg   **b** ⌐┬┬┬┬┐ miles
    14   ↑ 15   4   ↑ 5

. . . .

a This scale goes up in 1000s of g.   **b** This scale goes up in 1 mile.
    5 spaces represent 1000 g.   4 spaces represent 1 mile.
    Each space represents 200 g.   Each space represents 0.25 mile.
    The scale reads 14 kg 800 g. or 14.8 kg   The scale reads 4.75 miles.

Exercise 2b

1 Charles Blondin was a French tightrope walker.
He crossed the gorge below Niagara Falls on a tightrope,
1100 feet long and 160 feet above the water.
Convert the distances to
  a inches   **b** centimetres   **c** metres.

2 Convert these measurements to the units in brackets.
  a 6 pints (l)   **b** 4.5 kg (lb)   **c** 10 gallons (l)
  d 70 miles (km)   **e** 36 inches (cm)   **f** 45 kg (lb)
  g 2.5 pints (ml)   **h** 5 feet (cm)   **i** 4.5 oz (g)

3 A litre of petrol costs £1.24.
What will a gallon cost?

4 The speed limit on a canal is 8 km per hour.
Convert this speed to miles per hour.

5 Convert these measurements to the units in brackets.
  a 30 cm (inches)   **b** 4.2 litres (pints)   **c** 12 km (miles)
  d 300 ml (pints)   **e** 40.5 litres (gallons) **f** 103.4 lb (kg)
  g 450 g (oz)   **h** 240 mm (inches)   **i** 6.6 m (feet)

6 You should drink between 1.5 and 2 litres of water every day.
How many pints is this in one year?

7 Write down the readings on each scale. Give two answers for
each arrow.

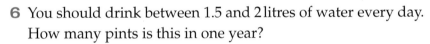

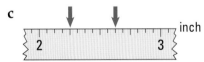

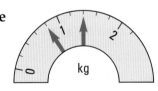

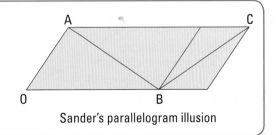

- Calculate the area of a rectangle and a triangle

Keywords
Area   Perpendicular
Base   Triangle

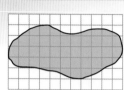

The **area** of a shape is the amount of surface it covers. You measure area in squares.

Use mm², cm², m² or km² to measure area.

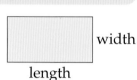
width

length

- The area of a rectangle = length × width

---

example

Calculate the perimeter and area of this shape made from rectangles.

Perimeter is the distance around the shape.

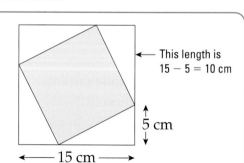
10 cm
4 cm
9 cm
7 cm

. . . .

First calculate the missing lengths.

$10 - 7 = 3\,\text{cm}$ $9 - 4 = 5\,\text{cm}$

Perimeter = 10 cm + 9 cm + 7 cm   Area = $10 \times 4 + 7 \times 5$
$\quad\quad\quad + 5\,\text{cm} + 3\,\text{cm} + 4\,\text{cm}$ $= 40 + 35$
$\quad\quad\quad = 38\,\text{cm}$ $= 75\,\text{cm}^2$

The shape is made from two rectangles.

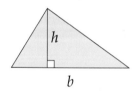 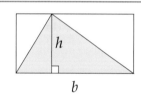 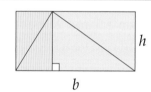

The area of a **triangle** is half the area of the surrounding rectangle.
The area of the rectangle $= b \times h$

b is the base.
h is the perpendicular height.

- The area of a triangle $= \frac{1}{2} \times b \times h$

$\quad\quad\quad\quad\quad\quad\quad = \frac{1}{2} \times$ **base** $\times$ **perpendicular** height

Perpendicular means 'at right angles to'.

---

example

A square is drawn inside another square.
Calculate the area of the shaded square.

. . . .

Area of the large square $= 15 \times 15 = 225\,\text{cm}^2$
Area of one triangle $= \frac{1}{2} \times 10 \times 5$
$\quad\quad\quad\quad\quad\quad\quad = 25\,\text{cm}^2$
Area of all four triangles $= 4 \times 25 = 100\,\text{cm}^2$
Area of the shaded square $= 225 - 100$
$\quad\quad\quad\quad\quad\quad\quad = 125\,\text{cm}^2$

This length is $15 - 5 = 10$ cm

5 cm

15 cm

Exercise 2c

1 Calculate the perimeter and area of these shapes made from rectangles. If necessary, draw the shapes on square grid paper.

a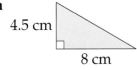
6 cm
2 cm
2 cm
3 cm

b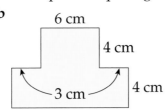
6 cm
4 cm
3 cm
4 cm

c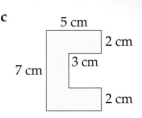
5 cm
2 cm
3 cm
7 cm
2 cm

2 Calculate the area of these triangles.

a
4.5 cm
8 cm

b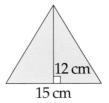
5 m
7.5 m

c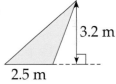
12 cm
15 cm

d
3.2 m
2.5 m

3 Calculate the unknown length in each of these shapes.

a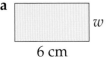
w
6 cm
Area = 18 cm²

b
w
6 mm
Area = 45 mm²

c
5 cm
b
Area = 20 cm²

d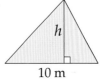
h
10 m
Area = 36 m²

4 Calculate the area of the shaded quadrilaterals.

a

b

c

5 The area of the rectangle and the triangle are the same.
Calculate the value of h.

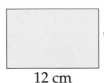
7.5 cm
12 cm

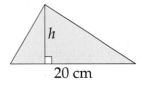
h
20 cm

A rope is knotted to form a loop of length 30 metres.
The rope forms a rectangle.
Calculate the largest area that can be enclosed by the rope.

2d Area of a parallelogram and a trapezium

- Calculate the area of a parallelogram and a trapezium

Keywords

Area	Parallelogram
Base	Perpendicular
Parallel	Trapezium

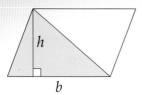
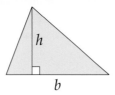

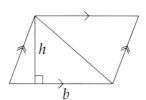

The **area** of the **parallelogram** is double the area of the triangle.

Area of the triangle $= \frac{1}{2} \times b \times h$

> A parallelogram has two pairs of **parallel** sides.

- The area of a parallelogram $= b \times h$

> b is the **base**.
> h is the **perpendicular** height.

example

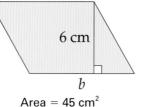

The area of the parallelogram is $45\,\text{cm}^2$. Calculate the length of the base.

· ·

Area $= b \times h$

$45 = b \times 6$

$b = 7.5\,\text{cm}$

$\boxed{45 \div 6 = 7.5}$

Area $= 45\,\text{cm}^2$

You can fit two identical **trapeziums** together to make a parallelogram.

> A trapezium has one pair of parallel sides.

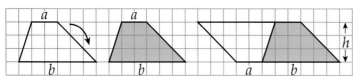

The area of the green trapezium is half the area of the parallelogram.

Area of the parallelogram $= (a + b) \times h$

> a and b are the lengths of the parallel sides. h is the perpendicular height.

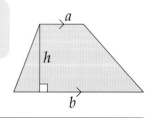

- The area of a trapezium $= \frac{1}{2} \times (a + b) \times h$

example

Calculate the area of this trapezium.

· ·

Area $= \frac{1}{2} \times (a + b) \times h$

$\quad = \frac{1}{2} \times (2.4 + 4.8) \times 5$

$\quad = \frac{1}{2} \times 7.2 \times 5 = 18\,\text{m}^2$

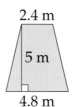

2.4 m

5 m

4.8 m $a = 2.4, b = 4.8, h = 5$

Exercise 2d

1 Calculate the area of these shapes.

Always state the units of your answers.

a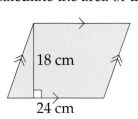
18 cm
24 cm

b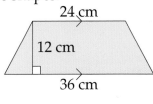
24 cm
12 cm
36 cm

c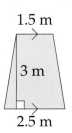
1.5 m
3 m
2.5 m

d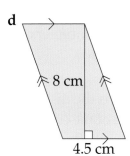
8 cm
4.5 cm

e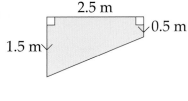
2.5 m
0.5 m
1.5 m

f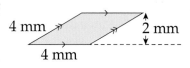
4 mm
2 mm
4 mm

2 Find the unknown lengths in these parallelograms.

a
h
4 cm
Area = 10 cm²

b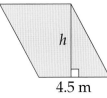
h
4.5 m
Area = 27 m²

c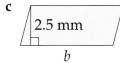
2.5 mm
b
Area = 12.5 mm²

3 Mike wants to paint the end wall of his terrace house with a protective weather-resistant paint.
   a Calculate the area of the wall.
   b One litre of paint covers approximately 5 m².
   How many litres of paint does Mike need?

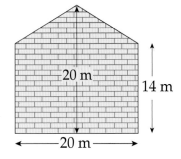
20 m
14 m
20 m

The area of this trapezium is 25 cm².
The length *a* is less than the length *b*.
Write down five different sets of possible values for *a* and *b*.

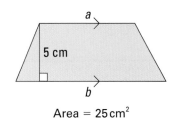
a
5 cm
b
Area = 25 cm²

2e Circumference of a circle

- Know the names of parts of a circle
- Calculate the circumference of a circle

Arc · Diameter
Centre · Pi (π)
Circumference · Radius

p. 230

- A circle is a set of points equidistant from its **centre**.
  Equidistant means 'the same distance'.

 The **circumference** (C) is the distance around the circle.

The perimeter of the circle is called the circumference.

The **radius** (r) is the distance from the centre to the circumference.

Radii is the plural of radius.

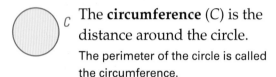 Part of the circumference is called an **arc**.

 The **diameter** (d) is the distance across the centre of the circle.

The diameter is twice the length of the radius. $d = 2 \times r$

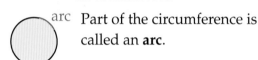

The circumference of the circle is '3 and a bit' × the diameter.
You can use the symbol
π (pi) for the exact
value of '3 and a bit'.

The exact value of π can never be written down. The numbers go on for ever without making a pattern.

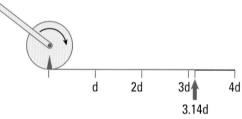

d   2d   3d   4d

3.14d

- Circumference = π × diameter $C = \pi d$

where C = circumference, d = diameter, r = radius and $\pi = 3.141\,592\ldots$

- Circumference = π × 2 × radius $C = 2\pi r$

---

example

Calculate the circumference of each circle. Take π to be 3.14.

a

8 cm

diameter = 8 cm

b
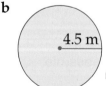
4.5 m

radius = 4.5 m

. . . .

a $C = \pi d$

$= 3.14 \times 8$

$= 25.12 \, cm$

b $C = 2\pi r$

$= 2 \times 3.14 \times 4.5$

$= 28.26 \, m$

Circumference is a distance and is measured in units of length.

26 **Geometry** Measures

Exercise 2e

1 $\pi = 3.141\,592\,653\,589\,793\,238\,46\ldots$

Which of these approximations is the nearest to π?

  a 3.1   **b** $\frac{22}{7}$ **c** 3   **d** 3.142

2 Measure and write down the radius and diameter of each circle.

State the units of your answers.

  a   **b**   **c**

Calculate the circumference of each circle. (Take $\pi = 3.14$)

3 Calculate the circumference of each circle. (Take $\pi = 3.14$)

  a 7 cm   **b** 8 m   **c** 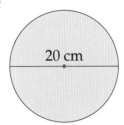 20 cm   **d** 2.5 m

4 A circle fits exactly inside a square.

The square has sides of length 10 cm.

  a Calculate the perimeter of the square.

  b Using $\pi = 3.14$, calculate the circumference of the circle.

  c Explain why you know the answer to part **a** should be larger than the answer to part **b**.

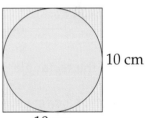

10 cm

10 cm

Make a collection of circular objects, such as coins, plates and so on.

Use a ruler and string to measure the diameter and the circumference of your objects.

Copy and complete the table to show your results.

	Circumference (C)	Diameter (d)	$C \div d$
Coin			
Plate			

Circumference ÷ diameter should be about the same number for each circle.

What is this number?

- Know the names of parts of a circle
- Calculate the area of a circle

Keywords
Chord   Segment
Sector   Semicircle

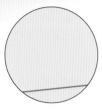 A **chord** is a line joining two points on the circumference.

 A **segment** is the region enclosed between a chord and an arc.

A **diameter** is a chord passing through the centre of the circle.

 A diameter divides a circle into two **semicircles**.

 A **sector** is the region enclosed by an arc and two radii.

You can divide a circle into lots of tiny sectors and rearrange them into a rectangle.

 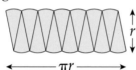

The length of the rectangle is half the circumference, πr, and the width of the rectangle is r.

The smaller you make the sectors, the closer the shape becomes to a rectangle.

Area of the rectangle $= \pi r \times r$

- **Area of a circle $= \pi \times$ radius $\times$ radius**
  Area $= \pi r^2$

where r = radius
$\pi = 3.141\,592\ldots$

example

Calculate the area of each circle. Take π to be 3.14.

a
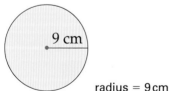
9 cm

radius = 9 cm

b

24 cm

diameter = 24 cm

a Area $= \pi r^2$
   $= 3.14 \times 9 \times 9$
   $= 254.34 \, \text{cm}^2$

b Radius $= 24 \div 2 = 12 \, \text{cm}$
   Area $= \pi r^2$
      $= 3.14 \times 12 \times 12$
      $= 452.16 \, \text{cm}^2$

Area is measured in square units, such as square centimetres.

Exercise 2f

1 Draw these circles on centimetre square grid paper.
First estimate and then calculate the area of each circle.

a   **b** 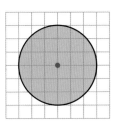   **c**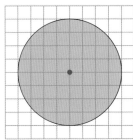

Take $\pi = 3.14$ for all the questions on this page.

2 Calculate the area of each circle.

a 7 cm

b 16 cm

Did you know?

Archimedes (287–212 BC) showed that the area of a circle equals the area of a right-angled triangle of base the circle's circumference and height its radius.

3 Calculate the area of these shapes.

a 10 cm

b 16 cm

c 3 cm

4 Calculate the area of the shaded regions.

a 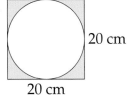 20 cm / 20 cm

b 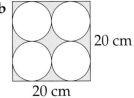 20 cm / 20 cm

5 A church window is made using a semicircle and a rectangle.
Calculate the area of glass in the window.

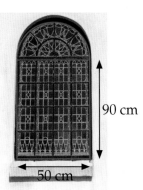

90 cm

50 cm

task

The radius of a circle is doubled.
Does the area of the circle double?
Explain your answer.

2a

1 Calculate the number of 10 cm lengths of string that can be cut from a 5 m ball of string.

2 Convert these measurements to the units indicated in brackets.
 a 8.5 l (ml)   **b** 456 mm (cm)   **c** 8.5 ha (m²)   **d** 25 cl (ml)   **e** 4.2 t (kg)

2b

3 Convert these measurements to the units indicated in brackets.
 a 27.5 kg (lbs)   **b** 120 cm (inches)   **c** 135 g (oz)
 d 750 ml (pints)   **e** 850 miles (km)

4 Write down each reading on the scales.
Give an answer for each arrow.

a  cm   **b** kg   **c** litres

2c

5 Six identical rectangles are arranged in the shape of a large rectangle.

Calculate the area of one of the rectangles.

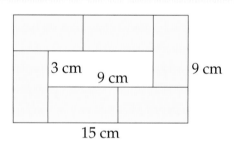

6 The area of all these triangles is 40 cm².
Calculate the unknown values.

a h, 8 cm   **b** 5 cm, b **c** h, 6.4 cm   **d** h, 4 cm

2d

7 Calculate the areas of the parallelogram and trapezia.

a 7.5 cm, 9 cm   **b** 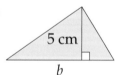 20 cm, 12 cm, 36 cm   **c** 0.5 m, 2 m, 2 m

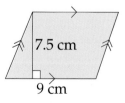
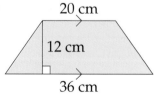
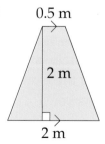
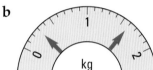

8 The area of the parallelogram and the trapezium are the same.
Calculate the value of h.

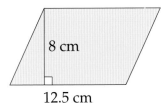

8 cm

12.5 cm

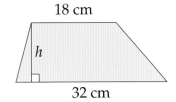

18 cm

h

32 cm

9 A penny-farthing was a type of bike used in the 19th century.
The diameter of the large wheel is 120 cm and is 3 times larger than the diameter of the small wheel.
Calculate
a the diameter of the small wheel
b the circumference of the small wheel
c the circumference of the large wheel.

The large wheel turns one complete revolution.
d How many times will the small wheel turn?

Use $\pi = 3.14$ for the remaining questions on this page.

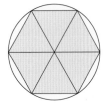

10 Six equilateral triangles of side 6 cm are arranged to form a hexagon.
A circle is drawn passing through the vertices of the hexagon.
Calculate the circumference of the circle.

11 A circular pond has a radius of 5 metres.
Calculate the surface area of the water.

12 The 'No entry' sign consists of a white rectangle on a red circle of radius 30 cm.
The rectangle has dimensions of 50 cm by 11.5 cm.
Calculate the red area of the sign.

Assessment criteria
- Use the formulae for the area of a triangle and a parallelogram **Level 6**
- Know and use the formulae for the circumference and area of a circle **Level 6**

Level 6

1 Calculate the perimeter of the semicircle.
State the units of your answer.

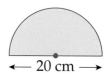

← 20 cm →

Rowais' answer ✔

The circumference of the circle	$= \pi \times diameter$
	$= 3.14 \times 20$
	$= 62.8$ cm
Half of the circumference	$= 31.4$ cm
Perimeter of the semicircle	$= 31.4 + 20$
	$= 51.4$ cm

Rowais first calculates the circumference of a circle with a diameter of 20 cm.

He remembers that perimeter is a length and uses centimetres.

Level 6

2 The diagram shows a shaded parallelogram drawn inside a rectangle.

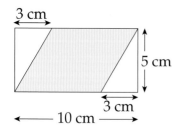

3 cm

5 cm

3 cm

← 10 cm →

What is the area of the shaded parallelogram?
You must give the correct unit with your answer.

KS3 2007 4–6 Paper 2

3 Data

Probability

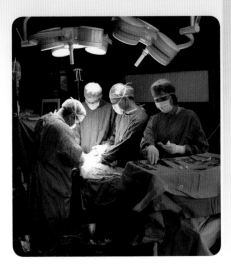

When you go into hospital for an operation many factors affect the chances of success. The reliability of the diagnosis, the risks and success rates for various treatment options, the surgeon's experience, your general state of health, the cleanliness of the hospital,...

You will be expected to weigh up the various options and give your consent for a treatment plan.

What's the point? Knowing how to estimate and combine probabilities can help you make better informed decisions about risky situations.

Check in

1 Simplify

a $\frac{6}{8}$ **b** $\frac{85}{100}$ **c** $\frac{18}{27}$ **d** $\frac{21}{35}$ **e** $\frac{51}{85}$

2 Estimate these probabilities
  a obtaining an odd number on the roll of a fair die.
  b that you get heads tossing a biased coin if P(tails)=0.45
  c that you get a head and tail when you toss two fair coins
  d that two people in a class of 30 share a birthday.

3 Evaluate

a $\frac{3}{16} + \frac{4}{16}$ **b** $\frac{5}{16} + \frac{3}{8}$

c $\frac{3}{7} + \frac{5}{21}$ **d** $\frac{1}{3} + \frac{1}{5} + \frac{1}{7}$

4 A bag contains a large number of sweets. There are as many mints as jelly beans. Complete this table.

	Fraction	Percentage	Decimal
Liquorice		25%	
Chocolate button	$\frac{7}{20}$		
Toffee			0.15
Mint			
Jelly bean			

- Show all the possible outcomes of two or more events in a list or table form

- A list of all the possible **outcomes** of an event or combination of events is called the **sample space**.

example

A restaurant offers a set meal.
How many meal combinations could I choose?

Number of combinations = 2 × 3
= 6

I could have either the soup or the pate with any one of the three main courses.

MENU CARD
Daily Specials
Starters: Tomato Soup
Salmon Pate
Mains: Chicken Casserole
Beef Curry
Mushroom
stroganoff

- A table is useful way to show a sample space when two events have **equally likely** outcomes.

Outcomes that occur with the same probability are called equally likely outcomes.

example

Two fair dice are thrown.
a Show all possible outcomes in a table.

b Calculate the probability of getting a total score of 5.

a

	1	2	3	4	5	6
1	1,1	1,2	1,3	1,4	1,5	1,6
2	2,1	2,2	2,3	2,4	2,5	2,6
3	3,1	3,2	3,3	3,4	3,5	3,6
4	4,1	4,2	4,3	4,4	4,5	4,6
5	5,1	5,2	5,3	5,4	5,5	5,6
6	6,1	6,2	6,3	6,4	6,5	6,6

Each of the 36 outcomes is equally likely.

b

Sum	1	2	3	4	5	6
1	2	3	4	5	6	7
2	3	4	5	6	7	8
3	4	5	6	7	8	9
4	5	6	7	8	9	10
5	6	7	8	9	10	11
6	7	8	9	10	11	12

The sum of the two scores is shown in each of the 36 cells.
Those with a total of 5 are shaded.
$$P\{Sum = 5\} = \frac{4}{36} = \frac{1}{9}$$
You write P(A) for the probability that the event A occurs.

- Probability = $\dfrac{\text{favourable outcomes}}{\text{all outcomes}}$

Exercise 3a

1 Two fair coins are tossed.

   a List all the possible outcomes.

   b Give the probabilities of obtaining

     i 0 heads   **ii** 1 head   **iii** 2 heads.

   c How can you check your answers to part **b**?

To avoid missing outcomes, be methodical when making your list.

2 A fair coin is tossed three times.

   a List all the possible outcomes.

   b In how many of these are

     i exactly 2 heads seen

     ii at least 2 heads seen?

   c What is the probability of getting exactly 2 heads when 3 fair coins are tossed?

3 Anneka goes on a weekend break taking 1 skirt, 3 pairs of trousers and 4 tops.

How many different combinations can she wear of a top with either a skirt or trousers?

4 Anil is buying an ice-cream. He has to choose between having it in a cone or a tub, whether to have vanilla or strawberry flavour and whether to have a flake, sprinkles or not to have either.

Make a list of all the possible combinations he could choose.

5 Two fair dice are thrown.

   a Construct a sample space diagram which shows the higher score showing on the two dice.

   b What is the probability that the higher score showing is a 4?

Hint: your diagram should look similar to that in part **b** of the third example.

investigation

The set menu in a restaurant has these options.

How many menu combinations are possible for someone

   a who has no restrictions on what they will eat

   b who does not like cheese

   c who is a vegetarian?

Set Menu

Starters
Melon (V)
Pâté
Vegetable Soup (V)

Main Courses
Chicken Maryland
Baked Cod
Beef Lasagne
Peppers stuffed
  with stilton cheese (V)

Desserts
Fresh Fruit Salad
Raspberry Pavlova
Cheese selection
Trio of Ice-Creams

(V) beside a starter or main course indicates that it is suitable for vegetarians.

- Construct a simple tree diagram

Keywords
Tree diagram

- A **tree diagram** is used to show a sample space.

This representation is useful when you have more than two events or when the outcomes are not equally likely.

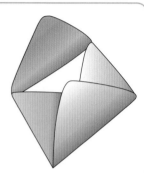

example

Jacques wins a competition and gets to pick one of three identical envelopes which contain £100, £200 or 300. Before he opens his chosen envelope he also gets to decide whether to accept a 50:50 'double or nothing' option.

a Show all the possible outcomes in a tree diagram.

b i What is the probability that he wins a least £300?

  ii What is the probability that he wins nothing?

a Envelope   Double money? ◄──────── Label each tier of branches.

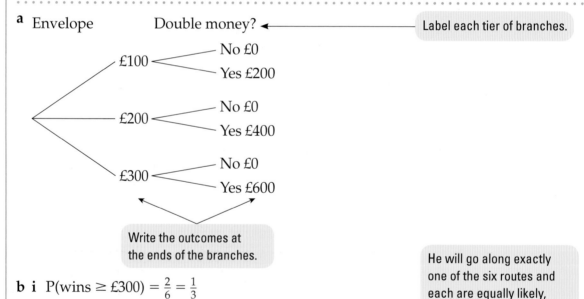

Write the outcomes at the ends of the branches.

b i P(wins ≥ £300) = $\frac{2}{6} = \frac{1}{3}$

  ii P(wins nothing) = $\frac{3}{6} = \frac{1}{2}$

He will go along exactly one of the six routes and each are equally likely, P = $\frac{1}{6}$.

The outcomes at the end of each set of branches are all distinct and can only be reached via one route through the tree.
You select either the £100, £200 or £300 envelope and say either yes or no to the 'double or nothing' option.

Exercise 3b

1 A bag contains one red, one blue and one green ball which are identical except for their colours. A ball is taken out, its colour noted and it is put back in the bag, then a second ball is taken out.

   a Draw a tree diagram to show all the possibilities for the colours of the two balls.

   b i What is the probability that red is seen at least once?

     ii What is the probability that green is not seen?

2 Repeat question 2 but this time assume that the first ball is not put back in the bag.

3 The journey Ms Atmar takes to school goes through two sets of traffic lights.

   a Draw a tree diagram to show all the possibilities for having to 'stop' or 'go' at the two sets of lights.

She notices that the first set of lights is on red $\frac{1}{3}$ of the time and the second $\frac{2}{5}$ of the time.

   b If she makes 150 journeys to school in a year, add to the label on each branch the number of journeys that satisfy the conditions for that branch.

   c Using your results from part b calculate the probabilities that she stops at

     i neither set of lights

     ii one set of lights

     iii both sets of lights.

50 journeys will involve stopping at the first set of lights.

In the example, if Jacques could open the envelope before deciding whether to accept the 'double or nothing' option, what would you advise him to do?

- Be able to identify mutually exclusive outcomes.
- Know that probabilities for mutually exclusive events add.

Keywords
Mutually exclusive

- Two outcomes are **mutually exclusive** if they can not happen at the same time.

example

You throw a die; which pairs of these events are mutually exclusive?

A: an odd number   B: a factor of 6   C: a multiple of 4

- -

A: 1, 3 or 5   B: 1, 2, 3 or 6   C: 4 only

A and C together with B and C are mutually exclusive
A and B are not mutually exclusive

A and B both occur if a
1 or a 3 is thrown.

- If a set of mutually exclusive events covers all possible outcomes then their sum of probabilities is 1.

A special case is
$P(\text{not } A) = 1 - P(A)$

example

I roll two fair dice and am interested in whether they show a 5 or 6.
a Illustrate the outcomes using a sample space diagram.
b Calculate the probabilities that
  i   neither dice shows 5 or 6   **ii** both dice show 5 or 6
  iii only one die show 5 or 6   **iv** at least one die shows 5 or 6

- -

a

	1	2	3	4	5	6
1	1, 1	1, 2	1, 3	1, 4	1, 5	1, 6
2	2, 1	2, 2	2, 3	2, 4	2, 5	2, 6
3	3, 1	3, 2	3, 3	3, 4	3, 5	3, 6
4	4, 1	4, 2	4, 3	4, 4	4, 5	4, 6
5	5, 1	5, 2	5, 3	5, 4	5, 5	5, 6
6	6, 1	6, 2	6, 3	6, 4	6, 5	6, 6

Check: since the four outcomes are mutually exclusive $\frac{1}{9} + \frac{2}{9} + \frac{2}{9} + \frac{4}{9} = 1$ the total probability

b i P(neither dice shows 5 or 6)   blue cells
    $= \frac{16}{36} = \frac{4}{9}$

ii P(both dice show 5 or 6) $= \frac{4}{36} = \frac{1}{9}$ green cells

iii P(only one die shows 5 or 6)
    = P(first die shows a 5 or 6   purple cells
       and second does not)   and
    + P(second die shows a 5 or 6   yellow cells
       and first does not)
    $= \frac{8}{36} + \frac{8}{36} = \frac{4}{9}$

iv P(at least one die shows 5 or 6)
    $= 1 - P(\text{neither die shows 5 or 6}) = 1 - \frac{4}{9} = \frac{5}{9}$

Exercise 3c

1 For each of the following pairs of events say whether or not they are mutually exclusive.
  a i   March 2nd will be the hottest day of next year.
    ii it will snow on March 2nd next year.
  b the total score when three ordinary dice are thrown will be
    i prime   ii even
  c a rugby player can play international rugby for
    i New Zealand   ii Ireland.

2 A red and a blue dice are thrown together.
  a Which pairs of the following events are mutually exclusive?
    A the sum of the scores is odd
    B the red and the blue dice show the same score
    C the total score is less than 5
    D the red dice is at least 3 more than the blue dice.
  b Give three more pairs of mutually exclusive events.
    Define any new events that you use.

3 A die is thrown twice and whether the score is even or odd is recorded each time.
  a Draw a sample space diagram to represent this situation.
  b Calculate the probability that the **product** of the scores showing is even.
  c Using the answer to part **b**, write down the probability that the product of the scores is odd.

4 A fair coin is tossed three times.
  a Draw a tree diagram to show all the possible outcomes.
  b Use your tree diagram to calculate the probability of getting
    i exactly 2 heads.   ii at least 2 heads.
  c The event 'not at least 2 heads' is the same as '0 or 1 head'.
    i Use the tree diagram to calculate the probability of getting 0 or 1 head.
    ii Show that this equals 1 − P(at least 2 heads).

Without making a new list, answer the following.
  a i   If I toss a coin 4 times and list all possible outcomes, many are there?
    ii How many of these would have exactly 1 head?
  b If the coin was tossed 5 times how many possible outcomes would a complete list contain?
    How many of these would have exactly 1 head?
  c Can you see any way to generalise to say what these would be if there were 10 tosses?

Hint: look back at the list in questions **1** and **2**, spread **3a**

- Estimate probabilities based on an experiment or simulation

Keywords
Experimental probability
Simulation

It is not always possible to calculate probabilities using reasoning.

- To estimate a probability, repeat an experiment several times and calculate the proportion of successes

Experiments are sometimes called trials.

$$\text{Experimental probability} = \frac{\text{number of successes}}{\text{number of trials}}$$

You can also use historic data to estimate probabilities

example

Hans is a zoologist who wants to know the relative sizes of the populations of three species of African monkeys, labelled A, B and C. He records 60 observations.
a Estimates the proportions of each species.
b How could Hans get better estimates?
c Out of another 120 monkeys, Hans counted 62 As, 47 Bs and 11 Cs.
  Give the best estimate you can now of the proportions.

A- 26
B- 27
C- 7

a Number A = 26   Best estimate $= \frac{26}{60} = 43\%$

    B = 27 $= \frac{27}{60} = 45\%$

    C = 7 $= \frac{7}{60} = 12\%$

If Hans recorded another 60 observations, it is almost certain that he would get different results.
Therefore it does not make sense to give exact values, like 43.3%.

b If Hans took a larger sample, he is more likely to get estimates close to the true proportions.

c Combining the two samples gives the best estimates.

    Number A = 26 + 62 = 88   Best estimate $= \frac{88}{180} = 49\%$

    B = 27 + 47 = 74 $= \frac{74}{180} = 41\%$

    C = 7 + 11 = 18 $= \frac{18}{180} = 10\%$

There are about 50%, 40% and 10% of the three species of monkey.

- The larger the sample size, the more accurate the estimated probabilities are likely to be.

Computer **simulations** are now used widely to estimate probabilities of complicated sequences of events, where to calculate the theoretical probability by a tree diagram or similar would be too difficult.

Exercise 3d

1 Keith has a swipe card to enter the building he works in.
The system records the time the card is first used each day.
He is supposed to be at work by 8.30 am.
Over a month the times recorded were:

8.27	8.24	8.27	8.31	8.30	8.26	8.25	8.29	8.32	8.26	8.28
8.31	8.25	8.27	8.26	8.35	8.26	8.24	8.27	8.27	8.25	8.27

Estimate the probability that Keith is late for work on a
randomly chosen day.

2 a Make up a tally chart and frequency table for the number
of times the vowels (a, e, i, o and u) appear on the page
facing this one.
 b Give an estimate of the probability of a vowel in English
being an e.

3 Choose another page from this book at random.
 a Would you expect the proportion of vowels which
are e to be the same on that page?
 b Repeat question **2** for that page.
 c Is the answer the same?
 d How could you get a more reliable estimate of the
probability of a vowel being an e?

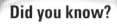

Did you know?

The relative frequency
of letters and letter
combinations is used to
crack secret ciphers.

4 a What is the probability that the page number of a page
chosen at random from the first chapter of this book will
contain the digit 1?
 b Could this be used as an estimate of the probability that a
page chosen at random from the book will contain the digit 1?

5 How could you estimate the probability of
 a being struck by lightening
 b it raining on your next birthday
 c Liverpool winning the next premiership league title?

> If you used a story book for children or a university history textbook, instead of this
> textbook, would you expect the estimate of the probability of a vowel being e to be
> the same, or higher, or lower?

- Compare experimental observations and theoretically predicted probabilities

Keywords

Experimental probability
Sample

example

A coin is tossed 40 times and shows 18 heads and 22 tails.

a Do these results suggest the coin is biased?

b If it is tossed another 40 times, will it show 18 heads again?

. . . .

a No. On average a fair coin will show 20 heads in 40 tosses, but anything from about 15 up to about 25 heads will be seen quite frequently in 40 tosses of a fair coin.

b It is possible to get 18 heads again but not very likely.

> There is about a 10% chance of getting 18 heads in 40 tosses of a fair coin.

- The more data used to estimate an **experimental probability,** the more reliable is the result.

example

Harriet is an archaeologist studying skeletons found at an ancient burial site. It is known that people who lived in that area had head circumferences in three size categories which occurred in the proportions:

A 20%   B 50%   C 30%

Historians speculate that the area was invaded about this time.

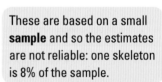

a Of the first 12 skeletons which Harriet studied, 1 is of size A, 7 are size B and 4 are size C.

Does this suggest that the proportions of the different sizes of heads are different from the known population of the area?

b A total of 236 skeletons are recovered, with 27 of size A, 161 of size B and 48 of size C. Does this support the suggestion that a different group of people invaded the area?

. . . .

a The estimated proportions are:

A $\frac{1}{12} = 8\%$ B $\frac{7}{12} = 58\%$ C $\frac{4}{12} = 33\%$

It is not possible to say anything strong in support of a difference.

> These are based on a small **sample** and so the estimates are not reliable: one skeleton is 8% of the sample.

b The estimated proportions are:

A $\frac{27}{236} = 11\%$ B $\frac{161}{236} = 68\%$ C $\frac{48}{236} = 20\%$

The evidence suggests that the people were not from the local population.

> These are based on a large sample so the estimates should be close to the true proportions: one skeleton is 0.4% of the sample.

Exercise 3e

1 Darrell says that the chance of getting 1 head when you toss 2 fair coins is $\frac{1}{3}$.
Ekaterina says he is wrong, and she will prove it to him. She tosses a pair of
fair coins 40 times and the table shows the outcomes.

Number of heads	0	1	2
Frequency	8	21	11

   a Do you think Darrell is right that the probability of getting 1 head is $\frac{1}{3}$?

   b Has Ekaterina proved that Darrell is wrong?

2 Dr McDonald is overseeing a drug trial. He has given one
group of patients drug A, another drug B and a third group
a placebo. His results are shown in the table.

	Drug A	Drug B	Placebo
Number in trial	96	10	36
Number cured	72	7	17

Write a short report for Dr McDonald saying whether you
think the drugs are effective and how a future drug trial
might be improved.

A placebo is a 'dummy'
medicine.

3 Kenny is testing a set of roulette wheels to see if they
are biased. He spins each wheel 60 times and records how
often the ball lands in one of three groups of numbers.

	1–12	13–24	25–36
Wheel 1	23	22	15
Wheel 2	17	19	22
Wheel 3	16	17	27
Wheel 4	20	18	22

   a Calculate the theoretical probability of landing in each of
the three groups of numbers.

   b For each wheel, calculate the experimental probabilities of
landing in each of the three groups of numbers.

   c Should Kenny recommend that the casino continues to
use these wheels?

   d For each wheel, do the experimental probabilities add up to 1?
If not, why not?

A European roulette wheel
has numbers from 0 to 36
equally spaced around its
edge.

If Ekaterina had tossed the pair of coins 4000 times in question **1**, would this have
been a proof that Darrell is wrong?
Can you think of any way to provide a **proof** in a situation like this?

- Simulate experimental data using a model.

Keywords
Model
Simulate

Sometimes it is too difficult to calculate probabilities using reasoning. However it may be possible to use a **model** to **simulate** the physical situation.

> A model is a set of rules to describe a situation.
> A simulation is an implementation of the rules.

Mathematical models are now used widely. Examples include studying the aerodynamics of vehicles, the behaviour of financial markets, the growth of cancer cells, climate change,…

> The random number button on a calculator generates numbers between 0 and 1 in such a way that each number is equally likely.

example

Use a calculator to simulate the outcome of rolling a fair die 12 times.

. . . .

Generate a random number

If the tenths digit is 1, 2,…6 use this as the die's score
Else generate a new random number.
Repeat until you have 10 scores.

> $0.3247668 \rightarrow 3$
> $0.0982445 \rightarrow$ reject

A computer simulation using random numbers is highly unlikely to give the same results twice.

> A simulation should be run several times to see how the values vary.

example

A simulation of rolling a die ten times is repeated ten times and the number of occasions when a prime factor of 12 appears is recorded.
2, 4, 3, 6, 4, 7, 3, 4, 4, 5

a Calculate the theoretical probability of getting a prime factor of 12.
b Estimate the same probability using the results of the simulation.
c Do you think a fair die was being simulated?

. . . .

a P(prime factor of 12) = P(2 or 3) = $\frac{2}{6} = \frac{1}{3}$

b Each individual simulation gives probabilities $\frac{2}{10} = 0.2$, $\frac{4}{10} = 0.4$,…, $\frac{5}{10} = 0.5$

A better estimate would be to take the mean of the ten simulations

estimated P(prime factor of 12) = $\frac{(0.2 + 0.4 + … + 0.5)}{10} = \frac{4.2}{10} = 0.42$

The range of the estimates is $0.7 - 0.2 = 0.5$

c The theoretical probability for a fair die is 0.3 which is close to the majority of values obtained in the simulation.

Therefore it is reasonable to think that a fair die was being simulated.

Exercise 3e²

1 For each simulation write out the rules used.
  a Use a calculator to simulate tossing a fair coin ten times
  b Use a calculator to simulate tossing a biased coin ten times if
    i P(heads) = 0.6   ii P(heads) = $\frac{1}{3}$

2 a Estimate P(heads) using your results from question **1b i**.
  b Repeat part **a** of this question nine more times.
    Do you get the same estimate for P(heads) each time?
    If not, why not?
  c What is the best estimate of P(heads) using your
    simulated data?

3 a Using your ten experiments from questions **1a** and **2b**
    estimate the probability of getting a run of three or more
    consecutive heads.
  b How do you expect this probability to depend on P(heads)?

4 A coin is tossed 10 times and the number of heads recorded. The
  result of 30 repeat experiments is shown in the bar chart on the left.
  A simulation, using P(heads) = 0.5, is shown on the right.

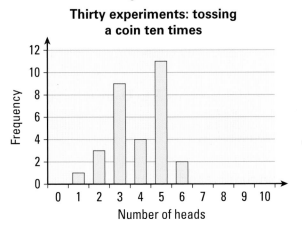

Thirty experiments: tossing a coin ten times

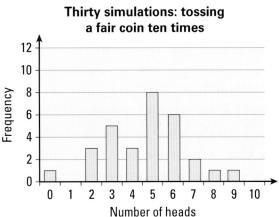

Thirty simulations: tossing a fair coin ten times

Do you think that the coin used in the experiment is biased?
Explain your reasoning.

Using the simulation in the spread sheet supplied, investigate the effect of changing P(heads) on the number of heads obtained when tossing a coin ten times.
Describe what you find.

Using your results from your investigation, estimate P(heads) for the coin used in the experiment in question **4**.

3a

1 A spinner with 3 equal sections coloured red, green and white is spun twice.
   a List all the possible outcomes.
   b In how many of these do you get a red and a green?
   c In how many of these do you not get a white?

2 Two fair dice are thrown.
   a Construct a sample space diagram which shows the product of the scores showing on the two dice.
   b What is the probability that the product is at least 20?

3 A lunch menu includes 3 starters, 4 main courses and 2 desserts. How many different menu combinations are there for someone who can eat anything on the menu?

3b

4 A bag contains one black, one white and one purple ball which are identical except for their colours. A ball is taken out, its colour noted and then replaced before a second ball is taken out.
   a Draw a tree diagram to show the possibilities of the colurs of the two balls.
   b **i** What is the probability that the two balls are a black and white?
      ii What is the probability that the two balls are the same colour?

3c

5 A white and a black dice are thrown together and the events A to D are defined as
      A the sum of the scores is even
      B the white and the black dice show different scores
      C the total score is less than 3
      D the difference between the scores is not more than 1.
   Explain why these pairs of events are mutually exclusive or not
   i A and B   **ii** B and D   **iii** B and C

6 The faces of a regular tetrahedron are labelled 1–4 and those of a regular octahedron 1–8. They are both rolled and the number on the bottom face is counted.
   a List all possible outcomes.
   b Use your list to calculate the probabilities that
      i both show prime numbers   **ii** only one shows a prime number.
   c Without looking at your list, what is the probability that neither shows a prime number?

7 Jorge is making stakes which should be about 1.3 m long.
The lengths of a number of stakes he has made are listed below.

1.27, 1.24, 1.27, 1.31, 1.30, 1.26, 1.25, 1.29, 1.32, 1.26, 1.28
1.31, 1.25, 1.27, 1.26, 1.35, 1.26, 1.24, 1.27, 1.27, 1.25, 1.27

  a Estimate the probability that one of his stakes is longer than 1.3 m.
  b Explain how a better estimate of this probability could be made.

8 How could you estimate the following probabilities?
  a A vowel chosen at random in French is an `a´.
  b The National Lottery has a single jackpot winner in the next draw.
  c Seeing at least 1 six when 3 dice are thrown together.

9 A trainee in a bank is surprised at how often transactions he sees start
with the digit 1. He does a quick tally of 100 transactions.

first digit	1	2	3	4	5	6	7	8	9
frequency	33	19	14	10	6	5	3	4	6

Do you think 1 to 9 are equally likely to occur as the first digit of
transactions?

10 An otherwise fair die is biased so that 5 and 6 are both three times as
likely to occur as the digits 1–4.
  a What are the individual probabilities of obtaining the numbers 1–6?
  b Use a calculator to simulate rolling such a die three times. Write
down the rules which you use and your results.
  c Repeat your simulation nine more times and use the results to
estimate the average sum of the three scores.
  d How could you improve the accuracy of your estimate?

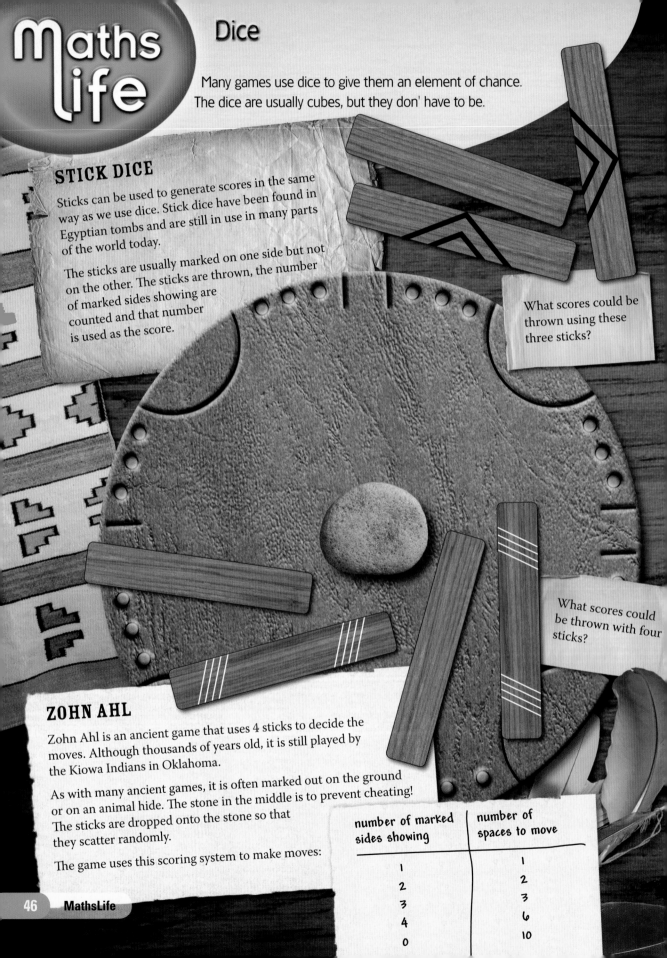

Maths Life

Dice

Many games use dice to give them an element of chance.
The dice are usually cubes, but they don' have to be.

STICK DICE

Sticks can be used to generate scores in the same way as we use dice. Stick dice have been found in Egyptian tombs and are still in use in many parts of the world today.

The sticks are usually marked on one side but not on the other. The sticks are thrown, the number of marked sides showing are counted and that number is used as the score.

What scores could be thrown using these three sticks?

What scores could be thrown with four sticks?

ZOHN AHL

Zohn Ahl is an ancient game that uses 4 sticks to decide the moves. Although thousands of years old, it is still played by the Kiowa Indians in Oklahoma.

As with many ancient games, it is often marked out on the ground or on an animal hide. The stone in the middle is to prevent cheating! The sticks are dropped onto the stone so that they scatter randomly.

The game uses this scoring system to make moves:

number of marked sides showing	number of spaces to move
1	1
2	2
3	3
4	6
0	10

GINS

This is another game that uses four sticks to generate scores. It is played by the Tohono O'odham, a group of aboriginal Americans who live in the Sonoran Desert, which links south west America and Mexico.

The sticks are traditionally made from cactus plants and are marked on one side only, with each stick having a different symbol. Points are scored like this:

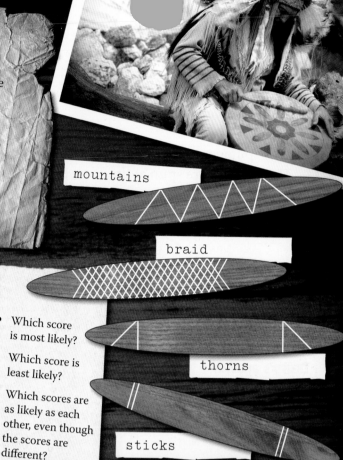

mountains

braid

thorns

sticks

Land showing	points
Sticks and 3 unmarked sides	4
Thorns and 3 unmarked sides	6
Braid and 3 unmarked sides	14
Mountains and 3 unmarked sides	15
Any 2 designs and 2 unmarked sides	2
Any 3 designs and 1 unmarked side	3
All 4 designs	5
All unmarked sides	10

- Which score is most likely?
- Which score is least likely?
- Which scores are as likely as each other, even though the scores are different?

DICE OF OTHER SHAPES

Some games use different shaped dice to give different ranges of numbers.

Make your own game of chance using dice of some sort. Weight the scores however you like.

- How many regular solids are there?
- Can a fair dice be made from a shape that is not a regular solid?
- What makes a dice fair?
- What other shapes would make fair dice?

- Why do you think these shapes have been chosen for the dice? Think about their faces and their angles.
- Would this be a good shape for a dice?

3 Summary

Assessment criteria
- Know the sum of probabilities of all mutually exclusive outcomes is 1 **Level 6**
- Systematically record mutually exclusive outcomes for single events and two successive events **Level 6**

1 Two spinners are numbered 1, 3, 5 and 2, 4, 6.
The pointers are spun at the same time.

Spinner A   Spinner B

a Draw a diagram to show all the possible outcomes.
b What is the probability that the sum of the spinners is 7?

Daisy's answer ✔

Daisy decides to draw a sample space diagram to show the outcomes.

a

		Spinner A		
		1	3	5
Spinner B	2	(2, 1)	(2, 3)	(2, 5)
	4	(4, 1)	(4, 3)	(4, 5)
	6	(6, 1)	(6, 3)	(6, 5)

b $\frac{3}{9} = \frac{1}{3}$

Daisy decides to write the probability as a fraction.

The 3 outcomes when the sum is 7 are (6, 1), (4, 3) and (2, 5)

2 In a bag, there are only red, white and yellow counters.
I am going to take a counter out of the bag at random.

> The probability that it will be red is more than $\frac{1}{4}$.
> It is twice as likely to be white as red.

Give an example of how many counters of each colour there could be.
Write numbers in the sentence below.

There could be _____ red, _____ white and _____ yellow counters.

KS3 2008 4–6 Paper 2

4 Number

Fractions, decimals and percentages

Try multiplying these Roman numerals.

XXIV × CLX

It is much easier written as 24 × 160. Working with fractions was even harder — the Romans wrote these in base 12.

Life became easier with the adoption of Arabic numerals. John Napier (1550–1617) improved things further by promoting the use of a decimal point to tell us where the integer part of a number stops and the fractional part starts.

What's the point? Using good notation allows calculations to be done efficiently and reliably.

✓ Check in

1 Write these decimals as fractions.

   a 1.5   **b** 0.78   **c** 0.125

> Write any fractions in their simplest form.

2 Write these fractions as decimals without using a calculator.

   a $\frac{7}{10}$ **b** $\frac{27}{20}$ **c** $\frac{13}{25}$ **d** $\frac{35}{40}$

3 Calculate each of these additions and subtractions, giving your answer as a fraction.

   a $\frac{2}{5} + \frac{1}{4}$ **b** $\frac{6}{7} - \frac{2}{3}$

4 Use a mental method to calculate

   a $1\frac{2}{3}$ of £39   **b** $\frac{7}{8}$ of 400 kg

5 Calculate each of these.

   a $10 \times \frac{4}{7}$ **b** $8 \div \frac{2}{3}$

6 Copy and complete this table.

Fraction	Decimal	Percentage
$\frac{13}{20}$		
	0.125	

- Convert between decimals and fractions
- Order fractions

Keywords
Recurring decimal
Terminating decimal

- A decimal is another way of writing a fraction.

To write a terminating decimal as a fraction you can use your knowledge of place values.

A **terminating decimal** is one whose last digits are all zero.
0.01206
= 0.01206000000...

example

Convert these decimals into fractions in their simplest form.

a 0.6   **b** 0.15   **c** 0.315

$$0.6 = \frac{6}{10} \xrightarrow[\div 2]{\div 2} \frac{3}{5} \qquad 0.15 = \frac{15}{100} \xrightarrow[\div 5]{\div 5} \frac{3}{20} \qquad 0.315 = \frac{315}{1000} \xrightarrow[\div 5]{\div 5} \frac{63}{200}$$

- You can use division to convert a fraction into a decimal by dividing the numerator by the denominator.

A **recurring decimal** is one whose last digits keep repeating.
0.3333333...
0.012345454545 ...

example

Convert $\frac{4}{33}$ into a decimal using short division.

$$\frac{4}{33} = 4 \div 33$$
$$= 0.1212...$$
$$= 0.1\dot{2}$$

$$\begin{array}{r} 0.1212... \\ 33\overline{)4.0000} \\ {}^{4\,7\,4\,7} \end{array}$$

In a recurring decimal you use dot notation to show which digits repeat.
0.1111...   = 0.$\dot{1}$
0.0121212... = 0.0$\dot{1}\dot{2}$
0.00123123... = 0.00$\dot{1}$2$\dot{3}$

- You can compare and order fractions and decimals by converting them into decimals.

example

Put these fractions and decimals in order from lowest to highest.

$\frac{2}{9}$ $\frac{3}{11}$ 0.22

Convert any fractions into decimals using division.

$\frac{2}{9} = 2 \div 9 = 0.222...$ $\frac{3}{11} = 3 \div 11 = 0.2727...$ 0.22

Order the decimals.   0.22   0.222...   0.2727...

So the order is   0.22 $\frac{2}{9}$ $\frac{3}{11}$

Exercise 4a

1 Write these decimals as fractions in their simplest form.

    a 0.4   **b** 1.12   **c** 0.36   **d** 0.98   **e** 0.166

2 Write these fractions as decimals without using a calculator.

    a $\frac{3}{10}$ **b** $\frac{23}{20}$ **c** $\frac{19}{25}$ **d** $\frac{63}{50}$ **e** $\frac{55}{25}$

    f $\frac{8}{5}$ **g** $\frac{3}{20}$ **h** $\frac{33}{40}$ **i** $\frac{14}{16}$ **j** $\frac{85}{80}$

3 Change these fractions into decimals using division. Use an appropriate method. Give your answers to 5 decimal places where appropriate.

    a $\frac{5}{16}$ **b** $\frac{3}{32}$ **c** $\frac{4}{11}$ **d** $\frac{3}{7}$ **e** $\frac{17}{6}$

4 Place < or > between these pairs of numbers to show which number is the largest.

    a $0.5 \square \frac{4}{7}$ **b** $\frac{7}{12} \square \frac{5}{8}$ **c** $\frac{3}{7} \square 0.42$ **d** $0.69 \square \frac{11}{16}$

    e $\frac{4}{9} \square 0.45$ **f** $0.462 \square \frac{6}{13}$ **g** $\frac{7}{9} \square 0.8$ **h** $0.1765 \square \frac{3}{17}$

5 Put these fractions and decimals in order from lowest to highest.

    a $\frac{3}{7}$ 0.43 $\frac{7}{16}$ 0.425

    b $\frac{1}{9}$ $\frac{1}{8}$ 0.11   0.12

    c $\frac{4}{7}$ $\frac{19}{33}$ 0.6 $\frac{571}{999}$

6 The variable p represents a decimal number with one decimal place. Write a list of the possible values of p if

    a $\frac{3}{7} < p < \frac{5}{7}$ **b** $\frac{1}{4} < p < \frac{3}{4}$ and $\frac{3}{8} < p < \frac{7}{8}$

7 Given that $\frac{1}{11} = 0.0909\ldots$, work out the decimal equivalents of these fractions without a calculator.

    a $\frac{2}{11}$ **b** $\frac{3}{11}$ **c** $\frac{4}{11}$ **d** $\frac{5}{11}$ **e** $\frac{6}{11}$

    Write down what you notice.

> **Did you know?**
>
> 1 ÷ 81
>
> 0.012 345 678 901
>
> $\frac{1}{81} = 0.012345678$
>
> 901234567890123 …
>
> $= 0.01\overset{\bullet}{2}34567\overset{\bullet}{8}9$

Challenge

Petra changes a fraction into a decimal using her calculator. The answer on her calculator says 0.684 210 526 3. Both the numbers in her fraction are less than 20. What fraction did Petra type into her calculator?

4b Adding and subtracting fractions

- Add and subtract fractions with different denominators

Keywords
Common denominator
Equivalent fractions

- You can add or subtract fractions with different denominators by first writing them as **equivalent fractions** with the same **common denominator**.

example

Calculate

a $\frac{7}{12} + \frac{1}{5}$

b $\frac{7}{18} - \frac{5}{24}$

a

$$\frac{7}{12} \overset{\times 5}{\underset{\times 5}{=}} \frac{35}{60} \qquad \frac{1}{5} \overset{\times 12}{\underset{\times 12}{=}} \frac{12}{60}$$

The common denominator is 60.
This is the LCM of 12 and 5.

Add the numerators

$$\frac{35}{60} + \frac{12}{60} = \frac{35 + 12}{60} = \frac{47}{60}$$

b

$$\frac{7}{18} \overset{\times 4}{\underset{\times 4}{=}} \frac{28}{72} \qquad \frac{5}{24} \overset{\times 3}{\underset{\times 3}{=}} \frac{15}{72}$$

The common denominator is 72.
This is the LCM of 18 and 24.

Subtract the numerators

$$\frac{28}{72} - \frac{15}{72} = \frac{28 - 15}{72} = \frac{13}{72}$$

example

Calculate $2\frac{3}{8} - 1\frac{7}{12}$

$$2\frac{3}{8} = \frac{19}{8} \qquad 1\frac{7}{12} = \frac{19}{12}$$

$$\frac{19}{8} \overset{\times 3}{\underset{\times 3}{=}} \frac{57}{24} \qquad \frac{19}{12} \overset{\times 2}{\underset{\times 2}{=}} \frac{38}{24}$$

The common denominator is 24.
This is the LCM of 8 and 12.

$$\frac{57}{24} - \frac{38}{24} = \frac{57 - 38}{24} = \frac{19}{24}$$

$$2\frac{3}{8} - 1\frac{7}{12} = \frac{19}{24}$$

MEMO

Adding and subtracting fractions

- Convert mixed numbers to improper fractions (that's top heavy ones).
- Use a common denominator (LCM).
- Only add or subtract the numerators.
- Change back to a mixed number.
- Write the fraction in its lowest terms.

Exercise 4b

1 Calculate each of these.

a $\frac{3}{7} + \frac{1}{7}$ **b** $\frac{17}{20} - \frac{7}{20}$ **c** $1\frac{7}{12} + 2\frac{6}{12}$ **d** $3\frac{4}{9} - 1\frac{7}{9}$

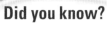

> Give each answer as a fraction in its simplest form.

2 Calculate each of these additions and subtractions.

a $\frac{3}{8} + \frac{5}{9}$ **b** $\frac{4}{7} + \frac{6}{11}$ **c** $\frac{3}{15} + \frac{4}{7}$ **d** $\frac{12}{13} - \frac{13}{15}$

e $\frac{14}{17} - \frac{11}{15}$ **f** $\frac{14}{27} + \frac{3}{16}$ **g** $\frac{5}{16} - \frac{2}{13}$ **h** $\frac{7}{12} + \frac{5}{16}$

3 Work out these.

a $\frac{13}{15} - \frac{7}{30}$ **b** $\frac{14}{15} + \frac{9}{20}$ **c** $\frac{17}{28} - \frac{14}{35}$ **d** $\frac{17}{20} + \frac{7}{24}$

e $\frac{11}{16} + \frac{7}{24}$ **f** $\frac{21}{32} - \frac{7}{16}$ **g** $\frac{29}{36} + \frac{17}{45}$ **h** $\frac{17}{60} + \frac{11}{36}$

4 a Paige wants to download a very big file from a website. In the first hour she downloads $\frac{2}{7}$ of the file. In the second hour she downloads the next $\frac{3}{8}$ of the file.

     i What fraction of the file has she downloaded after 2 hours?

     ii What fraction of the file has she not yet downloaded?

b Dylan is making a cake. He uses $\frac{3}{4}$ kg of flour, $\frac{3}{8}$ kg of butter and $\frac{7}{16}$ kg of sugar. He puts all the ingredients into a bowl. What is the total weight of the ingredients?

> **Did you know?**
>
>
>
> Musicians use notes of fractional duration:
>
> | | |
> |---|---|
> | breve | 2 notes |
> | semibreve | 1 note |
> | minim | $\frac{1}{2}$ note |
> | crotchet | $\frac{1}{4}$ note |
> | quaver | $\frac{1}{8}$ note |
> | semiquaver | $\frac{1}{16}$ note |

5 Work out these.

a $1\frac{3}{8} + \frac{1}{2}$ **b** $2\frac{1}{4} - \frac{3}{8}$ **c** $2\frac{2}{3} + 2\frac{5}{6}$ **d** $3\frac{3}{10} - 2\frac{3}{5}$

e $2\frac{3}{7} + 1\frac{4}{9}$ **f** $2\frac{3}{5} + 1\frac{2}{3}$ **g** $3\frac{4}{5} - 2\frac{7}{8}$ **h** $1\frac{4}{7} + 2\frac{1}{3}$

6 a A photograph has a length of $4\frac{3}{4}$ inches and a width of $3\frac{1}{3}$ inches. Calculate the perimeter of the photograph.

b Naomi takes a bus journey from Keswick to Seatoller. The total distance is 12 km. How far is it from Rosthwaite to Seatoller?

Keswick

$6\frac{2}{5}$ km

Grange

$3\frac{1}{8}$ km

Seatoller

Rosthwaite

Here are five weights, each with a different mass. You can use the weights to measure the mass of different amounts.

$\frac{3}{4}$ kg $\frac{1}{2}$ kg $\frac{1}{8}$ kg   1 kg $\frac{3}{16}$ kg

a What is the total mass of all five weights?

b Which two weights have a combined mass of $\frac{15}{16}$ kg?

c Investigate what different masses you could weigh using these weights.

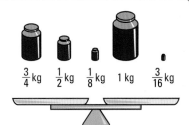

$\frac{3}{4}$ kg $\frac{1}{2}$ kg $\frac{1}{8}$ kg   1 kg $\frac{3}{16}$ kg

- Multiply an integer by a fraction
- Multiply a fraction by a fraction
- Divide a fraction by a fraction

Keywords
Fraction of a number
Inverse rule
Mixed number

- You can find a **fraction of a number** or quantity using multiplication.

example

Calculate $\frac{5}{18}$ of $30\,\text{kg}$.

$\frac{5}{18}$ of 30

$= \frac{5}{18} \times 30 = \frac{5}{18} \times \overset{5}{\cancel{30}}_{3}$ You can use cancellation to simplify the product.

$\qquad = \frac{25}{3} = 8\frac{1}{3}\,\text{kg}$ Convert your answer to a **mixed number** using division.

6 is the HCF of 18 and 30.

- You can multiply fractions using cancelling to simplify the product.

example

Calculate

a $\frac{3}{5} \times \frac{4}{7}$ **b** $\frac{7}{12} \times \frac{6}{11}$

When you multiply a pair of fractions, the numerators are multiplied together and the denominators are multiplied together.

a $\frac{3}{5} \times \frac{4}{7} = \frac{3 \times 4}{5 \times 7}$ **b** $\frac{7}{12} \times \frac{6}{11} = \frac{7}{\cancel{12}_{2}} \times \frac{\cancel{6}^{1}}{11}$

$\qquad\qquad = \frac{12}{35}$ $\qquad\qquad = \frac{7 \times 1}{2 \times 11} = \frac{7}{22}$

Cancel by dividing by 6.

- You can use the inverse rule to divide fractions.

example

Calculate $\frac{2}{5} \div \frac{3}{7}$

$\frac{2}{5} \div \frac{3}{7} = \frac{2}{5} \times \frac{7}{3}$ Change the division into a multiplication and invert the fraction.

$\qquad = \frac{2 \times 7}{5 \times 3}$

$\qquad = \frac{14}{15}$

Inverse rule

Dividing by $\frac{1}{7}$ is the same as multiplying by 7.

Dividing by $\frac{3}{7}$ is the same as multiplying by $\frac{7}{3}$.

Exercise 4c

1 Calculate

a $3 \times \frac{2}{7}$ **b** $4 \times \frac{1}{9}$ **c** $2 \times \frac{5}{16}$ **d** $3 \times \frac{3}{11}$

e $2 \times \frac{5}{14}$ **f** $3 \times \frac{5}{8}$ **g** $4 \times \frac{3}{5}$ **h** $5 \times \frac{7}{8}$

> Always simplify any fractions and write improper fractions as mixed numbers.

2 Calculate

a $6 \times \frac{2}{3}$ **b** $15 \times \frac{3}{10}$ **c** $18 \times \frac{5}{12}$ **d** $15 \times \frac{11}{12}$

e $18 \times \frac{7}{24}$ **f** $15 \times \frac{13}{25}$ **g** $35 \times \frac{9}{14}$ **h** $16 \times \frac{5}{28}$

> Remember to cancel if you can.

3 Calculate

a $\frac{5}{8}$ of 6 feet   **b** $\frac{6}{13}$ of 52   **c** $\frac{4}{9}$ of 12 inches

d $\frac{17}{12}$ of 66 mins   **e** $1\frac{3}{16}$ of 30 GB   **f** $2\frac{7}{10}$ of 110 m

4 Calculate

a $\frac{3}{5} \times \frac{2}{7}$ **b** $\frac{3}{8} \times \frac{5}{6}$ **c** $\frac{3}{4} \times \frac{5}{9}$ **d** $\frac{5}{6} \times \frac{3}{10}$

e $\frac{4}{9} \times \frac{3}{8}$ **f** $\frac{5}{6} \times \frac{9}{20}$ **g** $\frac{6}{7} \times \frac{14}{15}$ **h** $\frac{12}{25} \times \frac{10}{21}$

5 a What is the area of the postcard?

A postcard is $4\frac{1}{2}$ inches wide and $7\frac{3}{4}$ inches long.

b A bag of cherries weighs $\frac{7}{10}$ kg. In a week Hanif eats $2\frac{1}{4}$ bags of cherries.

How many kilograms of cherries does he eat?

$4\frac{1}{2}$ inches

$\longleftarrow 7\frac{3}{4}$ inches $\longrightarrow$

6 A bag of sugar weighs 1 kg. Nial uses $\frac{1}{4}$ of the bag to make some biscuits. Colleen uses $\frac{2}{3}$ of the remaining sugar to make a cake.

i How many grams of sugar are left?

ii What fraction of the bag of sugar is left?

7 Calculate

a $5 \div \frac{5}{6}$ **b** $8 \div \frac{4}{5}$ **c** $6 \div \frac{2}{5}$ **d** $9 \div \frac{3}{7}$

e $5 \div \frac{4}{9}$ **f** $10 \div \frac{4}{7}$ **g** $12 \div \frac{8}{11}$ **h** $15 \div \frac{12}{13}$

8 Calculate

a $\frac{3}{5} \div \frac{4}{7}$ **b** $\frac{5}{8} \div \frac{5}{6}$ **c** $\frac{7}{9} \div \frac{2}{3}$ **d** $\frac{7}{10} \div \frac{5}{7}$

e $\frac{4}{5} \div \frac{3}{8}$ **f** $\frac{8}{9} \div \frac{4}{3}$ **g** $\frac{5}{16} \div \frac{15}{21}$ **h** $\frac{7}{5} \div \frac{21}{10}$

---

a Choose a starting fraction, such as $\frac{3}{7}$.

b Work out $\dfrac{1 - \text{your fraction}}{1 + \text{your fraction}}$ then $\dfrac{1 - \text{new fraction}}{1 + \text{new fraction}}$

c Repeat for several different starting fractions.

d Write what you notice and try to explain what has happened.

4d Percentage change

- Calculate a percentage of an amount
- Calculate a percentage change

Keywords
Percentage increase
Percentage decrease

- You can calculate a percentage of an amount using mental, written and calculator methods.

example

Calculate 11% of £45.

> Remember that $11\% = \frac{11}{100} = 0.11$

Mental method
10% of £45 = £4.50
+ 1% of £45 = £0.45
11% of £45 = £4.95

Written method
11% of £45 = $\frac{11}{100}$ of 45
= $\frac{495}{100}$ = £4.95

Calculator method
11% of £45 = 0.11 of 45
= £4.95

- You can calculate a **percentage increase** or **decrease** in a single calculation using an equivalent decimal.

example

a

b

In a sale all prices are reduced by 22%. A pair of trainers normally cost £80. What is the sale price of the pair of trainers?

Jasmine earns £24 a week from her newspaper round. This week her wage is increased by 7%. What is her new weekly wage?

a Reduce by 22%

78%   100%

In the sale the prices decrease by 22%
Sale price = (100 − 22)% of old price
= 78% of £80
= 0.78 × 80
= £62.40

b Increase by 7%

100% 107%

Jasmine's wage increases by 7%
New wage = (100 + 7)% of old wage
= 107% of £24
= 1.07 × £24
= £25.68

Exercise 4d

1 Calculate these using an appropriate method.

  a 15% of £70 **b** 25% of 180 m **c** 78% of 58 kg **d** 35% of 240 ml
  e 62% of £99 **f** 35% of 85 GB **g** 45% of $58 **h** 99% of 99 m
  i 3% of 120 mm **j** 17.5% of 250 MB **k** 3.5% of 3 m **l** 4.75% of £27 000
  m 60% of 245 km **n** 105% of 665 g **o** 11% of 6 tonnes **p** 2% of £2 500 000

2 Thomas can buy a QII Games Console for one cash payment of £299, or pay a deposit of 30% and then twelve equal monthly payments of £19. Which is the better option? Explain and justify your answer.

> Give all answers to 2dp as necessary

3 Calculate these percentage changes.

  a Increase £40 by 12% **b** Decrease £360 by 21%
  c Increase 48 km by 5% **d** Decrease 36 mm by 15%
  e Increase 125 kg by 18% **f** Decrease £3700 by 35%
  g Increase £19 by 17.5% **h** Decrease 68 kJ by 4.5%

4 a Heather weighs 45 kg.
   Two weeks later her weight has increased by 8%.
   What is Heather's new weight?

  b In a sale all prices are reduced by 30%.
   A CD costs £13 before the sale.
   What is the sale price of the CD?

  c Last month Chris scored 40 marks on a history test.
   This month he improves his score by 15%.
   How many marks did he score in his history test this month?

  d Shahida is given £240 by her uncle. She spends 23% of the money.
   How much money does she have left?

5 Barry plays a computer game every week. Each week he improves his highest score by 13%. This week his highest score is 282 500.
  a What will his highest score be next week?
  b What was his highest score last week?

Did you know?

Metals expand when heated, for example, the length of a copper bar will increase by 0.17% if heated by 100°C. Differences in expansion rates are used to make bimetallic strips that bend when heated or cooled.

---

problem solving

Imran is 6 years old and is 90 cm tall. His father notices that Imran has increased in height by 9% each year for the last two years. If Imran grows at 9% a year:
  a How tall will Imran be when he is 7 years old?
  b How tall will Imran be when he is 10 years old?
  c How tall will Imran be when he is 16 years old?
  d Do you think Imran will grow at 9% a year?
   Explain your answer.

- Use percentage change to solve problems

- You can use **percentage change** to solve problems.

example

In a sale all the prices are reduced by 20%.
A football shirt costs £36 in the sale.
What was the original price of the football shirt?

SALE
20% OFF

SALE PRICE
ONLY £36

Using the **unitary method**
In this method you find
1% of the original price.
So you can say that 80%
of the original price is £36

A 20% reduction means
that the shirt cost 80% of
the original price.

Reduce by 20%

80%   100%

÷80 (80% of the original price = £36) ÷80
×100 { 1% of the original price = £0.45 } ×100
      ↖100% of the original price = £45 ↙

Using the **inverse operation**
method
In this method you use
division to work back to the
original amount.
To work out 80% of the price
you multiply by 0.8

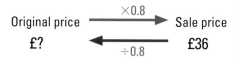

Original price —×0.8→ Sale price
£? ←÷0.8— £36

The inverse of multiplying by
0.8 is dividing by 0.8
Original price = Sale price ÷ 0.8
= £36 ÷ 0.8 = £45

example

Next year the number of students at Notterhall Sports College is expected to increase
by 15% to 966 students. How many students are there in the current year?

A 15% increase means that the number of students will increase to 115% of what it is in
the current year.

Using the **unitary method**

115% of students in current year = 966 students
  1% of students in current year = 966 ÷ 115
                                 = 8.4 students
100% of students in current year = 8.4 × 100
                                 = 840 students

Using the **inverse operation** method

To work out an increase of 15% you
multiply by 1.15
The inverse of multiplying by 1.15 is
dividing by 1.15
Students in current year = 966 ÷ 1.15
                         = 840 students

Exercise 4e

1 Jackson decides to increase the wages of everybody in his factory by 4%.
Copy and complete his new payroll list.

Name	Old wage	New wage
James	£300	
Bernie	£275	
Vikki		£520
Rufus		£364

2 a A pair of trainers are on sale for £84 which is 70% of the original price.
What was the original price of the trainers?

b A computer has been reduced in price by 25% to £345.
What was the original price of the computer?

c A packet of McDitty's chocolate fingers is increased in mass. The label says that the packet is now 35% bigger. The weight of the packet is now 324 g.
What was the original weight of a packet of McDitty's chocolate fingers?

3 a Gareth bought a computer game in a sale and saved £5. The label said that it was a 25% reduction.
What was the original price of the computer game?

b Mandy bought a box of cereal on Monday. On Friday she bought a box of the same cereal but with 30% extra free. Mandy worked out that she got an extra 150 g of cereal in the new packet.
How much cereal was there in the original packet?

4 Violet and Nita each bought an identical coat from the same shop. Violet bought hers on Saturday when there was 20% off the original price. Nita bought hers on Monday when there was 30% off the original price. Violet paid £15 more than Nita.
a What was the original price of the coat?
b How much did Violet pay for the coat?
c How much did Nita pay for the coat?

The population of the Earth in the year 2007 was 6649 million.
a If the population of the Earth has increased by 2% a year, what was the population of the Earth in 2006?
b What was the population of the Earth in the year 2000?
c Investigate the population of the Earth at different times in history.

investigation

- Convert between percentages, fractions and decimals
- Order fractions and percentages by converting them to decimals
- Write a number as a percentage of another number

Keywords
Conversion Fraction
Decimal   Percentage

- You can **convert** between **fractions**, **decimals** and **percentages** using a range of methods.

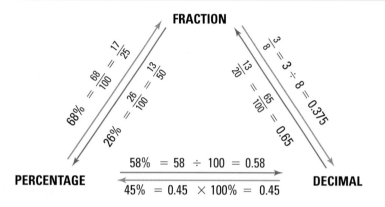

example

Copy and complete this table.

Fraction	Decimal	Percentage
	0.325	
$\frac{3}{7}$		

$0.325 = \frac{325}{1000} \xrightarrow{\div 25} = \frac{13}{40}$ with $\div 25$ below

$0.325 = 0.325 \times 100\% = 32.5\%$

$\frac{3}{7} = 3 \div 7 = 0.429 \, (3\,dp)$

$\frac{3}{7} = (3 \div 7) \times 100\% = 42.9\% \, (1\,dp)$

- You can express the **change** in an amount as a percentage of the original amount.

example

A computer is reduced in price from £420 to £357.
What is the percentage reduction?

Price reduction $= £420 - £357$ Calculate the reduction in price.
        $= £63$

Reduction $= \frac{63}{420}$ of the original price   Express the reduction as a fraction.

Percentage reduction $= (63 \div 420) \times 100\%$ Change the fraction into a percentage using
        $= 15\%$ division.

Check your answer by working out 15% reduction of £420 = 0.85 × 420 = £357

Exercise 4f

1 Copy and complete this table. Clearly show your working out.

Fraction	Decimal	Percentage
$\frac{7}{40}$		
	0.07	
		135%
$\frac{7}{12}$		
	0.0475	

Give your answers as
- decimals to 4 decimal places
- percentages to 2 decimal places
- fractions in their simplest form.

2 These are the marks scored by Seung in his recent exams. He needs to score 35% or more to pass.

a In which subjects did he pass the exam? Explain your answer.

b In which subject did he do the worst? Explain your answer.

c By changing each of his marks to a percentage, put the subjects in order from Seung's worst subject to his best.

EXAM REPORT

Engineering	9/24
Maths	14/40
Media	45/56
German	11/30
Art	12/35
Geography	17/49
Sports Studies	34%

3 a A HD TV is reduced in price from £480 to £408. What is the percentage reduction?

b Last month Vikram earned £2300. This month his pay is £2369. What is the percentage increase in Vikram's pay?

c Last year, the average number of people watching Manchester Rovers home games was 68 000. This year there are an average of 71 400 people watching the games. What is the percentage increase in the crowd at Manchester Rovers?

4 A water tank contains 800 litres of water. At night the water freezes and expands in volume to 872 litres of ice.

a Use this information to work out the percentage increase in volume of water when it turns into ice.

b What practical evidence is there that water expands when it freezes?

---

investigation

Over time the prices of things you buy usually increase. These are the prices of six items in 1982 and in 2007.

a For each item, work out the percentage increase (or decrease) over the 25-year period.

b Investigate price increases over longer periods of time.

c Find out why prices usually increase.

Object	1982 price	2007 price	% increase or decrease
House	£23 000	£195 000	
Salary	£7000	£23 000	
TV	£300	£150	
Petrol (litre)	£0.34	£1.04	
Marz bar	£0.16	£0.45	
Milk (pint)	£0.20	£0.36	
Men Utd season ticket	£64	£437	
Portable music player	£80	£20	

4a

1 Change these fractions into decimals using division. Use an appropriate method.

Give your answers to 5 decimal places where appropriate.

  a $\frac{9}{16}$ **b** $\frac{5}{17}$ **c** $\frac{3}{13}$ **d** $\frac{6}{7}$ **e** $\frac{11}{19}$

2 Place $<$ or $>$ between these pairs of numbers to show which number is the largest.

  a $0.4 \,\square\, \frac{3}{7}$ **b** $\frac{6}{13} \,\square\, \frac{7}{15}$ **c** $\frac{5}{8} \,\square\, 0.6$ **d** $0.39 \,\square\, \frac{7}{19}$

3 Put these fractions and decimals in order from lowest to highest.

  a $\frac{8}{13}$ 0.623 $\frac{5}{8}$ 0.63 **b** $\frac{3}{13}$ $\frac{4}{17}$ 0.229 0.23

4b

4 Work out

  a $\frac{12}{15} - \frac{7}{18}$ **b** $\frac{13}{15} + \frac{11}{25}$ **c** $\frac{14}{27} + \frac{13}{18}$ **d** $\frac{7}{14} + \frac{7}{21}$

  e $\frac{13}{16} + \frac{7}{20}$ **f** $\frac{24}{35} - \frac{5}{28}$ **g** $\frac{23}{36} + \frac{7}{54}$ **h** $\frac{13}{60} + \frac{8}{15}$

In your answers, convert any improper fractions to mixed numbers and write fractions in their simplest form.

5 Hector has $2\frac{1}{2}$ litres of water. Jenny has $\frac{3}{5}$ of a litre of blackcurrant cordial. They mix the two drinks together. What is the total amount of liquid?

6 Work out

  a $2\frac{1}{5} + \frac{1}{3}$ **b** $1\frac{1}{4} - \frac{5}{8}$ **c** $3\frac{2}{5} + 1\frac{2}{3}$ **d** $2\frac{5}{8} - 1\frac{11}{12}$

4c

7 Calculate

  a $\frac{3}{4}$ of 5 yards   **b** $\frac{5}{12}$ of 60 kg   **c** $\frac{3}{8}$ of 20 mm   **d** $\frac{4}{13}$ of 39 km

  e $1\frac{5}{16}$ of 40 miles   **f** $3\frac{7}{8}$ of 200 m²   **g** $1\frac{5}{12}$ of 340 ml   **h** $3\frac{8}{25}$ of 1 century

8 Calculate

  a $\frac{4}{7} \times \frac{5}{3}$ **b** $\frac{2}{5} \times \frac{3}{8}$ **c** $\frac{5}{6} \times \frac{4}{5}$ **d** $\frac{7}{8} \times \frac{3}{4}$

  e $\frac{14}{15} \times \frac{12}{35}$ **f** $\frac{12}{35} \times \frac{15}{21}$ **g** $\frac{27}{16} \times \frac{32}{18}$ **h** $\frac{5}{8} \times \frac{24}{15}$

Use cancellation whenever possible.

9 Calculate

  a $4 \div \frac{4}{7}$ **b** $12 \div \frac{4}{3}$ **c** $16 \div \frac{8}{9}$ **d** $10 \div \frac{5}{7}$

  e $3 \div \frac{5}{11}$ **f** $14 \div \frac{7}{4}$ **g** $15 \div \frac{10}{11}$ **h** $18 \div \frac{9}{13}$

10 Calculate

  a $\frac{4}{7} \div \frac{5}{8}$ **b** $\frac{6}{9} \div \frac{6}{7}$ **c** $\frac{8}{11} \div \frac{3}{4}$ **d** $\frac{8}{13} \div \frac{4}{7}$

  e $\frac{5}{6} \div \frac{4}{9}$ **f** $\frac{9}{10} \div \frac{3}{5}$ **g** $\frac{3}{14} \div \frac{12}{35}$ **h** $\frac{8}{9} \div \frac{32}{45}$

11 Calculate these percentage changes.

    a Increase £50 by 28%   **b** Decrease £640 by 45%

    c Increase 180 km by 6%   **d** Decrease 270 mm by 3.5%

    e Increase 85 kg by 8%   **f** Decrease £9 000 000 by 1.2%

12 **a** Monica earns £35 each weekend, working in her mum's shop.
      Next weekend her pay will be increased by 4%.
      How much will Monica earn next weekend?

    b In a sale all prices are reduced by 15%.
      A DVD costs £12.49 before the sale.
      What is the sale price of the DVD?

13 **a** A computer is on sale for £330 which is 60% of the original price.
      What was the original price of the computer?

    b A Porsche 911 increased in price from 1982 to 2007 by 263%.
      The price for a Porsche 911 in 2007 was £60 621.
      What was the price of the Porsche in 1982?

14 **a** Kerry bought a mobile phone in a sale and saved £12.
      The label said that it was a 15% reduction.
      What was the original price of the mobile phone?

    b In a special offer, a packet of biscuits says that it contains 20% extra.
      The weight of the packet is 64 g heavier than it was before the special offer.
      How much did the packet of biscuits used to weigh?

15 Copy and complete this table.
Show clearly your working out.

Give your answers as
- decimals to 4 decimal places
- percentages to 2 decimal place
- fractions in their simplest form.

Fraction	Decimal	Percentage
$\frac{7}{15}$		
	0.995	
		12.5%
$\frac{4}{13}$		
	1.0377	

16 **a** A CD costs £13. In a sale the price is reduced to £11.44.
      What is the percentage reduction?

    b A computer is reduced in price from £880 to £836.
      What is the percentage reduction?

4 Summary

Assessment criteria
- Calculate percentage increases and decreases **Level 6**
- Add, subtract, multiply and divide fractions **Level 6**

1 Here is some information about some children.

	Boys	Girls
Number of children	23 900	27 000
Percentage of left-handed children	9%	12%

How many more children were left-handed girls than left-handed boys?

Danny's answer ✔

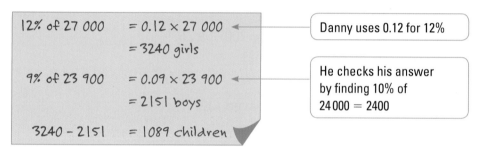

12% of 27 000 $= 0.12 \times 27\ 000$ ← Danny uses 0.12 for 12%
$= 3240$ girls

9% of 23 900 $= 0.09 \times 23\ 900$ ← He checks his answer by finding 10% of 24 000 = 2400
$= 2151$ boys

$3240 - 2151 = 1089$ children

2 a Add $\frac{6}{10}$ and $\frac{6}{5}$

Now use an arrow (↓) to show the result on the number line.

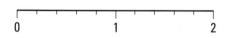

0   1   2

b How many sixths are there in $3\frac{1}{3}$?

c Work out $3\frac{1}{3} \div \frac{5}{6}$

Show your working.

KS3 2003 4–6 Paper 1

5 Algebra

Expressions and formulae

"Philosophy is written in this grand book, the Universe ... which stands continually open to our gaze, but it cannot be understood unless one first learns to comprehend the language and interpret the characters in which it is written. It is written in the language of mathematics ... without which it is humanly impossible to understand a single word of it."

Galileo Galilei, Il Saggiatore (*The Assayer*, 1623)

What's the point? Scientists and engineers use the language of formulae to help them understand and build the world around us.

Check in

1 Evaluate each of these.

   a $4 - 9$ **b** $(-2) + 5$ **c** $6 - (-4)$ **d** $(-2) - 7$

   e $4 \times (-5)$ **f** $(-21) \div 3$ **g** $(-6) \times (-7)$ **h** $(-48) \div (-8)$

2 Given that $a = 2$ and $b = 5$, evaluate each of these.

   a $5a$ **b** $b + 3$ **c** $4b - 3$ **d** $3a + 2b$

   e ab **f** $2(a + 4)$ **g** b^2 **h** $\dfrac{b + 7}{3}$

3 Simplify these algebraic expressions, where possible.

   a $x + x$ **b** $y + y + y$ **c** $2a + a$ **d** $5b - 3b$

   e $5p + q$ **f** $8k - 3$ **g** $7x + y - 2x$ **h** $10m - 4n - 6m + n$

- Use index notation including negative indices
- Use letter symbols
- Substitute into expressions involving powers

Keywords

Base   Reciprocal
Index   Substitute
Indices   Variable

 p. 12

- Long products of the same number can be written using **index** notation.

  $$2 \times 2 \times 2 \times 2 \times 2 \times 2 \times 2 \times 2 = 2^8 = 256$$

2 is the **base** and 8 is the **index** or power.

2^8 is not the same as $2 \times 8 = 16$

- A number raised to the power 0 is always 1.

  $$10^0 = 1 \qquad\qquad 2009^0 = 1$$

---

example

Evaluate these numbers without a calculator.

a 4^3 **b** 22^0

....

a $4^3 = 4 \times 4 \times 4 = 64$ **b** $22^0 = 1$

- To work out a number raised to a negative index, write the **reciprocal** with a positive index. $3^{-2} = \dfrac{1}{3^2} = \dfrac{1}{9}$

---

example

Evaluate these numbers without a calculator.

a 2^{-5} **b** $\left(\dfrac{2}{5}\right)^{-2}$

a $2^{-5} = \dfrac{1}{2^5} = \dfrac{1}{32}$

b $\left(\dfrac{2}{5}\right)^{-2} = \left(\dfrac{5}{2}\right)^2 = \dfrac{25}{4} = 6\dfrac{1}{4}$

The numerator and denominator are both squared.

$$\left(\dfrac{5}{2}\right)^2 = \dfrac{5}{2} \times \dfrac{5}{2}$$

- **Indices** in algebra follow the same rules as arithmetic.

  $$x^5 = x \times x \times x \times x \times x \qquad\qquad n^0 = 1$$

- Operations in algebra, like those in arithmetic, follow the rules of BIDMAS.

Brackets, **I**ndices, **D**ivision and **M**ultiplication, **A**ddition and **S**ubtraction

---

example

Given that $a = 3$, $b = -2$ and $c = \frac{1}{2}$, evaluate these expressions.

a $5a^2$ **b** $10 - b^2$ **c** $bc + a^3$

To evaluate an algebraic expression you **substitute** a given number for a **variable**.

....

a $5a^2 = 5 \times 3^2$ **b** $10 - b^2 = 10 - (-2)^2$ **c** $bc + a^3 = -2 \times \frac{1}{2} + 3^3$

        $= 5 \times 9$ $= 10 - 4$ $= -1 + 27$

        $= 45$ $= 6$ $= 26$

Exercise 5a

1 Evaluate these indices without a calculator.

   a 3^2 **b** 2^6 **c** 10^5 **d** 1^{10}

   e 0^4 **f** 4^0 **g** $(-1)^3$ **h** $(-3)^4$

2 Evaluate these negative indices without a calculator.

   a 2^{-4} **b** 6^{-2} **c** 5^{-3} **d** 1^{-8}

   e $\left(\frac{1}{2}\right)^{-5}$ **f** $\left(\frac{1}{3}\right)^{-3}$ **g** $\left(\frac{2}{3}\right)^{-4}$ **h** $\left(\frac{4}{9}\right)^{-2}$

3 State whether each of these algebraic statements is true or false. If false, give a reason.

   a $a + a + a = 3a$ **b** $x^3 = x \times 3$ **c** $p \times 9 = 9p$

   d $xy = yx$ **e** $t \div 7 = \frac{t}{7}$ **f** $y - 4 = 4 - y$

   g $n \times n = n^2$ **h** $3b^2 = (3b)^2$ **i** $-n \times -n = -n^2$

> Are these statements true if you substitute numbers for the variables?

4 Given that $a = -3$, evaluate these algebraic expressions and arrange the cards in ascending order.

   $\boxed{4a}$ $\boxed{a^3}$ $\boxed{2a^2}$ $\boxed{a^0}$ $\boxed{(2a)^2}$ $\boxed{a^{-2}}$

5 Given that $x = 2$ and $y = -5$, find the value of these algebraic expressions.

   a x^7 **b** y^3 **c** $5x^3$ **d** $(2x)^3$

   e $3x + y^2$ **f** $2x^3 - y$ **g** x^2y **h** $(x^4 - y^2)^2$

6 A mouhefanggai is a solid shape made from two cylinders meeting at right angles. If the cylinders have radius r, the volume of the mouhefanggai is $\frac{16}{3}r^3$.

Find the volume of a mouhefanggai made from cylinders with these radii.

   a $r = 3$ **b** $r = 6$ **c** $r = 2$ **d** $r = 4$

Mouhefanggai is Chinese for 'two square umbrellas'.

$(2^2)^2 = 2^2 \times 2^2 = 2^{2+2} = 2^4$

Giving your answers in index form, work out

   a $(2^2)^3$ **b** $(3^2)^4$ **c** $(4^5)^3$

Can you write a rule to work out a power of a power:

   $(2^m)^n = 2^{\square}$

- Collect like terms including powers
- Simplify algebraic expressions

Keywords
Collect   Like terms
Expression   Simplify

- Terms which involve the same unknown are called **like terms**.

$3a$, $12a$ and $-5a$ are like terms $2x$ and $-2x^2$ are not like terms
$8xy$ and $-3yx$ are like terms

$2x$ and $4x^2$ are not like terms because $2x$ involves only x and $4x^2$ involves $x \times x$.

- You can **collect** together terms that involve exactly the same combination of letters to **simplify** an algebraic **expression**.

example

Simplify these algebraic expressions by collecting like terms.

a $3a + 8b + 7a + 2$

b $8xy + 4y - 3yx - 3y$

c $4x^2 - 2x + x^2 - 3$

a $3a + 8b + 7a + 2$
$= 3a + 7a + 8b + 2$
$= 10a + 8b + 2$

b $8xy + 4y - 3yx - 3y$
$= 8xy - 3xy + 4y - 3y$
$= 5xy + y$

c $4x^2 - 2x + x^2 - 3$
$= 4x^2 + x^2 - 2x - 3$
$= 5x^2 - 2x - 3$

Rearrange the terms, placing like terms together; remember to keep the signs.

Write mixed terms in alphabetical order: $yx = xy$. Write y for $1y$.

- To simplify expressions involving multiplications, rearrange the multiplication so that all the numbers are together and all the letters are together.

$2t \times 3t^2 = 2 \times t \times 3 \times t \times t$
$\quad\quad\quad\; = 2 \times 3 \times t \times t \times t$
$\quad\quad\quad\; = 6t^3$

$t^2 = t \times t$

$t \times t \times t = t^3$

- To simplify expressions involving divisions, cancel common factors. Deal with the numbers and letters separately.

$$\frac{10a^2}{5a} = \frac{10 \times a \times \cancel{a}}{5 \times \cancel{a}}$$
$$\quad\;\; = 2a$$

$10 \div 5 = 2$

Exercise 5b

1 Copy the table. Place each of these algebraic expressions under the correct heading in the table and simplify where possible.

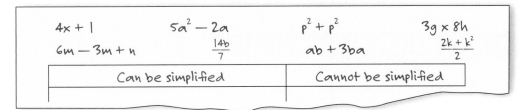

$4x + 1$
$5a^2 - 2a$
$p^2 + p^2$
$3g \times 8h$

$6m - 3m + n$
$\dfrac{14b}{7}$
$ab + 3ba$
$\dfrac{2k + k^2}{2}$

Can be simplified	Cannot be simplified

2 Simplify these expressions, where possible, by collecting like terms.

a $x + x + x$ **b** $4m + 8m$ **c** $10t - 3t$

d $3a^2 + 5a^2 - 7a^2$ **e** $4p^2 + 7p - p^2 + 2p$ **f** $7k + 3 - 2k^2$

g $9ab + 6bc - 4ba - 1$ **h** $8g^3 + 5p^2 - 7g^3 - 2p$ **i** $2 + 2x + x^0 + x^2$

3 Sort these cards into pairs of equivalent algebraic expressions. Show all your working.

$4 \times a \times a$	$4a^2 b^2$	$4a \times 2$	$8ab$

$2a \times 4b$	$4a^2$	$2ab \times 2ba$	$8a$

4 Simplify these expressions as fully as possible.

a $x \div 3$ **b** $8a \div 2$ **c** $\dfrac{3p}{3}$ **d** $\dfrac{12t}{3t}$ **e** $\dfrac{25gh}{5h}$

f $\dfrac{20b^2}{4b}$ **g** $\dfrac{30p^2q}{6p}$ **h** $\dfrac{24mn^2}{8mn}$ **i** $\dfrac{4a + 8}{4}$ **j** $\dfrac{3k - k^2}{k}$

5 Write an algebraic expression for the volume of these solids.

a
$2a$
$2a$
$2a$

b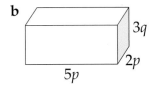
$3q$
$2p$
$5p$

> The volume of a cube or cuboid is given by its length × width × height.

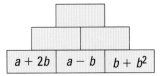

In this algebra pyramid, each brick is the sum of the two bricks below it.

$a + 2b$	$a - b$	$b + b^2$

a Copy and complete the pyramids.

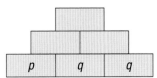

In this algebra pyramid, each brick is the product of the two bricks below it.

p	q	q

b Design some pyramids of your own.

- Expand brackets and simplify expressions
- Multiply a negative term over a bracket

Keywords

Bracket   Expression
Expand   Simplify

- To **expand** a **bracket** you multiply each term inside the bracket by the term outside the bracket.

---

example

Expand these brackets.

a $k(k + 2)$ **b** $-2(3p + 1)$

. . . .

a $k(k + 2) = k \times k + 2 \times k$ **b** $-2(3p + 1) = -2 \times 3p + -2 \times 1$
              $= k^2 + 2k$ $= -6p + -2$
                                                  $= -6p - 2$

p.2

Use the rules for multiplying with negative numbers.

- An **expression** may have several pairs of brackets. Expand each pair of brackets and then **simplify** by collecting like terms.

---

example

Find the difference in area between these rectangles.
Fully simplify your answer.

$2x + 1$ $x - 1$

5   **A**   3   **B**

area of A $= 5(2x + 1)$
area of B $= 3(x - 1)$
area A $-$ area B $= 5(2x + 1) - 3(x - 1)$
                      $= 10x + 5 - 3x + 3$
                      $= 7x + 8$

- An expression may involve indices. Terms which have different powers of a variable are not like terms and must be treated separately.

---

example

Expand and simplify
$x(2x - 5) - 6(x - 2)$.

$x(2x - 5) - 6(x - 2)$
$= 2x^2 - 5x - 6x + 12$
$= 2x^2 - 11x + 12$

Exercise 5c

1 Expand these brackets.
- **a** $3(x + 4)$
- **b** $4(2f - 1)$
- **c** $t(t + 9)$
- **d** $m(n - 7)$
- **e** $p(10 - q)$
- **f** $3a(a + b)$
- **g** $-8(4 - 2y)$
- **h** $-x(x - 10)$

2 Write an algebraic expression using brackets for the areas of these rectangles.

a

$3x - 4$

5

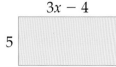

b

p

$2p + q$

Expand the brackets.

3 Expand and simplify these expressions.
- **a** $4(x + 2) + 3(x + 5)$
- **b** $2(3p + 2) + 5(p + 3)$
- **c** $3(3a - 4) + 6(2a + 1)$
- **d** $7(t - 3) + 3(9 - 2t)$
- **e** $5(k + 4) - 3(k + 1)$
- **f** $2(2y - 1) - 3(y + 2)$
- **g** $4(3m + 1) - 5(2m - 3)$
- **h** $8(2n - 5) - 4(3n - 10)$

4 Write an algebraic expression for the total area of these rectangles. Expand the brackets.

a

$k - 1$

6

b

k

$k + 5$

5 Find the surface area of this cuboid.

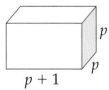

p

p

$p + 1$

To find the surface area of
a cuboid, calculate the area
of each individual face and
then sum your answers.

6 Sort these algebraic expressions into pairs by expanding the brackets and simplifying. Write the odd one out.

$x(x + 1) + 2(x - 5)$

$2x(x - 2) + 3(2 - x)$

$x(x + 5) - 2(x + 5)$

$3(x + 2) - 2x(2 - x)$

$5x(x + 1) - 3x(x + 4) + 6$

These brackets have been expanded.
Can you work out each original expression?
- **a** $3(\square + 2) = 3x + 6$
- **b** $2(p + \square) = 2p + 8$
- **c** $5(y - \square) = 5y - 10$
- **d** $4(\square + \square) = 4k + 12$
- **e** $\square(2t + \square) = 6t + 15$
- **f** $\square(\square - 2) = 15a - 10$

5d Factorising

- Find common factors
- Factorise an expression by taking out a common factor

Keywords
Factorise
Factors
Highest common factor (HCF)

- Factorising is the reverse of expanding. When factorising an expression you put brackets back into the expression.

$$3(x + 2) \xrightarrow[\text{Factorise}]{\text{Expand}} 3x + 6$$

A factor of a number is any number that divides into it without leaving a remainder.

 p. 8

- To **factorise**, look for **factors** that are common to all terms and choose the **highest common factor (HCF)**.

---

example

Factorise

a $5x + 15$

b $8a + 12$

a $5x + 15 = 5 \times x + 5 \times 3$
$= 5(x + 3)$

The HCF of $5x$ and 15 is 5.

b $8a + 12 = 4 \times 2a + 4 \times 3$
$= 4(2a + 3)$

The HCF of $8a$ and 12 is 4.

Expressions to be factorised can involve powers.

example

Factorise

a $y^2 + 3y$

b $2p^2 - 10pq$

a $y^2 + 3y = y \times y + y \times 3$
$= y(y + 3)$

b $2p^2 - 10pq = 2p \times p - 2p \times 5q$
$= 2p(p - 5q)$

To fully **factorise** an expression:
- Write the HCF outside a bracket.
- Divide each term in the expression by the HCF and write the answer inside the bracket.

Factorising is useful when trying to solve equations.

example

Solve $30x - 18 = 42$

$30x - 18 = 42$
$6(5x - 3) = 42$ Factorise the left-hand side of the equation.
$5x - 3 = 7$ Divide each side by 6.
$5x = 10$ Add 3 to each side.
$x = 2$ Divide each side by 5.

Exercise 5d

1 Write the HCF of these.
  a 4 and 6   **b** 9 and 15   **c** 12 and 18   **d** 15 and 20
  e $3x$ and $9x$ **f** $8x$ and $20y$ **g** $6p$ and $18p^2$ **h** $4t$, $10t$ and $14t^2$

2 Factorise fully these expressions.
  a $3x + 6$ **b** $4a - 12$ **c** $12b - 15$ **d** $10k + 15$ **e** $16 - 6p$
  f $7 - 7t$ **g** $mn + 2m$ **h** $8a - 2b$ **i** $5pq + 2$ **j** $6xy - 18x$

3 Ada and Ava are twins. Using a to stand for Ada and Ava's age, you can write an equation using Ada's description

    Ada says …   Ava says …

Mum's age $= 4a - 12$

  a Write an equation using Ava's description.
  b Use factorisation to convince Ada and Ava that they are both right.
  c Ada and Ava are 14 years old.
    Work out their Mum's age.

To find my Mum's age, I multiply my age by 4 and then subtract 12 from my answer.

To find my Mum's age, I subtract 3 from my age and then multiply my answer by 4.

4 Maggie has got all of her factorisation homework wrong. Explain each mistake.

5 Solve this equation using two different methods.

$$4x + 20 = 32$$

Check that your answer is the same for each method.

a $3x^2 + 6x$	**b** $8a + 10a^2$	**c** $8k^2 - 16k$
$= 3(x^2 + 2x)$	$= a(8 + 10a)$	$= 4k(2k - 4)$
d $9t^2 - 15t$	**e** $2p + 6p^2$	**f** $15xy - 10x^2$
$= 3t(3t - 15)$	$= 2p(3p)$	$= 5x(3y - 10^2)$

Think up other equations that can be solved using two methods and swap with a partner.

Factorise the left-hand side.

Alexander thinks of a number, adds 2 and multiplies by 5.
William takes the same number, subtracts 2 and multiplies by 3.
  a Write Alexander's thought process as an algebraic expression.
  b Write William's thought process as an algebraic expression.
  c Prove that the difference between these two expressions is always an even number.

* Substitute into a formula
* Derive a formula

* A **formula** is a relationship or rule expressed in symbols. The formula for the area of a triangle is $A = \frac{1}{2} bh$.

It connects the **variables** A = area, b = base and h = height.

The **subject** of this formula is A, it is the variable that equals an expression.

You can **substitute** into a formula to find an unknown variable.

> **example**
>
> Isla bakes fairy cakes in her gas oven at Gas Mark 4. What temperature should Flora use in her electric oven?
>
> $T = 14g + 121$, In this formula T is the temperature in °C and g is the Gas Mark.
>
> Substitute 4 (Gas Mark) for g.
> $$T = 14g + 121$$
> $$= 14 \times 4 + 121$$
> $$= 177°C$$

You can derive a formula to suit a real-life situation.

Derive means find or deduce from the information given.

> **example**
>
> A plumber's call-out charge is £50. His hourly rate is £25. Derive a formula for the cost of hiring this plumber.
>
> | Number of hours worked, h | Cost of hours worked in £ | Call-out charge in £ | Total cost, C |
> |---|---|---|---|
> | 1 | $1 \times 25 = 25$ | 50 | 75 |
> | 2 | $2 \times 25 = 50$ | 50 | 100 |
> | 3 | $3 \times 25 = 75$ | 50 | 125 |
> | h | $h \times 25 = 25h$ | 50 | $25h + 50$ |
>
> Construct a table containing examples. Generalise to derive a formula.
>
> $C = 25h + 50$

You may be able to use diagrams to derive a formula and explain how it works.

> **example**
>
> Write a formula for the perimeter, P, of any rectangle whose length is twice its width, w.
>
> $$P = 2w + w + 2w + w$$
> $$P = 6w$$
>
> Collect like terms.
>
>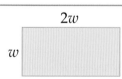

Exercise 5e

1 Find the value of the required variable in each of these formulae.

a $P = 4l$

Find P when $l = 7$.

b $s = \frac{d}{t}$

Find s when $d = 120$ and $t = 2.5$.

c $F = \frac{9}{5}C + 32$

Find F when $C = 30$.

d $s = ut + \frac{1}{2}at^2$

Find s when $u = 0$, $a = 2$ and $t = 5$.

2 Jason uses two routes to cycle from his house to Clare's house.

> Route A: 10 miles

> Route B: 14 kilometres

To convert a distance in miles, m, to a distance in kilometres, k, use the formula $k = \frac{8}{5}m$

Advise Jason of the shortest route.

3 The sum of all the numbers from 1 to n is given by the formula

$$\text{Sum} = \frac{n(n + 1)}{2}$$

a Use this formula to find the sum of the numbers from 1 to 5. Check your answer mentally.

b Calculate the sum of the first 100 numbers.

4 Lynda sees these two adverts for plumbers in her area.

a Derive a formula to find the cost of hiring out
  i Mike the Plumber   **ii** Phil's Plumbing.

b Use your formulae to advise Lynda of the cheapest plumber if the work takes
  i 2 hours   **ii** 5 hours.

c Find the number of hours work for which these plumbers charge the same amount.

PHIL'S PLUMBING

£50 call-out charge
£15 per hour thereafter

MIKE THE PLUMBER

Call-out fee £35
Hourly rate £20

5 The number of red squares, r, is connected to the length of a side of the inner white square, l, by the formula

$$r = 4l + 4$$

a Explain why this formula works.

b Use your formula to find the number of red squares surrounding a white square of length 10.

$l = 1$ $l = 2$ $l = 3$

> Research the formulae in question **1**. What are they used for? What do the variables stand for? Investigate other real-life formulae.

- Change the subject of a formula
- Use real-life formulae

Keywords
Evaluate   Subject
Inverse   Variable
Rearrange

- The **subject** of a formula is the **variable** that stands alone on one side of the formula. You can **rearrange** a formula to make a different variable the subject.

$$s = \frac{d}{t}$$

s is the subject.

$$t = \frac{d}{s}$$

t is the subject.

$$d = st$$

d is the subject.

Addition is the inverse of subtraction.
$$+2 \leftrightarrow -2$$
Division is the inverse of multiplication.
$$\div 5 \leftrightarrow \times 5$$

- To change the subject of a formula you need to 'undo' each operation in turn. Use **inverse** operations.

example

Rearrange $y = mx + c$ to make x the subject.

. . . .

$y = mx + c$ This formula reads 'Start with x, multiply by m and add c to get y'.

$y - c = mx$ Subtract c from both sides.

$\dfrac{y - c}{m} = x$ Divide both sides by m.

Read the formula starting with the variable that you want to make the subject.

If you are given a formula you may need to change the subject of that formula to **evaluate** a variable.

example

A travel brochure gives the average temperatures during July. The formula that connects temperature in °F to temperature in °C is $F = \frac{9}{5}C + 32$.

Rearrange this formula and find the temperature in °C.

. . . .

$F = \dfrac{9}{5}C + 32$ This formula reads 'Start with C, multiply by 9, divide by 5 and add 32 to get F'.

$F - 32 = \dfrac{9}{5}C$ Subtract 32 from both sides.

$5(F - 32) = 9C$ Multiply both sides by 5.

$\dfrac{5(F - 32)}{9} = C$ Divide both sides by 9.

Substituting 77°F for F gives $C = \dfrac{5(77 - 32)}{9} = \dfrac{5 \times 45}{9} = \dfrac{225}{9} = 25$

The average July temperature in Positano, Italy is 25°C.

POSITANO ITALY
Average daily
temperature 77°F

Exercise 5f

1 Make x the subject of these formulae.

a $x + b = a$　　**b** $y = x - t$　　　　**c** $p + x = q + r$　　**d** $p = x + y + z$

e $x - y = 2y$　　**f** $m^2 = x - n$　　　**g** $ab + x = c$　　　**h** $pq + r = r + x$

2 The formula for the perimeter of this isosceles triangle is
$$P = 2a + b.$$

a Explain why this formula works.

b Rearrange this formula to make b the subject.

c Find b when $P = 33$ and $a = 12$.

3 Make y the subject of these formulae.

a $xy = z$　　　　　**b** $py = q + r$　　　**c** $a = by - c$　　　**d** $a = r + xy$

e $m + ny = p - m$　**f** $dy - e = f - e$　**g** $xyz = p$　　　　**h** $kly = m + n$

4 Victoria is rearranging this formula to make y the subject.
$$a = b(x + y)$$
The lines of her working have been muddled.
Can you put them back in the correct order?

$$\frac{a - bx}{b} = y$$　　　$a = bx + by$　　　$a - bx = by$

5 The formula for the perimeter of this rectangle is $P = 2l + 2w$.

a Explain why this formula works.

b Rearrange this formula to make w the subject.

c Find w when $P = 28$ and $l = 9$.

d Derive a formula to find the perimeter of a rectangle whose length is three times its width.

6 For each of these formulae, change the subject to the variable given in brackets.

a $P = x + y + z$　(x)　　　**b** $P = 4l$　　　　(l)

c $A = lw$　　　　(l)　　　　**d** $P = 2a + 2b$　(b)

e $C = 2\pi r$　　　(r)　　　　**f** $y = mx + c$　　(m)

g $v = u + at$　　(t)　　　　**h** $m = \frac{1}{2}(a + b)$　(a)

a Make x the subject of these formulae.

　i $a - x = b$　　　　**ii** $p - qx = r$

b Create some more formulae involving a negative x term and challenge your partner to rearrange your formulae to make x the subject.

Discuss your methods.

1 Evaluate these numbers without a calculator.

   a 5^2 **b** 3^4 **c** 2^8 **d** 6^0

   e 4^{-3} **f** 8^{-2} **g** $\left(\frac{1}{2}\right)^{-7}$ **h** $\left(\frac{3}{4}\right)^{-2}$

2 Given that $m = 3$ and $n = -2$, find the value of these algebraic expressions.

   a m^2 **b** n^3 **c** $2m^3$ **d** $6n^2$

   e $(2n)^2$ **f** $3m + n^4$ **g** mn^2 **h** $(m^2 - n^2)^2$

3 Simplify these expressions, where possible, by collecting like terms.

   a $3x + 8x - 2x$ **b** $4a^2 - 6a^2 + 10a^2$ **c** $10m + 7n - 3n - 5m$

   d $4p^2 + 8 - 3p$ **e** $12ab - 6ba + ab$ **f** $3g^3 - 4g^3 + 2g^2$

4 Simplify these expressions as fully as possible.

   a $\dfrac{20x}{5}$ **b** $\dfrac{12y}{4y}$ **c** $\dfrac{21pq}{7q}$

   d $\dfrac{30k^2}{18k}$ **e** $\dfrac{24gh^2}{16h}$ **f** $\dfrac{3b + 12}{3}$

5 Use brackets to write an expression for the area of this rectangle. Then expand the brackets.

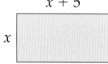

6 Expand and simplify these expressions.

   a $5(a + 2) + 3(a + 4)$ **b** $3(4x + 1) + 6(2x - 1)$

   c $3(4p + 3) + 7(1 - p)$ **d** $5(3b - 2) - 2(4b + 1)$

   e $8(m + 2) - 3(2m - 3)$ **f** $6(4n - 3) - 4(5n - 4)$

   g $x(x + 3) + 4(x - 2)$ **h** $y(2y - 5) - y(y - 3)$

7 Factorise fully these expressions.

   a $2x + 4$ **b** $5y + 20$ **c** $6g - 2$ **d** $8t - 12$

   e $18 - 15k$ **f** $10p + 15q$ **g** $7a + ab$ **h** $15mn - 9n$

8 **a** Three consecutive numbers are summed. Using n to represent the first of these numbers, write and simplify an algebraic expression.

   b Prove that the sum of three consecutive numbers is always equal to three times the middle number.

> Use factorisation.

9 Entry to the Cheeky Monkeys play barn costs £3.50 per child.
Accompanying adults are free.

   a Work out the cost of one child paying 4 visits to Cheeky Monkeys.

   b Derive a formula to work out the cost, C, of one child paying n visits
to Cheeky Monkeys.

A parent or carer can spend £10 for membership of Cheeky Monkeys
for one year. Members pay only £2.50 entry fee per child.

   c Derive a formula to work out the cost, C, of one child paying n visits
to Cheeky Monkeys if their parent or carer is a member.

   d Sam takes her only daughter, Aysha, to Cheeky Monkeys once a
month. Work out whether or not it is worth Sam becoming a member
of Cheeky Monkeys.

10 The diagrams show a pattern of red and white tiles.

   a Write a formula to connect the number of white tiles, w, with the
number of red tiles, r.

   b Explain why this formula works.

   c Use your formula to find the number of red tiles surrounding 100
white tiles.

11 Make x the subject of each of these formulae.

   a $p = x + r$ **b** $a + b = x - c$ **c** $x + 3y = z$

   d $3p + x = 5p$ **e** $a = x - a^2$ **f** $x - mn = p + mn$

12 Make y the subject of each of these formulae.

   a $m = ny$ **b** $b^2y = a$ **c** $p + 3 = qy$

   d $g = fy + h$ **e** $aby = x$ **f** $y(\pi + 2) = r$

5 Summary

Assessment criteria
- Use letter symbols to represent unknown numbers or variables **Level 5**
- Change the subject of a simple formula **Level 6**

Level 6

1 Rearrange the equations
a $f - 6 = g$ $f =$
b $3q = p$ $q =$

Aneela's answer ✔

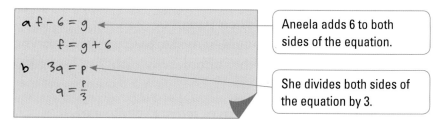

a $f - 6 = g$
  $f = g + 6$

Aneela adds 6 to both sides of the equation.

b $3q = p$
  $q = \frac{p}{3}$

She divides both sides of the equation by 3.

Level 6

2 You can often use algebra to show why a number puzzle works.
Write down the missing expressions.

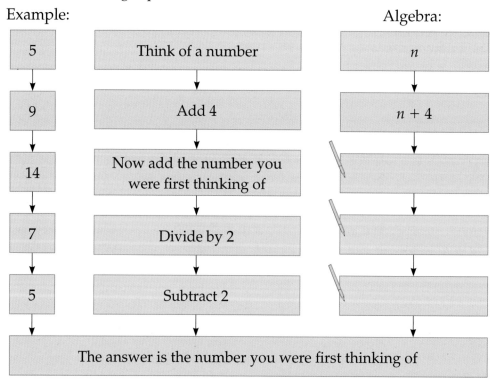

Example: Algebra:

5	Think of a number	n
9	Add 4	$n + 4$
14	Now add the number you were first thinking of	
7	Divide by 2	
5	Subtract 2	

The answer is the number you were first thinking of

KS3 2002 4–6 Paper 1

6 Geometry

Angles and 3-D shapes

The Eiffel Tower in Paris, France was completed in 1889. It is 324 metres high. The structure has to be extremely strong as it must withstand all weather conditions.

What's the point? Engineers use the properties of shapes to help them design buildings and to ensure that they are as safe as possible.

✓ Check in

1 Use a protractor to measure these angles.
State whether the angles are acute, obtuse or reflex.

a    b 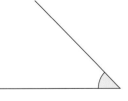   c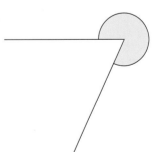

2 Solve these equations.
   a $5a = 180$ **b** $8b + 36 = 180$ **c** $15c = 360$

6a Angles and parallel lines

- Know facts about angles at a point and on parallel and intersecting lines

Keywords
Keywords
Alternate
Corresponding
Intersect
Parallel
Perpendicular
Vertically opposite

You should know these facts.

360°

There are 360° at a point.

180°

There are 180° on a straight line.

90°

Perpendicular lines meet at right angles.

- **Parallel** lines are always the same distance apart.

The arrows mean the lines are parallel.

When two lines **intersect**, 4 angles are formed.

When a line intersects two parallel lines, 8 angles are formed.

- **Vertically opposite** angles are equal.

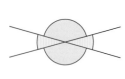

The 2 pink, acute angles are equal.
The 2 green, obtuse angles are equal.

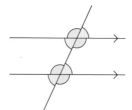

The 4 pink, acute angles are equal.

The 4 green, obtuse angles are equal.

- **Alternate** angles are equal.
- **Corresponding** angles are equal.

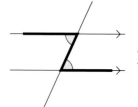

Alternate angles form a Z shape.

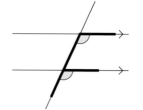

Corresponding angles form an F shape.

example
example

Calculate the values of the angles *a*, *b* and *c*.

$a = 135°$ Alternate angles are equal
$b = 45°$ Angles on a straight line add to 180°
$c = 135°$ Corresponding angles are equal
               or Vertically opposite angles are equal
               or Angles on a straight line add to 180°

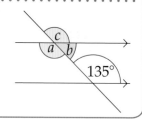

Geometry Angles and 3-D shapes

Exercise 6a

1 Calculate the unknown angles.

a

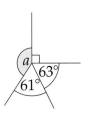

b

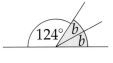

c

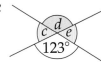

2 Calculate the angles marked with a letter, giving a reason in each case.

a

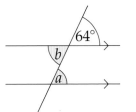

b

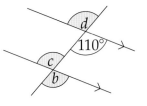

c

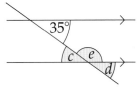

d

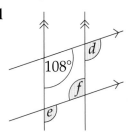

e

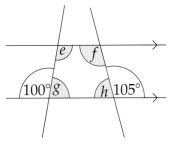

f

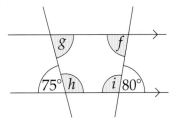

3 Calculate the value of the letters.

a

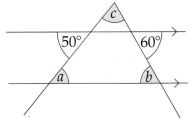

b

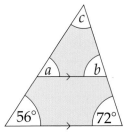

a Find the values of *a* and *b*.

b Using angles on a straight line, find the value of *c*.

c Find the total of *a*, *b* and *c*.

d Choose your own values for the angles marked 40°
   and 60° and find the new total of *a*, *b* and *c*.

e What does this prove?

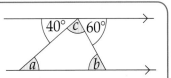

- Know facts about angles in a triangle and a quadrilateral
- Recognise types of triangles and quadrilaterals

Keywords
Quadrilateral   Exterior
Triangle   Interior

- The **interior** angles of a **triangle** add to 180°, $a + b + c = 180°$

You should know the mathematical names of these triangles.

Equilateral

3 equal sides
3 equal angles

Isosceles

2 equal sides
2 equal angles

Scalene

no equal sides
no equal angles

Right-angled

one 90° angle

p. 138

- The **exterior** angle of a triangle is equal to the sum of the two opposite interior angles.

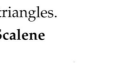

- The interior angles of a **quadrilateral** add to 360°.

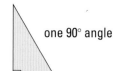

You should know the mathematical name of these quadrilaterals.

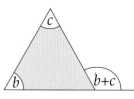

$p + q + r + s = 360°$

Square

4 equal sides
4 90° angles
2 sets of parallel sides

Rectangle

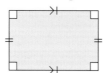

2 sets of equal sides
4 90° angles
2 sets of parallel sides

Rhombus

4 equal sides
2 pairs of equal angles
2 sets of parallel sides

Parallelogram

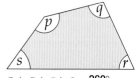

2 sets of equal sides
2 pairs of equal angles
2 sets of parallel sides

Trapezium

1 set of parallel sides

Isosceles trapezium

1 set of equal sides
2 pairs of equal angles
1 set of parallel sides

Kite

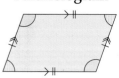

2 sets of equal sides
1 pair of equal angles
no parallel sides

Arrowhead

2 sets of equal sides
1 pair of equal angles
no parallel sides

Exercise 6b

1 Calculate the third angle in each of these triangles and state the type of triangle.

   a 60°, 60°   **b** 33°, 114°   **c** 36°, 54°

2 Name the different types of quadrilaterals you can see in this regular hexagon.

3 Calculate the fourth angle in each of these quadrilaterals. State the type of quadrilateral – there could be several answers for each question.

   a 45°, 45°, 135°   **b** 47°, 63°, 125°   **c** 20°, 20°, 65°

4 Name the quadrilaterals that have diagonals that

   a bisect each other

   b are perpendicular

   c are equal in length

   d are equal in length and are perpendicular

   e are equal in length but are not perpendicular.

5 Two identical equilateral triangles are placed together edge to edge.

   a What is the name of the shape that is formed?

   b Explain the angle properties of this shape to justify your answer.

6 Calculate the value of the unknown angles.

a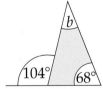

b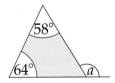

c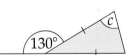

A rectangle is drawn inside a circle of radius 6 cm. The rectangle fits along two perpendicular radii of the circle. Find the length of the diagonal of the rectangle.

- Know some properties of polygons
- Calculate the interior and exterior angles of regular polygons

Keywords

Exterior	Regular
Interior	Tessellation
Polygon	

- A **polygon** is a 2-D shape with three or more straight sides.

You should know the names of these polygons.

Number of sides	Name
3	triangle
4	quadrilateral
5	pentagon
6	hexagon
7	heptagon
8	octagon
9	nonagon
10	decagon

You call the angles inside a shape **interior** angles.

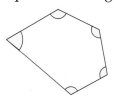

You find the **exterior** angles of a 2-D shape by extending one side at each corner.

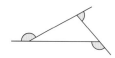

- The exterior angles of any polygon add to 360°.

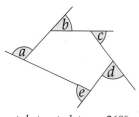

$a + b + c + d + e = 360°$

- Interior angle + exterior angle = 180°

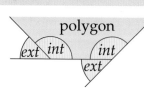

Angles on a straight line add to 180°.

- A **regular** shape has equal sides and equal angles.
  A regular pentagon has 5 equal sides and 5 equal angles.

example

Calculate the exterior and interior angle of a regular octagon.

· ·

The exterior angles of any polygon add to 360° and there are 8 equal exterior angles in a regular octagon.

360° ÷ 8 = 45°   Each exterior angle is 45°
180° − 45° = 135°   Each interior angle is 135°

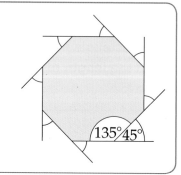

Exercise 6c

1 Tessellate each polygon on square grid paper.

a   b   c   d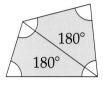

> A **tessellation** is a tiling pattern with no gaps.

2 When you draw the diagonal of a quadrilateral, two triangles are formed.

The sum of the interior angles of a quadrilateral is

$$2 \times 180° = 360°$$

a Draw a pentagon and draw the diagonals from one vertex to form three triangles.

b Copy and complete the table for all polygons up to a decagon.

Name	Number of triangles	Sum of the interior angles
triangle	1	$1 \times 180° = 180°$
quadrilateral	2	$2 \times 180° = 360°$
pentagon	3	

3 Calculate the exterior and interior angle of

  a an equilateral triangle   **b** a regular hexagon

  c a regular nonagon   **d** a regular decagon

  e a regular 18-sided polygon   **f** a regular 24-sided polygon.

4 Regular pentagons do not tessellate as rhombuses are needed to fill the gaps.

  a Calculate the size of the exterior angle of a regular pentagon.

  b Calculate the size of the interior angle of a regular pentagon.

  c Calculate each of the four angles in the rhombus.

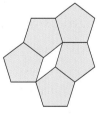

Draw a circle.

Use a protractor to mark off points at 60° intervals at 0°, 60°, 120° etc.

Draw the regular hexagon and six of the diagonals.

Cut out the 12 triangles and colour the obtuse angles.

a Rearrange the six isosceles triangles to make a regular hexagon.

b Use angles at a point to calculate this obtuse angle.

c Hence state the value of the interior angle of a regular hexagon.

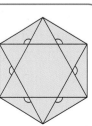

6d Congruent shapes

- Recognise congruent shapes

Keywords
Congruent
Corresponding angles
Corresponding sides

These figures may look different, but they are the same size and the same shape.

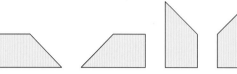

If you cut them out, they would all fit on top of each other. These figures are **congruent**.

- Congruent figures are exactly the same size and the same shape.

---

example

Write the letters of the congruent shapes.

 A   B   C   D   E

. . . .

A, B and D are congruent as they are the same size and the same shape.
C and E are congruent as they are the same size and the same shape.

- If shapes are congruent, then
  - **corresponding angles** are equal
  - **corresponding sides** are equal .

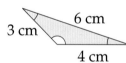

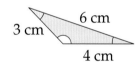

---

example

The green triangle and the yellow triangle are congruent. State the lengths of

a AB

b AC

c BC

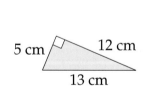

. . . .

Rotate and flip over the yellow triangle so that the triangle fits on top of the green triangle.

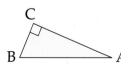

Compare the triangles.
a AB = 13 cm
b AC = 12 cm
c BC = 5 cm

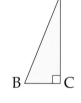

In a triangle, corresponding sides are opposite corresponding angles.

Exercise 6d

1 Draw the shape that is not congruent to the others.

a

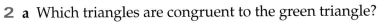

b

c

d

2 a Which triangles are congruent to the green triangle?
  b Which triangles are congruent to the orange triangle?
  c Which triangle is not congruent to the others?

3 The blue parallelogram and the green parallelogram are
congruent. State the values of angles A, B, C and D.

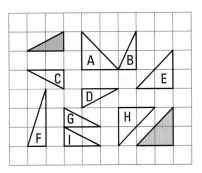

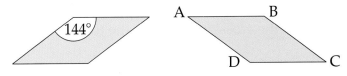

4 The yellow triangle and the orange triangle
are congruent.

  State the lengths of   **a** AB
                            b AC
                            c BC

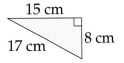

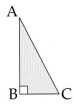

A 4 by 4 grid can be divided into two congruent shapes in
many different ways.
Find ten more different ways to divide the grid into two
congruent shapes.

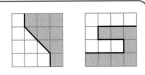

6e 3-D shapes

- Recognise and name 3-D solids
- Recognise the nets of 3-D solids

Keywords
Cross-
  section
Edge
Face
Net
Prism

Pyramid
Solid
Three
  dimensions (3-D)
Vertex

- A **solid** is a shape formed in **three dimensions (3-D)**.

- A **face** is a flat surface of a solid.

- An **edge** is the line where two faces meet.

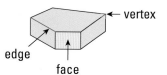

vertex

edge

face

- A **vertex** is a point at which three or more edges meet.

> The plural of vertex is vertices.

You should know the names of these solids.

Cube	Cuboid	**Prism**	**Pyramid**

All the faces
are square.

All the faces
are rectangles.

The **cross-section**
is the same
throughout the
length.

The base tapers
to a point.

> The base or cross-section decides the name of the solid. This is a triangular prism and a hexagonal pyramid.

A square-based pyramid is
sliced horizontally.
Describe the cross-sections at
different heights.

Each cross-section is a square.
The squares decrease in size the nearer
the cross-section is to the top vertex.

- A **net** is a 2-D shape that can be folded to form a solid.

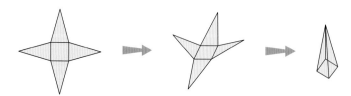

Colour the net of a cube so that the opposite faces have the same colour.
Use the colours yellow, red and green.

Exercise 6e

1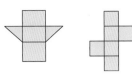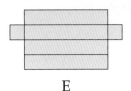

| A | B | C | D | E |

Each net forms a solid.

State   **a** the mathematical name of the solid

           b the solid's number of   **i**   faces

                                   ii   vertices

                                   iii edges.

2 A prism is shown.

State the prism's number of   **a** faces

                                        b vertices

                                        c edges.

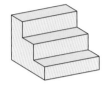

3 a Draw a 3-D shape with five faces.

   b State the number of vertices and edges on your shape.

4 A tetrahedron is made from two blue and two green equilateral triangles.

Find the number of edges where

a a blue face meets a blue face

b a blue face meets a green face

c a green face meets a green face.

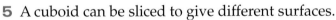

5 A cuboid can be sliced to give different surfaces.

   a Describe the shape of the surface if the cuboid is sliced through the points A, B, C and D.

   b Is it possible to cut a triangular surface? Draw a diagram to illustrate your answer.

An octahedron is made from eight equilateral triangles.

a State the shape's number of   **i**   faces

                                         ii   vertices

                                         iii edges.

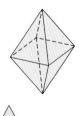

You can make an octahedron using this net.

b Copy the net and write the numbers 1 to 8 on the triangles so that the opposite faces of the octahedron add to 9.

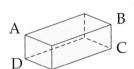

• Draw plans and elevations of 3-D shapes

Keywords
Dimensions   Plan
Front   Side
  elevation   elevation
Isometric   Solid
  paper

You can draw diagrams to show a **solid** viewed from different directions.

• A **front elevation** (F) is the view from the front.
• A **side elevation** (S) is the view from the side.
• A **plan** (P) shows the view from above.
   The plan is the bird's eye view.

These are the views of the cuboid.

3 cm This is the plan view (P).

P   5 cm

This is the front elevation (F). 2 cm

5 cm

F → 5 cm

2 cm

3 cm

S

2 cm This is the side elevation (S).

3 cm

The **dimensions** of this cuboid are 5 cm by 3 cm by 2 cm.

Label the edges with their lengths.

example

The diagram shows a square-based pyramid.
Sketch   **a** the front elevation (F)
          b the side elevation (S)
          c the plan view (P).

P

S

F

a

Front elevation

b

Side elevation

c

Plan view

example

The diagram shows the plan view of a solid made from cubes. The number in each square represents the number of cubes in that column.
Draw the solid on **isometric paper**.

1	2
	1

The bold lines show when the level of cubes changes.

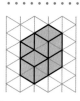

or

Notice the vertical lines. The isometric paper must be this way up.

Exercise 6f

1 Sketch the front elevation (F), the side elevation (S) and the plan view (P) of these cuboids.

Remember to label the edges with their lengths.

a

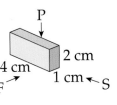

P
2 cm
4 cm
1 cm ← S
F

b

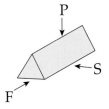

P
3 cm
2 cm   2 cm ← S
F

c

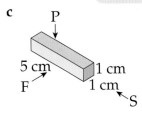

P
5 cm   1 cm
F   1 cm
S

2 Sketch the front elevation (F), the side elevation (S) and the plan view (P) of these solids.

a

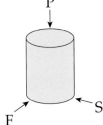

P
← S
F

b

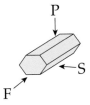

P
← S
F

c

P
F   ← S

3 The diagram shows the plan view of a solid made from cubes. The number in each square represents the number of cubes in that column.
a Draw the solid on isometric paper.
b Draw the front and side elevations.

| 1 | 2 | 1 |

4 A 3-D shape is made from cubes.
The elevations and the plan view are shown.

Front elevation   Side elevation   Plan view

a Draw the solid on isometric paper.
b How many cubes are needed to make the shape?

puzzle

The front and side elevations and the plan views of two solids are shown. The diagrams are jumbled up. Draw a sketch of each solid, showing the dimensions of the shape and giving the mathematical name in each case.

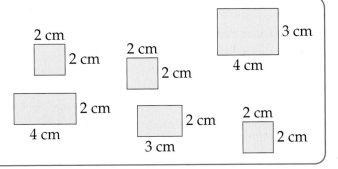

2 cm
2 cm
2 cm
2 cm
3 cm
4 cm
4 cm
2 cm
2 cm
2 cm
3 cm
2 cm
2 cm
2 cm

1 Calculate the angles marked with a letter, giving a reason in each case.

a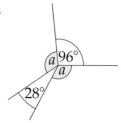

b

c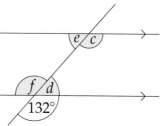

2 Find the value of
   a a
   b b
   c $a + b$

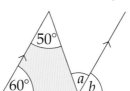

3 Calculate the value of the unknown angles.
Give a reason in each case.

a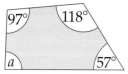

b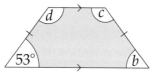

c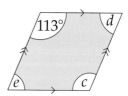

4 Two identical right-angled isosceles triangles are placed edge to edge.
Draw diagrams to show

   a a square
   b a right-angled isosceles triangle
   c a parallelogram.

Use the properties of the right-angled triangles to show that each
shape is the required quadrilateral.

5 Calculate the value of the unknown angles.

a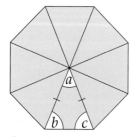

A regular octagon

b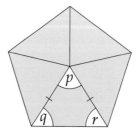

A regular pentagon.

6 a Copy these shapes and draw all the diagonals from each vertex.

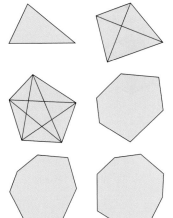

b Copy and complete the table.

Polygon	Number of sides	Number of diagonals
triangle	3	0
quadrilateral	4	2
pentagon	5	

7 a Tessellate four congruent 'L' shapes on a 4 by 4 square grid.
b Draw a different arrangement using the same shapes on the grid.

8 On square grid paper, draw the net of a cuboid with dimensions 3 cm by 4 cm by 5 cm.

9 Which shapes are the net of a square-based pyramid?

 A

 B

 C

10 On square grid paper, draw the front elevation (F), the side elevation (S) and the plan view (P) of each solid.

a
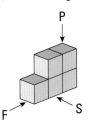

b
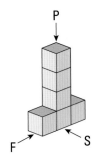

c
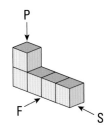

d
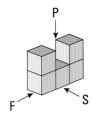

6 Summary

Assessment criteria
- Analyse 3-D shapes through plans and elevations **Level 6**
- Identify alternate and corresponding angles for parallel lines **Level 6**
- Use angle properties to solve geometrical problems **Level 6**

Level 6

1 The diagram shows 5 grey and 2 white cubes arranged to form an H shape.

On square grid paper draw

a the front view

b the side view

c the top view

Remember to colour the cubes grey and white.

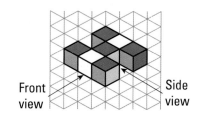

Front view   Side view

Paula's answer ✔

Paula realises only 3 cubes will be visible from the front.

The top view is the same as the plan view.

Paula uses bold lines where the shape alters its level.

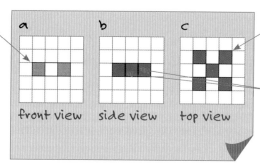

a   b   c

front view   side view   top view

Level 6

2 Look at the diagram, made from four straight lines. The lines marked with arrows are parallel.

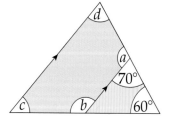

Work out the sizes of the angles marked with letters.

$a =$ ___ ° $b =$ ___ ° $c =$ ___ ° $d =$ ___ °

KS3 2006 4–6 Paper 2

7 Algebra

Equations and graphs

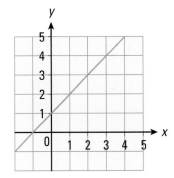

Robert Hooke was a 17th century scientist. He measured the distance a spring stretched when different weights were hung from it. He then plotted his results on a graph and found that they formed a straight line. The equation of the straight line is now called "Hooke's Law".

What's the point? Scientists can use graphs and equations to investigate the properties of different materials.

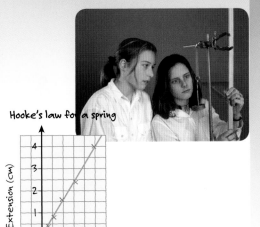

Hooke's law for a spring

Check in

1 Solve these equations.

a $x + 3 = 8$

b $2y + 7 = 15$

c $4p - 3 = 21$

d $8k - 4 = 20$

2 Expand these, simplifying where possible.

a $2(a + 5)$

b $3(b - 10)$

c $x(x + 2)$

d $a(b - 3)$

e $3t(t - 1)$

f $2p(3q + 4)$

g $4(k + 3) + 5(k - 2)$

h $5(3n + 2) - 2(4n - 1)$

3 a Copy and complete the table for some points on the line.

x	0		3
y		3	

b Copy and complete this sentence:

'The y-coordinate is equal to the x-coordinate ☐ ☐'

c Use part **b** to write the equation of the line.

- Solve linear equations with the unknown on one or both sides

Keywords
Equation   Solve
Expression Solution

- An **equation** is a mathematical statement that two expressions are equal.

$7x + 5 = 3x + 9$ is an equation. The two sides are equal.
$7x + 5$ and $3x + 9$ are **expressions**.

To **solve** an equation, you find the value of the unknown. Think of the equation $7x + 5 = 3x + 9$ as a set of scales, balanced at the equals sign.

- To ensure that the scales balance, you must perform the same operation on each side of the equation.

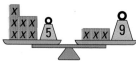

Subtract $3x$ from both sides: this is written as $4x + 5 = 9$

Subtract 5 from both sides: this is written as $4x = 4$

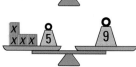

The **solution** of the equation is $x = 1$.

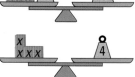

example

Solve these equations.
a $2(5x - 4) = 12$ **b** $\dfrac{3a + 4}{2} = 11$

- - - - - - - - - -

a $2(5x - 4) = 12$ Expand the brackets.
$10x - 8 = 12$ +8 to both sides.
$10x = 20$ ÷10 on both sides.
$x = 2$

b $\dfrac{3a + 4}{2} = 11$ ×2 on both sides.
$3a + 4 = 22$ −4 from both sides.
$3a = 18$ ÷3 on both sides.
$a = 6$

- To solve an equation with the unknown on both sides, subtract the smallest algebraic term from both sides.

example

Solve these equations.
a $4x + 6 = 9x - 4$ **b** $2(5n + 3) = 4(2n - 1)$

- - - - - - - - - -

a $4x + 6 = 9x - 4$ -4x from both sides.
$6 = 5x - 4$ +4 to both sides.
$10 = 5x$ ÷5 on both sides.
$2 = x$
$x = 2$

b $2(5n + 3) = 4(2n - 1)$ expand the brackets.
$10n + 6 = 8n - 4$ -8n from both sides.
$2n + 6 = -4$ -6 from both sides.
$2n = -10$ ÷2 on both sides.
$n = -5$

Exercise 7a

1 Solve these equations.

   a $x + 4 = 7$ **b** $5z = 20$ **c** $2n - 6 = 4$ **d** $11 = 3p + 2$

   e $9 + 6t = 9$ **f** $20 = 7h - 1$ **g** $4k - 1 = 1$ **h** $9 + 8y = 1$

2 Arrange these equations into pairs if they have the same
solution. Which is the odd equation out?

$3(x + 5) = 21$ $\dfrac{x}{2} + 9 = 8$ $12 = 4(x - 3)$

$2(10 + x) = 8$ $\dfrac{2x + 7}{3} = 1$ $\dfrac{5x + 4}{7} = 2$

$\dfrac{x}{3} + 5 = 7$

3 For each of these questions, form an equation and solve it to
find the answer to the problem.

   a I think of a number, add 6 and multiply the result by 3. I get 33.
      What is my number?

   b This rectangle has
      an area of 35 units².
      Calculate x.

   c Find x and hence
      the angles of this
      triangle.

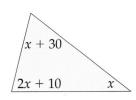

4 Solve these equations by expanding the brackets and collecting
like terms.

   a $2(x + 3) + 4(x + 1) = 22$ **b** $7(a - 3) + 5(a + 2) = 37$

   c $3(p - 2) + 2(p - 5) = 14$ **d** $2(2k - 1) + 4(3k + 1) = 18$

   e $5(2y + 3) - 6(y + 1) = 29$ **f** $4(5n - 2) - 6(3n - 1) = 12$

5 Solve these equations with unknowns on both sides.

   a $3x + 5 = 2x + 10$ **b** $6q - 10 = 2q + 10$ **c** $4a - 11 = 7a - 17$

   d $9b - 2 = 2(3b + 5)$ **e** $3m - 7 = 5m - 8$ **f** $3(4 + 3n) = 4(n - 2)$

6 For each of these questions, form an equation and solve to find
the answer to the problem.

   a I think of a number, multiply by 5 and add 4.
      I get the same answer when I multiply by 3 and add 14.
      What is my number?

   b This triangle is isosceles.
      Find x and hence the length of the sides of the triangle.

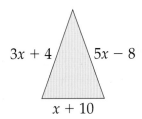

The sum of three consecutive even numbers is 48.
If x is the first number, form and solve an equation in x to find these numbers.
Can you make up some similar puzzles of your own?

- Solve linear equations with a negative algebraic term on one or both sides

Keywords
Equation
Solve

- To **solve** an **equation** with a negative algebraic term, add this term to both sides of the equation.

  $5 - 2x = 1$ involves the negative algebraic term $-2x$

example

Solve these equations.

a $12 - 5k = 2$ **b** $4 - 3a = 7$

$-(-5k) = +5k$
$-(-3a) = +3a$

. . . .

a $12 - 5k = 2$		**b** $4 - 3a = 7$	
$12 = 2 + 5k$	$+5k$ to both sides.	$4 = 7 + 3a$	$+3a$ to both sides.
$10 = 5k$	-2 from both sides.	$-3 = 3a$	-7 from both sides.
$2 = k$	$\div 5$ on both sides.	$-1 = a$	$\div 3$ on both sides.
$k = 2$		$a = -1$	

- To solve an equation with the unknown on both sides, subtract the smallest algebraic term from both sides.

If one or both of the algebraic terms is negative then subtracting the smallest term from both sides is the same as adding this term to both sides.

example

Solve these equations.

a $3x + 1 = 11 - 2x$ **b** $5 - 2n = 8 - 4n$

$-2x$ is smaller than $3x$
$-4n$ is smaller than $-2n$

. . . .

a $3x + 1 = 11 - 2x$	$+2x$ to both sides.	**b** $5 - 2n = 8 - 4n$	$+4n$ to both sides.
$5x + 1 = 11$	-1 from both sides.	$5 + 2n = 8$	-5 from both sides.
$5x = 10$	$\div 5$ on both sides.	$2n = 3$	$\div 2$ on both sides.
$x = 2$		$n = \dfrac{3}{2}$	
		$n = 1\tfrac{1}{2}$	

Exercise 7b

1 Solve these equations.

a $12 - x = 5$ **b** $-7a = 14$ **c** $6 - 4n = 2$ **d** $21 - 4m = 5$
e $15 - 3t = 0$ **f** $8 = 18 - 5p$ **g** $5 = 6 - 2k$ **h** $8 - y = 9$
i $5 - 4b = 13$ **j** $3 = 8 - 2d$

2 Prove that all of these equations have the same solution.

$2(5 - x) = 4$ $\dfrac{14 - 3x}{5} = 1$ $3x - 4(x - 2) = 5$

$12 - 4x = 0$ $4(9 - 2x) = 12$

3 Solve these equations with unknowns on both sides.

a $2x + 1 = 7 - x$ **b** $3t - 2 = 3 - 2t$ **c** $19 - 3p = 4p + 5$
d $14 - 5k = 3k - 10$ **e** $9n + 5 = 5 - n$ **f** $4 - a = 16 - 3a$
g $3 - 2b = 13 - 4b$ **h** $11 - 8m = 1 - 3m$ **i** $2(5 - y) = 22 - 5y$
j $3(5 - 2d) = 3 - 2d$ **k** $5(3 - 2q) = 2(7 - q)$ **l** $2(4 - x) = 5(1 - x)$

4 For each of these questions, form an equation and solve it to find the number that I am thinking of.

a I think of a number, multiply it by 2 and add 4.
   I get the same answer as when I subtract my number *from* 19.
b I think of a number, double it and subtract it *from* 10.
   I get the same answer as when I multiply my number
   by 4 and subtract 8.

5 Find the length of a side of this square.

6 The square and rectangle have the same perimeter.
   Find the length of the rectangle.

$5x + 2$

$50 - 3x$

$6 - x$

$2(x + 1)$

x

The equation $x^2 = 16$ has two solutions.
Work out these two solutions.

One solution is positive and one is negative.

Using this knowledge, can you now write the two solutions
for each of these equations?

a $x^2 = 4$ **b** $x^2 = 25$ **c** $x^2 = 100$ **d** $x^2 + 1 = 10$ **e** $2x^2 = 128$

Research the name of this type of equation.

- Generate outputs of functions
- Find inverse functions
- Use mapping diagrams

Keywords
Equation   Mapping
Function   diagram
Mapping   Rule

- A **function** is a **rule** that links a set of inputs with a set of outputs.

Find the function that maps these inputs to these outputs. Write the function as an equation.

x	1	2	3	4
y	7	9	11	13

The y-values increase in steps of 2, indicating that the 2 times table is involved.
The y-values are each 5 more than the first four multiples of 2, which are 2, 4, 6, 8.
The function is 'multiply by 2 and add 5' which is written as the equation $y = 2x + 5$.

- A function can be written in words, 'multiply by 2 and add 5' as a **mapping**, $x \rightarrow 2x + 5$,   or an **equation**, $y = 2x + 5$.

- A function can be represented by a **mapping diagram**.

- An **inverse** function reverses the direction of the mapping.

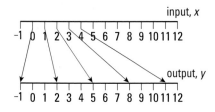

This mapping diagram represents the function 'multiply by 3 and subtract 1'.

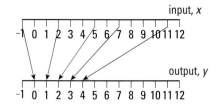

example

Find the inverse of the function $x \rightarrow 4x + 3$.
Use your answer to find a and b.

x	a	b
y	11	23

Read $x \rightarrow 4x + 3$ as 'multiply by 4 and add 3' and undo each operation in turn.
The reverse is 'subtract 3 and divide by 4'.

The inverse of $x \rightarrow 4x + 3$ is $x \rightarrow \dfrac{x - 3}{4}$.

Substituting 11 into the inverse function gives $\dfrac{11 - 3}{4} = 2$. Hence $a = 2$.

Substituting 23 into the inverse function gives $\dfrac{23 - 3}{4} = 5$. Hence $b = 5$.

Exercise 7c

1 For each function, copy and complete this table of values.

x	1	2	3	4	5
y					

  a $y = 5x$ **b** $y = 2x + 3$ **c** $y = 3(x - 1)$ **d** $y = 5 - x$

2 Copy and complete this mapping diagram for $x \rightarrow 8 - 2x$.
Use values of x from 0 to 5.

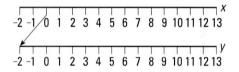

3 Find the function that maps these x-values to these y-values.
Give your answers as equations.

a

x	y
1	5
2	6
3	7
4	8

b

x	y
0	0
1	5
2	10
3	15

c

x	y
2	9
3	11
4	13
5	15

4 a Copy and complete this mapping diagram for $x \rightarrow 3x - 2$.
Use values of x from 0 to 5.

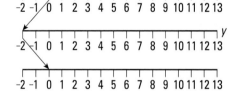

  b Reverse the direction of the mapping and draw the inverse of $x \rightarrow 3x - 2$.
Extend the mapping diagram from part **a** as shown.

  c Find the inverse of $x \rightarrow 3x - 2$.

5 Find the inverse of these functions.

  a $x \rightarrow 10x$ **b** $x \rightarrow x + 6$ **c** $x \rightarrow 2x + 1$

  d $x \rightarrow 7x - 4$ **e** $x \rightarrow 4(x - 1)$ **f** $x \rightarrow \dfrac{x + 5}{3}$

Draw mapping diagrams for each of these functions.
a $x \rightarrow 10 - x$ **b** $x \rightarrow 5 - x$ **c** $x \rightarrow 3 - x$
Draw mapping diagrams for the inverse of the functions in parts **a**, **b** and **c** and use your diagrams to write the inverse of these functions.

What can you conclude about the mapping diagrams and the inverses of functions of the form $x \rightarrow c - x$, where c is any number?
Investigate functions of the form $x \rightarrow x + c$.

- Draw graphs of linear functions
- Recognise the equation of a straight-line graph

Keywords
Function   Straight-line
Graph   graph
Linear   Variable
Plot

- A **graph** shows the relationship between two **variables**.

- To **plot** the graph of a **function**, generate three or more points that satisfy the given equation and produce a table of values.

A linear function will not contain variables with powers.

$x + y = 5$ is a linear function.

$y = x^2 + 3x + 2$ is not a linear function.

This is a table of values for the equation $y = x + 4$. The y-values are always 4 more than the x-values. You can read off a set of coordinate pairs: $(1,5)$, $(2,6)$ and $(3,7)$.

x	1	2	3
y	5	6	7

- The graph of a **linear** function will always be a **straight line**.

Plot the points $(1,5)$, $(2,6)$ and $(3,7)$ on a set of coordinate axes and join with a ruler.

If you plot three points and do not have a straight line then you have made a mistake!

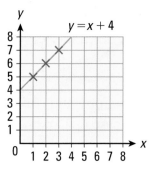

example

Plot the graphs $y = 3$ and $y = 2x - 1$ on the same set of coordinate axes. Write the coordinates of the point of intersection.

x	1	2	3
y	3	3	3

x	1	2	3
y	1	3	5

If $y = 3$ then the y-values are always 3.

If $y = 2x - 1$ then you double each x-value and subtract 1 to get each y-value.

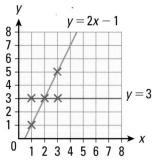

The point of intersection is $(2, 3)$.

- Equations of the form $y = c$ where c is a number, produce horizontal line graphs.

- Equations of the form $x = c$ where c is a number, produce vertical line graphs.

Exercise 7d

1 Match each equation with one of these cards.

| Horizontal line | Vertical line | Sloping line | Not a straight line |

- **a** $x = 5$
- **b** $y = 3x + 2$
- **c** $x + y = 10$
- **d** $y = 0$
- **e** $y = x^2$
- **f** $y = \frac{1}{3}x$
- **g** $x = -1$
- **h** $y = 2(x - 1)$

2 a Copy and complete the table of values for the equation $y = 3 - 2x$.

x	0	1	2
y		1	

b Plot these points on a set of coordinate axes with values from -2 to 4 in both the x and y directions.

c Write the coordinates of the point where the line $y = 3 - 2x$ cuts the x-axis.

3 a On a set of coordinate axes with values from 0 to 5 in both the x and y directions, plot the graphs of $x = 1$ and $y = 3$. Write the coordinates of the point where these lines intersect.

b Without drawing the graphs, write the coordinates of the point where these lines intersect.

- **i** $x = 2$ and $y = 4$
- **ii** $x = 3$ and $y = -1$
- **iii** $x = \frac{1}{2}$ and $y = 1$

4 Which of these lines passes through the point $(2, 5)$?

Line	$y = x + 3$	$x + y = 7$	$y = 3x$	$y = 2x - 1$	$y = \frac{3}{2}x + 2$
✓ or ✗					

x	0	1	2
y			

5 a For each equation, copy and complete this table of values.

- **i** $y = 2x - 1$
- **ii** $y = 2x$
- **iii** $y = 2x + 1$
- **iv** $y = 2x + 2$

b Plot the graph of each equation on the same set of coordinate axes.

c Comment on your graphs.
Compare each graph with its equation, mentioning both its slope and the coordinates of the point where the graph cuts the y-axis.

d Repeat parts **a**, **b** and **c** for each of these equations.

- **i** $y = \frac{1}{2}x + 1$
- **ii** $y = x + 1$
- **iii** $y = 2x + 1$
- **iv** $y = 3x + 1$

Here are the equations of five straight lines.
Can you find two pairs of parallel lines?
Which is the odd one out?
Suggest the equation of a line that is parallel to this line.

$y = x$

$y = x + 2$

$y = \dfrac{x + 1}{2}$

$y = 2x + 1$

$y = 2(x + 1)$

- Find the gradient and *y*-intercept of a straight-line
- Find the equation of a straight-line in the form
  $y = mx + c$

Keywords
Gradient
Intercept
Slope

- The equation of a straight-line graph can be written $y = mx + c$

- The **gradient**, *m*, describes the steepness or **slope** of the line.

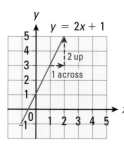

The gradient is 2.
This means that for every
1 unit across you move
2 units up.

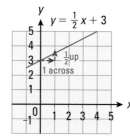

The gradient is $\frac{1}{2}$.
This means that for every
1 unit across you move $\frac{1}{2}$
a unit up.

- The *y*-**intercept**, *c*, is the point at which the line cuts the
  y-axis. The coordinates of this point are $(0, c)$.

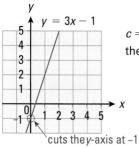

cuts the *y*-axis at –1

$c = -1$. The coordinates of
the *y*-intercept are (0, -1).

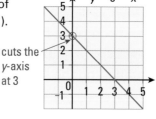

cuts the
y-axis
at 3

$c = 3$. The coordinates of
the *y*-intercept are (0, 3).

This line has a negative
gradient of -1. The line
slopes in a negative
direction.

example

Find the equation of each of these straight lines.

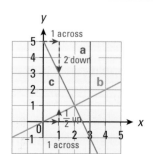

a The line is vertical. The coordinates of some points on
the line are (3,0), (3,1) and (3,2). The *x*-value is always 3.
The equation of the line is $x = 3$.

b $m = +\frac{1}{2}$ because for every 1 unit across you move $\frac{1}{2}$
a unit *up*. The *y*-intercept is (0,0) so $c = 0$.
The equation of the line is $y = \frac{1}{2}x$.

c $m = -2$ because for every 1 unit across you move 2 units *down*.
The *y*-intercept is (0,5) so $c = 5$.
The equation of the line is $y = -2x + 5$ or $y = 5 - 2x$.

Exercise 7e

1 Copy and complete the table for each of these equations.

Equation	Gradient	Coordinates of y-intercept

   a $y = 3x + 2$ **b** $y = 4x - 1$ **c** $y = 2x$ **d** $y = \frac{1}{4}x + 3$

   e $y = \frac{x}{2} - 5$ **f** $y = 3(x + 2)$ **g** $y = 4 - \frac{3}{2}x$ **h** $y = 10 - x$

2 Write the equations of these three straight lines.

   a Line A has a gradient of 2 and y-intercept at (0, 1).

   b Line B cuts the y-axis at -4 and has a gradient of 1.

   c Line C has $m = -3$ and $c = \frac{1}{2}$.

> Either make a sketch of these coordinates or look for patterns in the tables. For example, in part **b**, what must you multiply x by to get y? In part **c**, try adding the x and y values

3 For each of these tables of coordinates, write the equation of the line on which these points lie.

a
x	0	1	2	3	4
y	5	5	5	5	5

b
x	0	1	2	3	4
y	0	2	4	6	8

c
x	0	1	2	3	4
y	5	4	3	2	1

d
x	0	1	2	3	4
y	2	5	8	11	14

4 Find the equation of each of these straight lines.

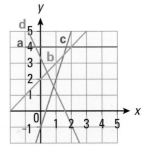

5 'Fab Cabs' taxis took these fares from three customers.

   a Plot this information on a graph. Use axes with x-values from 0 to 8 (representing the journey length in miles) and y-values from 0 to 20 (representing the fare).

   b Write the equation that the taxi company uses to calculate each fare.
Explain how this works, mentioning the cost per mile of hiring a taxi.

Name	Journey length (miles)	Fare
Mrs Mackay	4	£10
Mike	6	£14
Doris Williams	2.5	£7

   c 'Fair Fares' taxis charges £1 per mile and puts £5 on the meter at the start of each journey.
Add this information to your graph and determine which of these two companies you would choose to travel with.
Explain your decision.

| $x + y = 10$ | $2y = x + 4$ | $3y = 4x - 3$ | $2y + x = 6$ | $4y + 2x - 3 = 0$ |

Rearrange these equations so that y is the subject.
Write the gradient and y-intercept of each equation.

- Plot quadratic graphs

Keywords
Parabola
Quadratic

- A function which involves x^2 as its highest power of x is called a **quadratic** function.

  $y = x^2$, $y = x^2 + 2x - 3$ and $y = 4x^2 - 1$ are all quadratic functions.

  $y = x + 5$, $y = 3x$ and $y = 4 - 3x$ are all linear functions.

- A quadratic function produces a curved graph called a **parabola**.

This graph is a symmetrical ∪ shape.

This graph is a symmetrical ∩ shape.

example

Plot the graph of the function $y = x^2$.

Construct a table of values.

x	-3	-2	-1	0	1	2	3
y	9	4	1	0	1	4	9

$(-3)^2 = -3 \times -3 = 9$ $2^2 = 2 \times 2 = 4$

Plot the coordinate pairs
(-3, 9), (-2, 4), (-1, 1),
(0, 0), (1, 1), (2, 4) and (3, 9).

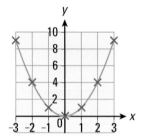

example

Plot the graph of the function $y = -x^2 + 2x + 1$.

Construct a table of values.

x	-3	-2	-1	0	1	2	3
$-x^2$	-9	-4	-1	0	-1	-4	-9
$+2x$	-6	-4	-2	0	+2	+4	+6
$+1$	+1	+1	+1	+1	+1	+1	+1
y	-14	-7	-2	+1	+2	+1	-2

Plot the coordinate pairs
(-3,-14), (-2,-7), (-1,-2),
(0, 1), (1, 2), (2, 1)
and (3,-2).

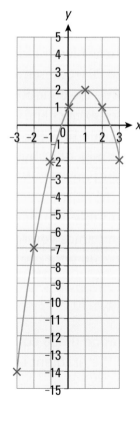

Exercise 7e²

1 Match each equation with one of these cards.

Linear graph	Quadratic graph

a $y = 10 - 3x$ **b** $y = 2$ **c** $x + y = 8$ **d** $y = x^2 - 7x + 10$

e $y = 2x^2$ **f** $x = -3$ **g** $y = 3(x + 1)$ **h** $y = x(x - 1)$

2 **a** Copy and complete the table of values for the equation $y = x^2 + 2$.

x	-3	-2	-1	0	1	2	3
x^2		4					
2		2					
y		6					

   b Plot these points on a set of coordinate axes with x-values from -4 to 4 and y-values from 0 to 12. Join the points with a smooth curve.

   c Write the coordinates of the point where the curve $y = x^2 + 2$ cuts the y-axis.

   d Write the coordinates of the minimum point of the curve $y = x^2 + 2$.

3 **a** Copy and complete the table of values for the equation $y = x^2 - 2x$.

x	-2	-1	0	1	2	3	4
x^2		1					
$-2x$		2					
y		3					

   b Plot these points on a set of coordinate axes with x-values from -3 to 5 and y-values from -2 to 10. Join the points with a smooth curve.

   c Write the coordinates of the points where the line $y = x^2 - 2x$ cuts the x-axis.

   d Write the equation of the vertical line about which $y = x^2 - 2x$ is symmetrical.

A function which involves x^3 as its highest power of x is called a **cubic** function.

a Copy and complete the table of values for the equation $y = x^3 - 4x$.

x	-3	-2	-1	0	1	2	3
x^3	-27	-8			1		
$-4x$	12				-4		
y	-15				-3		

b Plot these points on a set of coordinate axes with x-values from -3 to +3 and y-values from -15 to +15. Join the points with a smooth curve.

c Write the coordinates of the point where the line $y = x^3 - 4x$ cuts the y-axis.

challenge

• Find the midpoint of two coordinates

Keywords
Coordinate
Mid-point

A line segment AB can be defined by giving the **coordinates** of its end points: A (3, 2) and B (7, 4).

The **midpoint** M is the point that lies an equal distance from A and B on the line joining them.

The x-coordinate $= 3 + \frac{1}{2}(7 - 3) = \frac{1}{2}(3 + 7) = 5$

The y-coordinate $= 2 + \frac{1}{2}(4 - 2) = \frac{1}{2}(2 + 4) = 3$

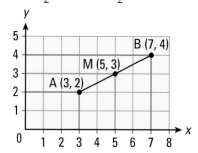

$7 - 5 = 5 - 3$
$4 - 3 = 3 - 2$

• The midpoint M of the line segment joining A (x_A, y_A) and B (x_B, y_B) is given by

You can write
$M = \frac{1}{2}(A + B)$

$$\left(\frac{x_A + x_B}{2}, \frac{y_A + y_B}{2} \right)$$

---

example

Let A and B be the end points of a line segment and M be its midpoint.

a Given A (4, -1) and B (-2, -2) find M.

b Given A (3, -1) and M (5, -2) find B.

. . . .

a $M = \left(\dfrac{4 - 2}{2}, \dfrac{-1 - 2}{2} \right) = \left(\dfrac{2}{2}, \dfrac{-3}{2} \right) = (1, -1.5)$

b Let B $= (x, y)$ then

$(5, -2) = \left(\dfrac{3 + x}{2}, \dfrac{-1 + y}{2} \right)$

$\dfrac{3 + x}{2} = 5 \qquad\qquad \dfrac{-1 + y}{2} = -2$

$3 + x = 10 \qquad\qquad -1 + y = -4$

$x = 7 \qquad\qquad\qquad y = -3$

B $(x, y) = (7, -3)$

For the x-coordinate
you go $+2 = 5 - 3$ units from A to M,
so B is $+2$ units from M: $5 + 2 = 7$

For the y-coordinate
you go $-1 = -2 - -1$ units from A to M
so B is -1 units from M: $-2 + -1 = -3$

Check: $\frac{1}{2}(3 + 7) = 5$
$\frac{1}{2}(-1 + -3) = -2$

Exercise 7f

1 Find the midpoints of these pairs of points.

a (2, 3) and (4, 7)

b (4, -2) and (4, -4)

c (6, 6) and (-6, -6)

d (-5, -2) and (-3, -8)

e (-2, 4) and (-1, 5)

f (1.2, 5.3) and (7.2, -3.2)

2 A line segment AB has midpoint M. Given A and M find the coordinates of B.

a A (2, 2) and M (3, 4)

b A (-1, 3) and M (3, 4)

c A (2, 2) and M (-1, 3)

d A(-1, -3) and M (-2, -3)

e A (7, -4) and M (3, -2)

f A (2.3, -1.3) and M (-3.4, -2.5)

3 The following sets of coordinates give the vertices of a quadrilateral ABCD. For each set

> The shapes will fit on a graph with x and y coordinates from -6 to 6.

i give the name of the quadrilateral

ii calculate the coordinates of the midpoints of the lines joining opposite vertices M_{AC} and M_{BD}

iii comment on what you find.

a A (0, -1) B (1, 2) C (5, 5) and D (4, 2)

b A (-5, -2) B (-5, 3) C (-1, 0) and D (-1, -5)

c A (2, -3) B (2, -1) C (5, 2) and D (5, -6)

4 Show that the points A, B and their midpoint lie on the given line.

a A (-1, -4)   B (3, 4)   line $y = -2 + 2x$

b A (1, 3)   B (2, 5)   line $y = 1 - 2x$

c A (0, 1)   B (6, -1)   line $x + 3y = 3$

d A (-2, 5)   B (3, $2\frac{1}{2}$)   line $y = 4 - \frac{1}{2}x$

---

challenge

Find the point P on the line segment AB which is one third of the way from A.

a A (0, 0)   B (3, 0)

b A (0, 2)   B (0, 8)

c A (1, 3)   B (7, 6)

d A (-2, -3)   B (-5, 3)

e A (4, -6)   B (-2, 2)

f A (1.2, 2.1)   B (0.6, 0.6)

7a

1 Solve these equations.

   a $7x + 3 = 6x + 8$ **b** $6y + 9 = 4y + 17$

   c $2a + 5 = 5a - 7$ **d** $5b - 3 = 9b - 7$

   e $p + 24 = 7p$ **f** $4(q - 1) = 6q - 5$

   g $3(k - 4) = 2(4k - 1)$ **h** $\frac{2}{3}t - 2 = \frac{1}{3}t + 2$

2 For each of these questions, form an equation and solve it to
   find the answer to the problem.

   a Find the length of   **b** The areas of these shapes are equal.
      this rectangle.

      $3x + 2$

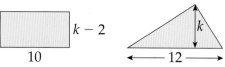

      $8(x - 1)$ 10 12

                                    Find k and hence the dimensions
                                  of each shape.

7b

3 Solve these equations.

   a $10 - x = 7$ **b** $15 - 2y = 5$ **c** $11 = 21 - 5m$ **d** $0 = 18 - 6n$

   e $9 - 3d = 8$ **f** $4 - 7f = 11$ **g** $8 - 2k = 5$ **h** $12 - 3t = 7$

4 Solve these equations.

   a $4x + 3 = 8 - x$ **b** $2k + 5 = 17 - 4k$

   c $3p - 5 = 5 - 2p$ **d** $10 - 3t = t - 2$

   e $7 - a = 15 - 2a$ **f** $11 - 5b = 5 - 2b$

   g $8(3 - y) = 2 + 3y$ **h** $2(7 - 2g) = 3(4 - g)$

7c

5 **a** Draw a mapping diagram for each of these functions.

    i

x	y
0	0
1	3
2	6
3	9

    ii

x	y
1	7
2	9
3	11
4	13

   b For each function in part **a**, write an equation that maps the x-values to
    the y-values.

6 Find the inverse of these functions.

   a $x \rightarrow x + 3$ **b** $x \rightarrow 5x$ **c** $x \rightarrow 4x - 2$ **d** $x \rightarrow \dfrac{x + 1}{6}$

7 a Copy and complete the table of values for the equation
$y = 2x + 1$.

x	0	1	2
$2x$			
$+1$			
y	1		

b Plot these points on a set of coordinate axes with x and y values from 0 to 8. Join your points with a straight line.

c On the same set of axes, plot the graph of $y = 7 - x$.

d Write the coordinates of the point of intersection of these graphs.

8 True or false?
The graphs of the functions $x = 2$ and $y = -3$ intersect at the point $(-3, 2)$.

9 Write the gradient and y-intercept of these straight lines.

a $y = 2x + 1$

b $y = 3x - 2$

c $y = \frac{1}{2}x + 5$

d $y = 8x$

e $y = x - 2$

f $y = 4 - 3x$

g $y = 1 - \frac{1}{3}x$

h $y = 3(2 - x)$

10 Find the equation of each of these straight lines.

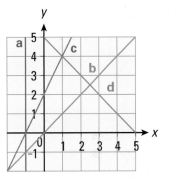

11 True or false?
The graph of the function $y = x^2 + 5x + 6$ passes through the point $(1, 12)$.
Explain your answer.

12 a Copy and complete the table of values for the equation $y = x^2 - x$.

b Plot these points on a set of coordinate axes with x-values from -3 to 4 and y-values from -1 to 8. Join the points with a smooth curve.

x	-2	-1	0	1	2	3
x^2	4					
$-x$	2					
y	6					

c Write the coordinates of the points where the line $y = x^2 - x$ cuts the x-axis.

d Write the equation of the vertical line about which $y = x^2 - x$ is symmetrical.

13 M is the midpoint of the line segment AB.
Find M or B given the following information.

a $A(4, 2)$ $B(6, 4)$

b $A(-1, 7)$ $B(3, 3)$

c $A(5, 6)$ $B(1, -2)$

d $A(-2, -3)$ $B(-4, 2)$

e $A(-2, -1)$ $M(0, 1)$

f $A(6, 4)$ $M(2, 2)$

7 Summary

Assessment criteria
- Construct and solve linear equations **Level 6**
- Recognise that $y = mx + c$ corresponds to a straight line graph **Level 6**

Level 6

1 Kate multiplies her age by 5 and then subtracts 60.
The result is the same as her age.
What is Kate's age?

Sally's answer ✔

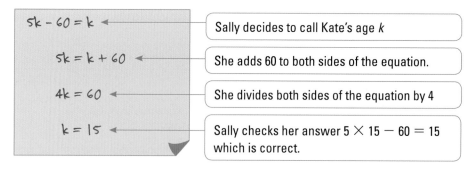

$5k - 60 = k$ ← Sally decides to call Kate's age k

$5k = k + 60$ ← She adds 60 to both sides of the equation.

$4k = 60$ ← She divides both sides of the equation by 4

$k = 15$ ← Sally checks her answer $5 \times 15 - 60 = 15$ which is correct.

Level 6

2 The graph shows a straight line with gradient 1.
  a On the graph, draw a different straight line with gradient 1.
  b The equation of another straight line is $y = 5x + 20$.
  Write the missing number.
  The straight line $y = 5x + 20$ passes through (0, ___).

  c A straight line is parallel to the line with equation $y = 5x + 20$.
  It passes through the point (0, 10).
  What is the equation of this straight line?

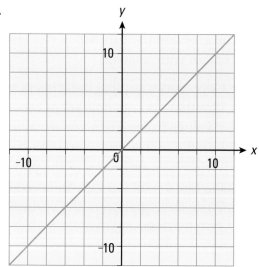

KS3 2007 5–7 Paper 2

8 Number

Calculations

Engineers rely on mathematics to be able to build and run the modern world.

In a power station they have to be able to calculate volumes of cooling water, power outputs, safety margins etc. quickly and accurately.

What's the point? If you want to be able to do calculations quickly and confidently it is important to be able to do them in several ways, using computers, pencil and paper, or in your head.

✓ Check in

1 Round each of these numbers to the nearest **i** integer **ii** 1 dp.
   a 6.0972   **b** 15.533   **c** 217.386

2 Calculate these using an appropriate method.
   a 8.7 + 3.4   **b** 15.7 − 7.29   **c** 29.46 + 8.7   **d** 12.3 − 8.49

3 Calculate
   a 12 × 10   **b** 38 × 0.1   **c** 3.7 × 0.01   **d** 48 ÷ 0.1

4 Calculate these using an appropriate method.
   a 21 × 2.8   **b** 39 × 42.2

5 Calculate these using an appropriate method.
   Give your answer to 1 dp as appropriate.
   a 260 ÷ 14   **b** 61.6 ÷ 8

6 Work out these calculations using the order of operations.
   a $(3 + 2^2) \times 4$ **b** $28 - 2^2 - 7$ **c** $2 \times 7^2 + 6$

- Round numbers to a given power of 10
- Use rounding to make estimates

Keywords
Decimal place
Estimate
Round down
Round up
Whole number

- To round a number to the nearest **whole number** or a given number of **decimal places** you look at the next digit.
  - if it is five or more, **round up**
  - if it is less than five, **round down**.

---

example

A space shuttle orbits the Earth at about 28 000 kilometres per hour. Mission control calculates that to slow down during re-entry the shuttle's nose must be raised 40.382 95° above the horizontal.

Write the re-entry angle to 3 decimal places.

re-entry angle

3 dp means to the nearest thousandth of a degree.

1000	100	10	1	.	$\frac{1}{10}$	$\frac{1}{100}$	$\frac{1}{1000}$	$\frac{1}{10\,000}$	$\frac{1}{100\,000}$
		4	0	.	3	8	2	9	5

Round to 3 dp therefore look at the 4th dp.
This is 9 therefore round up.
40.38295 = 40.383 (3 dp)

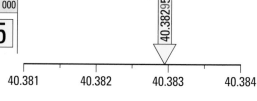

40.381   40.382   40.383   40.384

- Rounding is used to make **estimates** in real-life situations.

---

example

June works in the canteen of H.Elthy Eton School. She needs to calculate how many dinners to make each day.
In a recent poll, 73% of pupils at the school ate school dinners.
The school is an 11−16 sports college with four form groups in each year.
How many dinners should June make?

June estimates that there are about 30 pupils in each form group.
She knows that there are 4 × 5 = 20 form groups in the school.
She also knows that about $\frac{3}{4}$ of the pupils eat school dinners.

Number of dinners $\approx \frac{3}{4}$ of (30 × 20)

$= \frac{3}{4}$ of 600

$= 450$

$73\% \approx \frac{3}{4}$

Exercise 8a

1 Round each of these numbers to the nearest
    i 1000   **ii** 100   **iii** 10.
    a 12 093   **b** 2397   **c** 894   **d** 8498
    e 23 456   **f** 699   **g** 2987   **h** 1 436 384

2 Round each of these numbers to the nearest
    i whole number   **ii** 1 dp   **iii** 2 dp   **iv** 3 dp.
    a 5.0472   **b** 3.4539   **c** 17.5166   **d** 3.04925
    e 13.00854   **f** 130.2536   **g** 0.03047   **h** 7.90089

3 Here is some information about Brian the flea.
    Each of the measurements has been rounded.
    Length = 3.8 mm (1 dp)
    Width = 1.26 mm (2 dp)
    Write **i** the minimum value and
           ii the maximum value that each of Brian's measurements
           could be.

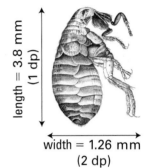

length = 3.8 mm (1 dp)

width = 1.26 mm (2 dp)

4 Work out an estimate for each of these problems.
    Show all the steps of your working out.
    a At R U Danzin Arts College the average height of a Y8 boy
      is 1.48 m and the average height of a Y8 girl is 1.35 m.
      There are 73 boys and 81 girls in the school.
      Estimate, to the nearest metre, the total height of the pupils in Y8.
    b A swimming club decided to raise money for charity by
      swimming the equivalent distance from Oxford to Carlisle.
      The distance from Oxford to Carlisle is 429.7 km.
      The length of the swimming pool was 24.6888 metres.
      The average time to swim one length was 51.3 secs.
      i Estimate, to the nearest length, the number of lengths swum.
     ii Estimate, to the nearest hour, the time taken for the swim.

Kevin has measured the walls of his bedroom.
    Length = 3.4 m (1 dp)   Width = 2.3 m (1 dp)
He buys a rectangular piece of carpet with an area of 7.9 m², in the same shape as
his bedroom. However the piece of carpet is not long or wide enough!
Explain what has happened.

- Consolidate and extend mental methods for addition and subtraction
- Use standard written methods for addition and subtraction

p. 258

Keywords
Compensation
Partitioning

- First, try to work out additions and subtractions in your head.

    Two methods are **partitioning** and **compensation**.

---

example

Calculate

a $9.6 + 8.8$

b $8.49 - 1.97$

. . . .

a Use partitioning

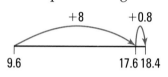

Split 8.8 into 8 and 0.8
Add the two parts to 9.6

$$9.6 + 8.8 = 9.6 + 8 + 0.8$$
$$= 17.6 + 0.8$$
$$= 18.4$$

b Use compensation

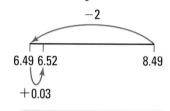

Subtract 2 then add 0.03

$$8.49 - 1.97 = 8.49 - 2 + 0.03$$
$$= 6.49 + 0.03$$
$$= 6.52$$

- When mental addition or subtraction is too hard, use a written method.

---

example

Calculate

a $4587 + 345.002 + 0.0067$

b $4783.29 - 36.8 - 0.8$

. . . .

a Use standard addition method

```
  4587.0000
   345.0020
 +   0.0067
 ----------
  4932.0087
    1 1
```

b Use standard subtraction method

```
     7 12 1
  4783.29
 -  37.60
 --------
  4745.69
```

Write the digits in columns, lined up on the decimal point. To make the calculations easier, add trailing zeros so that each number has the same number of decimal places.

You are taking away 36.8 and 0.8, so it is easier to subtract 37.6 in one step.

Exercise 8b

1 Choose an appropriate method to calculate each of these.

    a $12.7 + 8.6$ **b** $4.78 + 8.9$ **c** $7.8 + 8.95$

    d $3.29 + 7.99$ **e** $18.3 - 6.49$ **f** $8.76 - 4.93$

2 Find the missing numbers in each of these number sentences.

    a $3.73 + \square = 5$ **b** $6.85 + \square = 20$

    c $\square + 9.03 = 15$ **d** $2.99 + \square = 50$

3 Calculate these using a written method.

    a $645.9 - 77.3$ **b** $548.62 + 73.8$ **c** $45.75 + 730.4$

    d $963.2 - 271.6$ **e** $358.23 - 71.7$ **f** $213.8 + 7.26$

4 Calculate these using an appropriate method.

    a $6.72 + 524.3 + 7$ **b** $73.2 + 105.7 + 41.27$

    c $513.4 + 29.27 + 0.078$ **d** $1349.2 + 31.05 - 8.8$

    e $187.8 - 51 - 26.7$ **f** $48.7 + 193.5 - 89.37$

    g $423.79 - 75 - 1.8$ **h** $618.78 - 39.7 - 2 - 0.28$

5 a In an experiment Karl must mix three secret compounds
     in a flask. He uses 28 g of compound D, 0.0345 g of I
     and 7.4 g of H. The total mass of the flask and the three
     compounds is 3524.6 g.
     What is the mass of the flask?

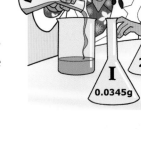

    b Hannibal designs cars. He knows that lighter cars use less
     fuel. Hannibal's car weighs 1142 kg. He decides to remove
     these items:

Tool box	8.4 kg	Radio	0.356 kg
GPS device	0.283 kg	Air freshener	0.0045 kg
Spare tyre	20.1 kg	CDs	0.44 kg
Floor mats	2.38 kg	Torch	1.2 kg

    i What is the new mass of the car?

    ii Explain which of the items Hannibal might choose not to remove.
      Work out the weight of the car if he removes only the items you
      think are appropriate.

Find the missing amount in each of these number sentences.

    a $\square + 4065\,g = 13\,kg$

    b $1570\,m + 0.08\,km + \square = 5\,km$

    c $908\,ml + \square + 1.02\,litres = 2\,litres$

    d $1.8\,tonnes + 1570\,kg + 2.6\,kg + 25\,g = \square\,tonnes$

    e $2.3\,km + 800\,m + 27\,cm + 76\,mm = \square\,km$

First, convert the
measurements to the
same units.

8c Powers of 10

- Multiply and divide numbers by powers of 10
- Use standard form

Keywords
Index notation
Standard form

- The decimal system is based upon powers of 10, and can be written using **index notation**.

1 thousand (kilo) $= 1000$ $= 10 \times 10 \times 10 = 10^3$

1 tenth $= \frac{1}{10} = 0.1 = \frac{1}{10^1}$ $= 10^{-1}$

1 hundredth (centi) $= \frac{1}{100} = 0.01 = \frac{1}{10^2}$ $= 10^{-2}$

> Science and engineering use very large and very small numbers, for example, $3\,400\,000\,000\,000 = 3.4 \times 10^{12}$.
> This is called writing a number in **standard form**.

- The decimal system makes it easy to multiply and divide by powers of ten.
  Multiplying by 0.1 is the same as **dividing** by 10.
  Multiplying by 0.01 is the same as **dividing** by 100.

---

example

Calculate

a 45×0.1 **b** 13×10^{-2}

. . . .

a 45×0.1

$= 45 \times \frac{1}{10}$ Multiplying by $\frac{1}{10}$ is the same

$= 45 \div 10$ as dividing by 10.

$= 4.5$

b 13×10^{-2}

$= 13 \times \frac{1}{100}$ Multiplying by $\frac{1}{100}$ is the same

$= 13 \div 100$ as dividing by 100.

$= 0.13$

- **Dividing** by 0.1 is the same as **multiplying** by 10.
- **Dividing** by 0.01 is the same as **multiplying** by 100.

---

example

Calculate

a $4.5 \div 10^{-1}$ **b** $0.13 \div 0.01$

. . . .

a $4.5 \div 10^{-1}$

$= 4.5 \div \frac{1}{10}$ Dividing by $\frac{1}{10}$ is the same as

$= 4.5 \times 10$ multiplying by 10.

$= 45$

b $0.13 \div 0.01$

$= 0.13 \div \frac{1}{100}$ Dividing by $\frac{1}{100}$ is the same

$= 0.13 \times 100$ as multiplying by 100.

$= 13$

Exercise 8c

1 Calculate

   a 26×0.1 **b** $338 \div 0.1$ **c** 4.7×0.1 **d** $5.3 \div 0.1$

   e $28.5 \div 0.01$ **f** $0.82 \div 0.01$ **g** 25.4×0.1 **h** 3.8×0.01

2 Calculate

   a 28×10^2 **b** 3×10^3 **c** $275 \div 10^2$ **d** $4170 \div 10^3$

   e 8.3×10^3 **f** 4.2×10^2 **g** $377 \div 10^2$ **h** $251 \div 10^2$

   i 0.32×10^3 **j** 1.07×10^3 **k** $4.1 \div 10^2$ **l** 0.038×10^2

3 Calculate

   a 29×10^{-1} **b** 3.8×10^{-1} **c** 51×10^{-2} **d** 3.2×10^{-2}

   e $36 \div 10^{-1}$ **f** $9.2 \div 10^{-1}$ **g** $65 \div 10^{-2}$ **h** $0.51 \div 10^{-2}$

   i 317×10^{-1} **j** 299×10^{-1} **k** 8.15×10^{-2} **l** 0.602×10^{-2}

4 Use one of the six number cards to complete each statement.

   a $4 \times \square = 400$ **b** $0.23 \div \square = 23$ **c** $24 \div \square = 0.24$ 10^2 10^1 10^3

   d $5 \times \square = 0.05$ **e** $0.08 \div \square = 80$ **f** $830 \times \square = 83$

5 Each of these numbers has been written in standard form. 10^{-2} 10^{-1} 10^{-3}

   Work out the size of each of the numbers.

   a 3.3×10^3 **b** 2.4×10^4 **c** 4.7×10^4 **d** 6.3×10^5

   e 2.7×10^7 **f** 4.7×10^{-3} **g** 2.9×10^{-5} **h** 1.01×10^9

6 Jack works out $15.8 \times 14.7 = 232.26$

   Use this information to work out these calculations.

   In each case, explain clearly the method you have used.

   a 158×14.7 **b** 1.58×1.47

   c 1580×0.147

   | 1.58×1.47 = | | 158×14.7 = |

   $15.8 \times 14.7 = 232.26$

   | 1580×0.147 = |

   d What other multiplications can you work out?

      Represent your answers on a spider diagram.

   e Can you use Jack's calculation to work out any divisions?

Brogan is explaining to Shane how she can multiply numbers by powers of 10.
Brogan says 'just look at the power and move the digits that number of places to the left of the decimal point'.

a Investigate Brogan's method by trying out some examples of your own.

b Does Brogan's method work for negative powers of 10?
   Explain your answer.

(8d) Multiplication

- Consolidate and extend mental methods for multiplication
- Use a standard written method for multiplication
- Make and justify estimates and approximations

Keywords
Equivalent whole number calculation
Estimate
Partitioning
Using factors

p. 262

- Always try to work out multiplications in your head.

example

Calculate
a 26×0.05 **b** 6.4×21

. . . .

a Using factors
$$26 \times 0.05 = 26 \times 5 \times 0.01$$
$$= 130 \times 0.01$$
$$= 1.3$$

Re-write 0.05 as the factors 5×0.01.

b Partitioning
$$6.4 \times 21 = (6.4 \times 20) + (6.4 \times 1)$$
$$= 128 + 6.4$$
$$= 134.4$$

Split 21 into two parts, 20 and 1.

For more difficult multiplications convert to an **equivalent whole-number calculation**.

example

Hugh is a baker. He orders 66.5 kg of raspberry jam to make 200 Bakewell tarts.
He is charged £0.93 for each kilogram of jam.
How much does Hugh have to pay for the jam?

. . . .

Always **estimate** the answer first.
$$66.5 \times 0.93 \approx 70 \times 1$$
$$= £70$$

Change the decimal multiplication into an equivalent whole-number calculation.
$$66.5 \times 0.93 \quad \text{is changed to} \quad 665 \times 93$$

Use an appropriate method, in this case the standard method.

$$665 \times 93 = 61\,845$$

$$
\begin{array}{r}
665 \\
\times\ 93 \\
\hline
90 \times 665 = 59850 \\
3 \times 665 = 1995+ \\
\hline
61845 \\
\end{array}
$$

Multiply 66.5×10 and 0.93×100 to make a whole-number calculation.
Altogether, multiply by $10 \times 100 = 1000$

The total cost of the jam $= 66.5 \times £0.93 = 61\,845 \div 1000$
$$= £61.845$$
$$= £61.85 \text{ (2 decimal places)}$$

At the end of the calculation, remember to divide by 1000.

120   **Number** Calculations

Exercise 8d

1 Calculate these using an appropriate method.

Remember to always do a mental approximation first.

   a 28 × 43   **b** 52 × 93   **c** 4238 × 7   **d** 2654 × 9

   e 284 × 45   **f** 19 × 716   **g** 8888 × 8 **h** 88 × 888

2 Calculate these using an appropriate method.

   a 21 × 5.8   **b** 24 × 0.02 **c** 31 × 0.33 **d** 49 × 7.1

   e 31 × 4.6   **f** 29 × 2.3   **g** 75 × 0.05 **h** 13 × 0.07

3 Calculate these using a written method.

   a 9 × 5.18   **b** 7 × 3.92   **c** 23 × 5.4   **d** 36 × 4.4

   e 28 × 0.26   **f** 56 × 0.45   **g** 78 × 29.1   **h** 43 × 6.18

   i 37 × 2.95   **j** 71 × 6.21   **k** 2.8 × 46.1   **l** 3.8 × 29.8

   m 8.3 × 2.04 **n** 16.3 × 0.35   **o** 27.5 × 0.57 **p** 46.5 × 0.78

4 a Jacob buys 37 kg of marmalade.
   The marmalade is sold in 1 kg jars at a cost of £1.45 a jar.
   How much does the 37 kg of marmalade cost?

  b K-Lee needs to make 385 small cakes.
   Each cake requires 100 g of flour.
   The flour costs £0.96 for 1 kg.
   How much does the flour cost to make all 385 cakes?

  c Every Monday morning Liam fills his car with petrol. He
   uses 45.6 litres of fuel each week. Petrol costs £0.99 per litre.
   His car travels 16.3 km for each litre of fuel.
   i How much does Liam pay for fuel each week?
   ii How far can he travel in his car each week?

  d Horse feed costs £0.49 per kg. Monika works out that on
   average her horse Neddy eats 19.6 kg of feed each week.
   i What is the weekly cost of feed for her horse?
   ii What is the annual cost of feeding her horse?

The sum of two numbers is 19.
  a What is the greatest product you could make with the two numbers?

The sum of three numbers is 19.
  b What is the greatest product you could make with the three numbers?
  c Investigate splitting different numbers. Can you generalise your results?

- Consolidate and extend mental division strategies
- Use an appropriate written method of division
- Make and justify estimates and approximations

Keywords
Equivalent calculation
Estimate
Partitioning
Repeated subtraction
Short division
Using factors

p. 262

- Always try to work out divisions in your head.

example

Calculate

a $435 \div 15$ **b** $450 \div 13$

Split 450 into 400 and 50.

a Using factors

$435 \div 15 = 435 \div 5 \div 3$

$\qquad = 87 \div 3$

$\qquad = 29$ Write 15 as 5×3.

b Partitioning

$450 \div 13 = (400 \div 13) + (50 \div 13)$

$\qquad = 30 \text{ r } 10 + 3 \text{ r } 11$

$\qquad = 33 \text{ r } 21$ Simplify the remainder,

$\qquad = 34 \text{ r } 8$ $21 \div 13 = 1 \text{ r } 8$

- When you are dividing a number by a decimal you need to change to an **equivalent calculation** with an integer divisor.

example

Calculate $532 \div 3.9$ giving your answer to 1 decimal place

Re-write the calculation
as an integer divisor

$532 \div 3.9 = 5320 \div 39$

Multiply the dividend and divisor by 10.

Work out $5320 \div 39$ using an appropriate written method.

Using **repeated subtraction**

```
        136.41
    39) 5320
       -3900      39 × 100 = 3900
        1420
       -1170      39 × 30 = 1170
        250
       -234       39 × 6 = 234
        16.0
       -15.6      39 × 0.4 = 15.6
        0.40
       -0.39      39 × 0.01 = 0.39
        0.01
```

$5320 \div 39 = 136.41 \text{ r } 0.01$

$5320 \div 39 = 136.4 \text{ (1 dp)}$

Using **short division**

```
        136.41
       14 25 16 4  1
    39) 5320.000
```

Think $53 \div 39 = 1$ remainder 14

$142 \div 39 = 3$ remainder 25

$250 \div 39 = 6$ remainder 16

$160 \div 39 = 4$ remainder 4

$40 \div 39 = 1$ remainder 1

$5320 \div 39 = 136.4 \text{ (1 dp)}$

Estimate
$532 \div 3.9 \approx 560 \div 4 = 140$

Exercise 8e

1 Calculate these using an appropriate mental method.
   a $84 \div 6$ **b** $135 \div 9$ **c** $156 \div 12$ **d** $315 \div 15$
   e $440 \div 20$ **f** $540 \div 12$ **g** $936 \div 18$ **h** $495 \div 15$

2 Calculate these using an appropriate mental method.
   Give your answer with a remainder where appropriate.
   a $240 \div 14$ **b** $330 \div 17$ **c** $341 \div 31$ **d** $368 \div 16$
   e $279 \div 15$ **f** $440 \div 19$ **g** $610 \div 21$ **h** $680 \div 12$

3 Calculate these using an appropriate method.
   Give your answer as a decimal to 1 dp where appropriate.
   a $45.6 \div 6$ **b** $60.8 \div 8$ **c** $68.8 \div 7$ **d** $78.2 \div 17$
   e $70.2 \div 18$ **f** $81.6 \div 16$ **g** $13 \div 8$ **h** $92 \div 7$
   i $115 \div 6$ **j** $265 \div 14$ **k** $38.7 \div 15$ **l** $44.5 \div 16$

4 Calculate these using an appropriate method.
   Give your answer as a decimal to 1 dp where appropriate.
   a $475 \div 3.6$ **b** $458 \div 2.8$ **c** $716 \div 1.9$ **d** $671 \div 4.1$
   e $538 \div 3.7$ **f** $625 \div 2.5$ **g** $196 \div 1.4$ **h** $782 \div 2.2$

> First re-write each division as an equivalent calculation with an integer divisor.

5 Give your answers to these as either a remainder or as a
   decimal to 2 dp, depending upon the problem.
   a Horace is an Olympic sprinter. In the semi-final he
   runs the 100 m in 9.8 seconds.
   What is his speed in metres per second?
   b Irene works on a coffee plantation in Africa. Each day
   she has to pack 350 kg of Fair Trade coffee. She packs
   the coffee into 1.5 kg packs.
   How many packs can she fill with coffee?

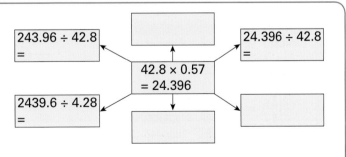

Investigation

Georgia works out 42.8×0.57
$= 24.396$

Use this information to work
out these calculations.
In each case, explain clearly
the method you have used.

$243.96 \div 42.8 =$

$2439.6 \div 4.28 =$

$42.8 \times 0.57 = 24.396$

$24.396 \div 42.8 =$

a i $24.396 \div 42.8$
   ii $243.96 \div 42.8$
   iii $2439.6 \div 4.28$
b What other divisions can you work out?
   Represent your answers on a spider diagram.

- Find the square root and cube root of a number by trial-and-improvement
- Solve problems involving square and cube roots

Keywords
Cube root
Square root

p. 208

- You can find the **square root** of a number by trial-and-improvement.

example

Estimate $\sqrt{60}$ to 2 dp.

First, you must find upper and lower bounds. $7^2 = 49$ and $8^2 = 64$ so $7 < \sqrt{60} < 8$

	A	B	C	D
1	Estimate	Estimate^2	Answer	Result
2	7	7^2	49	Low
3	8	8^2	64	High
4	7.5	7.5^2	56.25	Low
5	7.6	7.6^2	57.76	Low
6	7.7	7.7^2	59.29	Low
7	7.8	7.8^2	60.84	High
9	7.75	7.75^2	60.0625	High
10	7.74	7.74^2	59.9076	Low
11	7.745	7.745^2	59.98503	Low

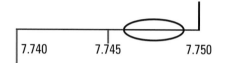

7.740   7.745   7.750

7.7 too small and 7.8 too big
therefore $7.7 < \sqrt{60} < 7.8$
7.74 too small and 7.75 too big
therefore $7.74 < \sqrt{60} < 7.75$
7.745 too small and 7.750 too big
therefore $7.745 < \sqrt{60} < 7.750$

$\sqrt{60}$ is between 7.745 and 7.750
This means that you can round to 2 dp
$\sqrt{60} = 7.75$ (2 dp)

- You can find the **cube root** of a number by trial-and-improvement.

example

Estimate $\sqrt[3]{100}$ to 2 dp.

$4^3 = 64$ and $5^3 = 125$ so $4 < \sqrt[3]{100} < 5$

	A	B	C	D
1	Estimate	Estimate^3	Answer	Result
2	4	4^3	64	Low
3	5	5^3	125	High
4	4.5	4.5^3	91.125	Low
5	4.6	4.6^3	97.336	Low
6	4.7	4.7^3	103.823	High
7	4.65	4.65^3	100.5446	High
9	4.64	4.64^3	99.89734	Low
10	4.645	4.645^3	100.2206	High

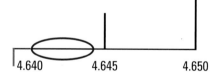

4.640   4.645   4.650

4.6 too small and 4.7 too big
therefore $4.6 < \sqrt[3]{100} < 4.7$
4.64 too small and 4.65 too big
therefore $4.64 < \sqrt[3]{100} < 4.65$
4.640 too small and 4.645 too big
therefore $4.640 < \sqrt[3]{100} < 4.645$

$\sqrt[3]{100}$ lies between 4.640 and 4.645
This means that you can round to 2 dp
$\sqrt[3]{100} = 4.64$ (2 dp)

Exercise 8f

1 Lavina is working out $\sqrt{75}$ to 2 dp.

Here is her working out.

a Does she need to do any more working to find the answer? Explain your thinking.

	Estimate	Estimate²	Answer	Result
	8.6	8.6^2	73.96	Low
	8.7	8.7^2	75.69	High
	8.66	8.66^2	74.996	Low
	8.67	8.67^2	75.169	High

b Find $\sqrt{75}$ to 2 dp.

c Continue Lavina's method to find $\sqrt{75}$ to 3 dp.

2 Use a trial-and-improvement method to find the square root of each of these numbers to 2 dp.

a $\sqrt{30}$ **b** $\sqrt{70}$ **c** $\sqrt{145}$

d $\sqrt{180}$ **e** $\sqrt{250}$ **f** $\sqrt{600}$

Use the square root key on your calculator to check your answers.

3 Use a trial-and-improvement method to find the cube root of each of these numbers to 1 dp.

a $\sqrt[3]{40}$ **b** $\sqrt[3]{200}$ **c** $\sqrt[3]{70}$ **d** $\sqrt[3]{13}$ **e** $\sqrt[3]{2000}$

Did you know?

This Babylonian tablet says

$\sqrt{2} = 1 + \frac{24}{60} + \frac{51}{60^2} + \frac{10}{60^3}$

$= 1.414\,213$ (6 dp)

The calculation was done 3700 years ago without calculators.

Investigation

Yvette is trying to find $\sqrt{60}$ using a method called iteration.

It takes an 'old' estimate and calculates an improved 'new' estimate.

Here is the formula she is using

$$\text{new} = \frac{1}{2} \times \left(\text{old} + \frac{60}{\text{old}}\right)$$

She tries 10 as her 'old' estimate.
She uses her 'new' estimate, 8, as the 'old' estimate.

$$\text{new} = \frac{1}{2} \times \left(10 + \frac{60}{10}\right) = 8$$

She uses her 'new' estimate, 7.75, as the 'old' estimate, and repeats …

$$\text{new} = \frac{1}{2} \times \left(8 + \frac{60}{8}\right) = 7.75$$

a Continue using Yvette's method for finding $\sqrt{60}$.

b After a few goes, use your calculator to check the value of $\sqrt{60}$. Write what you notice.

c Try finding $\sqrt{300}$ using the same method.

d If you have access to a computer, use this formula in a spreadsheet.

8g Calculator skills

- Use a calculator's fraction $\boxed{x/y}$, power $\boxed{x^y}$, sign change $\boxed{(-)}$ and square root $\boxed{\sqrt{}}$ keys to evaluate expressions
- Use rounding to check if an answer is of the correct order of magnitude

Keywords
Check
Fraction key
Order of magnitude
Power key
Sign change key
Square root key

- When solving more complex problems involving numbers with lots of decimal places, square roots, fractions and powers, use a calculator.

Fraction key

example

Calculate $\frac{3}{4} + \frac{2}{7}$

Using the calculator, type

The answer is $\frac{29}{28} = 1\frac{1}{28}$

Power key

example

Calculate $(6.34)^5$

Using the calculator, type

The answer is $10\,243.450\,88$

Sign change

example

Calculate $5.67 \times (-3.45)^2$

Using the calculator, type

> The brackets ensure you calculate
> -3.45 × -3.45 not -3.45 × 3.45

The answer is $67.487\,175$

Square root key

example

Calculate $\sqrt{12.65 \times 3.98}$ to 3 dp.

Using the calculator, type

> The brackets ensure you calculate
> $\sqrt{12.65 \times 3.98}$
> not $\sqrt{12.65} \times 3.98$

The answer is 7.096 to 3 dp

- When using a calculator, it is very important to regularly **check** the answer.

  Use mental estimates to see if the answer is the correct **order of magnitude**.

  $5.67 \times (-3.45)^2 \approx 6 \times (-3)^2 = 6 \times 9 = 54 \approx 67.487175$ ✓

Exercise 8g

1 Without using a calculator, choose the most likely answer for each of these questions.
In each case explain the reasoning behind your choices.
a $(297)^2 = 88\,209$ or $91\,204$ or 5940
b $155 \div 0.62 = 96.1$ or 250 or 961

Beware, not all calculators are the same!
shift might be 2nd fn
y^x might be ^
Compare calculators with your friends.

2 a The rectangle and the square have exactly the same area.
How long is each side of the square?
Give your answer to 2 dp.

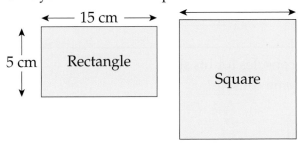

b The area of the new school sports building is $593\,m^2$.
The width of the changing room is $\frac{2}{5}$ of the length of the changing room.
What is the length of the side of the sports hall?
Give your answer to 2 dp.

3 a Kevin says that when you square a number the answer always gets bigger.
Give two examples to show that this is not always true.
b Griselda says that when you find the square root of a number the answer always gets smaller.
Give two examples to show that this is not always true.
c Write a sentence which explains what happens to the size of a number when you find the square and the square root of it.

Olaf is trying to solve a puzzle.
He must use each of the numbers 1, 3, 5, 7 and 9 only once to make this mathematical calculation correct.
Copy and complete the calculation so that it is correct.

$$\frac{\sqrt{\square\square^2 + \square\square}}{\square} = 2$$

8h Calculators in context

- Carry out more complex calculations using a calculator
- Interpret the display on a calculator in different contexts
- Convert between units by finding integer remainders after division

Keywords
Converting
Divisor
Remainder

p. 60

- When doing division using a calculator, you must decide how best to write and interpret any **remainder** in the context of the problem.

  It could be written as a whole number, a fraction or a decimal.

example

Tyrone pays £10 000 for 60 video game consoles for his shop. How much did he pay for each video game console?

Using a calculator

```
10000÷60
    166.6666667
```

Because the answer is money, you should round it to 2 decimal places.

Answer   Each console cost £166.67

- It is very important to interpret the remainder when you are **converting between units**.

example

a Convert 10 000 seconds into hours, minutes and seconds.
b Convert 10 000 ounces into kilograms.

a Convert the secs into mins $10\,000 \div 60 = 166.6666\ldots$

Change the remainder to $0.6666\ldots$ mins $= 0.6666\ldots \times 60$ secs
an integer by multiplying $= 40$ seconds
it by the **divisor**

1 min = 60 secs

This is 166 mins and 0.6666… of a min.

Convert the mins into hrs $166 \div 60 = 2.7666\ldots$

Change the remainder $0.7666\ldots$ hours $= 0.7666\ldots \times 60$ mins
to an integer by multiplying $= 46$ minutes
it by the **divisor**

1 hour = 60 mins

This is 2 hours and 0.7666… of an hour.

Answer   10 000 seconds = 2 hours, 46 minutes and 40 seconds

b Convert the ounces into grams $10\,000 \times 30 = 300\,000$ g

Convert the g into kg $300\,000 \div 1000 = 300$ kg

1 oz ≈ 30 g
1000 g = 1 kg

Answer   10 000 ounces ≈ 300 kg

Exercise 8h

1 Convert these metric measurements to the units indicated in brackets.

   a 3865 cm (m and cm)
   b 373 068 cm (km, m and cm)
   c 7427 ml (ℓ and ml)
   d 15 863 320 g (tonnes, kg and g)
   e 12.25 m (feet and inches)
   f 58 000 cm² (m²)
   g 25 kg (pounds)
   h 400 mm² (cm²)

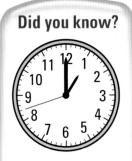

1 inch ≈ 2.5 cm
10 000 cm² = 1 m²
100 mm² = 1 cm²
1 kg ≈ 2.2 pounds

2 Convert these measurements of time into the units indicated in brackets.

   a 5420 secs (hours, mins and secs)
   b 400 000 secs (days, hours, mins and secs)
   c 100 000 days (years, weeks and days)
   d 9 999 999 secs (years, weeks, days, hours, mins and secs)

Did you know?

Sexagesimal (base 60) numbers originated with the ancient Sumerians. We still use them to tell the time and measure angles.

3 Solve these problems.

Give each of your answers in a form appropriate to the question.

   a Hanif sells small cars at his garage. He finds the total cost of his 5 small cars is £59 647. What price should he quote in his newspaper advert for a 'typical small car'?

   b The Year 8 pupils at Heswick High School are going on a trip to Alton Towers theme park. There are 233 pupils and 20 staff going on the trip. Each coach can hold 43 people. How many coaches should be ordered?

   c Ben takes an exam. There are 60 marks in total available on the exam paper and Ben gets 38 marks correct. How well did Ben do on the test?

Jimmi McFast is an athlete. He completes the 100 m at the Olympics in 9.92 seconds.

a How fast did he run the 100 m race?
Give your answer in metres per second (to 1 dp).

b Convert Jimmi's speed into kilometres per hour.

c Investigate some other speeds using these examples.
- An aeroplane's cruising speed is 400 miles per hour.
- A cheetah can run at 110 km per hour.
- A TGV train can travel at 105 metres per second.
- A space shuttle needs to travel at about 17 000 miles per hour to escape from the Earth.

1 mile ≈ 1.6 km

- Know and use the order of operations, including powers and the use of brackets
- Use the bracket keys on a calculator
- Use the square and square root keys on a calculator

Keywords

BIDMAS Order

Brackets Operation

An operator does something to one or a pair of numbers. Examples are
Addition ($+$)
Subtraction ($-$)
Multiplication ($\times$)
Division ($\div$)
Square (x^2)
Square root ($\sqrt{x}$)

- When a calculation contains more than one **operation**, you must do the operations in the correct **order**.
  The correct order for working out operations follows **BIDMAS**.

example

Calculate

a $(5 - 3^2)^2 - 2^3$

b $(3^2 + 5)^2 - 2^3$

. . . .

a $(5 - 3^2)^2 - 2^3$ ⬭ Brackets

$= (5 - 9)^2 - 2^3$

⬭ Indices

$= (-4)^2 - 2^3$

$= 16 - 8$ ⬭ Multiply   ⬭ Divide

$= 8$ ⬭ Add   ⬭ Subtract

b $(3^2 + 5)^2 - 2^3$ Work out the brackets
Inside the brackets there is a power

$= (9 + 5)^2 - 2^3$ and also a subtraction/addition

$= (14)^2 - 2^3$ work out the powers

$= 196 - 8$ work out the subtraction

$= 188$

Beware!
$-3^2 = -(3 \times 3) = -9$
$(-3)^2 = -3 \times -3 = +9$

- A fraction often hides as a pair of **brackets**.
  It is very useful to write the brackets when using a calculator.

example

Calculate $\dfrac{\sqrt{(8 + 3)}(5 - 2)^3}{2 \times 8}$. Give your answer to 2 dp.

. . . .

Rewrite using brackets $[\sqrt{(8 + 3)} \times (5 - 2)^3] \div [2 \times 8]$

Key in

Put brackets around the numerator and the denominator.

The calculator displays 5.596 804

$$= 5.60 \text{ to 2 dp}$$

Exercise 8i

1 Fern and Caroline both sat a test but did not agree on the answers.

Question	Fern	Caroline
a $(3 + 4^2) \times 2$	38	
b $5 - 3^2 - 3$	1	98
c $6 - 5^2$	31	-7
d $(-5)^2 + 6$	31	-19
e $60 \div (4 + 8) - 7 + (5 - 2)^3$	25	-19
f $(3 \times 5^2) \div (3 \times 5)$	15	39
g $(3 \times 8)^2 \div (3 \times 2)$	96	5
		16

For each question, calculate the correct answer to see who is right.

Show your workings.

Explain the mistake made for each incorrect answer.

2 Calculate these giving your answer to 2 dp where appropriate.

a $\dfrac{(8 - 3)^2}{(5 - 2)^2}$ **b** $\dfrac{(3^2 - 1)(5 - 2)^2}{(9 - 4)^2}$ **c** $\dfrac{(7 - 3)^2 \sqrt{(28 - 3)}}{(10 - 8)^3}$

3 Use a calculator to work out these calculations.

Give your answers to 2 dp where appropriate.

a $[2.5^2 + (5 - 2.8)]^2$ **b** $3.4 + [6.8 - (11.7 \times 3.2)]$

c $8 \times (2.5 - 4.6)^2$ **d** $\dfrac{4.37 \times 31.6}{1.09 \times (6.4 - 2.8)^2}$

e $\dfrac{3 \times \sqrt{(4.3^2 + 6^2)}}{5}$ **f** $\dfrac{(5^2 + 2)^2}{6 \times \sqrt{(7.8^2 - 9)}}$

---

a Jackie and Vlad are working out this calculation. $\left(\dfrac{5}{3}\right)^2$

Jackie types $\frac{5}{3}$ into her calculator and squares it.

Vlad works out 5^2 and divides by 3^2.

They both get the same answer.

Explain how and why both methods work.

b Investigate

i $3^2 \times 5^2$ **ii** $\sqrt{12} \times \sqrt{3}$ **iii** $\sqrt{12} \div \sqrt{3}$

8a

1 Round each of these numbers to the nearest
  i whole number   ii 1 dp   iii 2 dp   iv 3 dp.
  a 6.1583   **b** 4.5648   **c** 18.6262   **d** 4.154 94
  e 3.909 09   **f** 9.999 99   **g** 87.654 32   **h** 0.000 707

2 Work out an estimate for each of these problems.
  Show all the steps of your working out.
  a The average height of a man in Scotland is 1.78 m. There are
    662 954 people living in Glasgow, of whom 49% are men.
    Estimate the combined height of all the men in Glasgow.
    Give your answer to the nearest kilometre.
  b Giuseppe runs the marathon which is 42.195 km in length.
    He covers each km in 3 mins 48 secs.
    Estimate the time it will take Giuseppe to complete the race.
    Give your answer to the nearest minute.

8b

3 Calculate these using an appropriate method.
  a $7.6 + 4.3 + 11$ **b** $79 + 115.6 + 41$ **c** $9.27 + 0.9 + 9 + 0.95$
  d $999.9 + 99.99 + 0.099$ **e** $33.3 + 333.3 - 3.33$ **f** $2473.5 + 40.79 - 4.6$

8c

4 Calculate
  a 39×10^3 **b** 7×10^2 **c** $416 \div 10^1$ **d** $3703 \div 10^2$
  e 5.3×10^{-1} **f** 7.7×10^1 **g** $562 \div 10^3$ **h** $327 \div 10^3$
  i 0.49×10^2 **j** 2.7×10^{-1} **k** $6.4 \div 10^{-2}$ **l** 0.057×10^2

5 Each of these numbers has been written in standard form.
  Work out the size of each of the numbers.
  a 4.7×10^3 **b** 3.9×10^{-2} **c** 8.2×10^4 **d** 2.9×10^5
  e 7.3×10^6 **f** 8.07×10^{-4} **g** 6.3×10^5 **h** 2.05×10^7

8d

6 Calculate these using a written method.
  Remember to do a mental approximation first.
  a 82×0.65 **b** 64×0.57 **c** 82×91.3 **d** 93×26.5
  e 36×1.86 **f** 72×9.51 **g** 16×2.19 **h** 8.3×86.7
  i 63.7×0.91 **j** 38.4×0.69 **k** 57.2×0.61 **l** 93.9×0.93

7 Calculate these using an appropriate method.
Give your answer as a decimal to 1 dp where appropriate.

a $48.6 \div 6$	**b** $67.4 \div 8$	**c** $82.8 \div 7$	**e** $38.5 \div 14$
e $62.5 \div 15$	**f** $31.2 \div 16$	**g** $327 \div 4.6$	**h** $912 \div 5.6$
i $304 \div 2.4$	**j** $441 \div 2.1$	**k** $327 \div 8.2$	**l** $955 \div 3.7$

8 Use a trial and improvement method to find the square root of each of these numbers to 2 dp.

a $\sqrt{45}$ **b** $\sqrt{13}$ **c** $\sqrt{361}$ **d** $\sqrt{876}$ **e** $\sqrt{2640}$

Use the square root key on your calculator to check your answers.

9 Use a trial and improvement method to find the cube root of each of these numbers to 1 decimal place.

a $\sqrt[3]{95}$ **b** $\sqrt[3]{300}$ **c** $\sqrt[3]{10}$ **d** $\sqrt[3]{999}$ **e** $\sqrt[3]{87654}$

10 Use your calculator to work out the answer to these sets of instructions.
a Input the number 12. Square your answer. Add 23.
Find the square root. Add -8. Cube your answer.
b Input the fraction $\frac{7}{8}$. Square your answer. Divide by 2.
Add 14. Square root your answer.
c Write the sets of instructions in parts **a** and **b** as calculations using the correct order of operations.

11 Solve these problems.
Give each of your answers in a form appropriate to the question.
a Jasmine's syndicate wins £3 454 123.23 on the Euro millions. There are 17 people in the syndicate. How much does each person receive?
b The population of Smalltown is 48. Each year the population is predicted to increase by 6%. What will the population be in one year's time?

12 Calculate these, giving your answer to 2 dp where appropriate.

a $\dfrac{(7-2)^3}{(8-3)^2}$ **b** $\dfrac{(4^2-1.2)(7-2.5)^2}{(9-4.1)^3}$ **c** $\dfrac{(3^2-2)^2\sqrt{(31-2^3)}}{(17-5)^2}$

13 Use a calculator to work out these calculations.
Give your answers to 2 dp where appropriate.
a $[1.8^3 + (17 - 2.3^2)]^2$ **b** $8.2 + [3.7^2 - (12.7 \div 2.6)]$

c $9.2 \times (1.05 - 2.1)^3$ **d** $\dfrac{5.03 \times 1.9^3}{4.23 \times (8.7 - 3.3)^2}$

Assessment criteria
- Multiply and divide numbers by powers of 10 **Level 6**
- Give solutions to an appropriate degree of accuracy **Level 6**

Level 6

1 Find the missing numbers.
   a $4.8 \times 0.01 = \square$
   b $0.6 \div 0.1 = \square$
   c $0.01 \times \square = 3.4$

Barry's answer ✔

Barry thinks 'How many 0.1 s in 0.6?'
The answer should be 6.

a $4.8 \times 0.01 \quad = 4.8 \times \frac{1}{100}$
$= 4.8 \div 100$
$= 0.048$

b $0.6 \div 0.1 \quad = 0.6 \div \frac{1}{10}$
$= 0.6 \times 10$
$= 6$

c $0.01 \times \square \quad = 3.4$
0.01 is the same as $\frac{1}{100}$
So $\frac{1}{100} \times \square = 3.4$
$3.4 \times 100 = 340$

He decides multiplying by $\frac{1}{100}$ is the same as dividing by 100.

He decides dividing by $\frac{1}{10}$ is the same as multiplying by 10.

Barry checks that $0.01 \times 340 = 3.4$

Level 6

2 The value of π correct to 7 decimal places is:

   3.1415927

   a Write the value of π correct to 4 decimal places.
   b Which value below is closest to the value of π?
      Put a ring round the correct one.

   $\dfrac{179}{57}$ $\qquad$ $3\dfrac{1}{7}$ $\qquad$ $\left(\dfrac{16}{9}\right)^2$ $\qquad$ $\dfrac{355}{113}$

KS3 2007 4–6 Paper 2

9 Geometry

Transformations

The geometric shapes and constructions in crop circles are often quite complex, and the patterns illustrate mathematics in a beautiful way.

What's the point? Are these intricate and fascinating designs constructed by aliens or are they man made?

✓ Check in

1 Convert these measurements to the units in the brackets.
   a 80 cm (mm)   **b** 0.2 km (m)   **c** 3.5 m (cm)
   d 450 m (km)   **e** 75 cm (m)   **f** 15 mm (cm)

2 **a** Copy this grid. Plot and join the points
      (-4, 2), (-2, 3), (0, 2) and (-2, -2) to form a kite.

   The kite is moved 4 units to the right.
   b Draw the new position of the kite and give
      the coordinates of the vertices.

   This kite can be reflected back to the starting
   position.
   c Describe where you would put the mirror line.

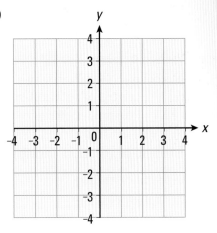

• Reflect, rotate and translate 2-D shapes

Keywords
Centre of rotation
Congruent
Image
Object
Reflection
Rotation
Transformation

• A **transformation** moves a shape to a new position.

The starting shape is called the **object**.
The **image** is the shape after the transformation.

• A **reflection** flips an object over a mirror line.

You describe a reflection by giving the mirror line.

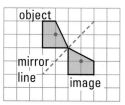

• A **rotation** turns an object about a point, called the **centre of rotation**.

You describe a rotation by giving
– the centre of rotation
– the angle of rotation
– the direction of turn (clockwise or anticlockwise).

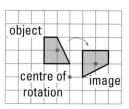

• A **translation** slides an object.

You describe a translation by giving the distance moved left or right, then the distance moved up or down.

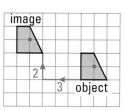

p. 88

The object and the image are **congruent** for reflections, rotations and translations.

Congruent shapes are the same size and the same shape.

example

The orange octagon is rotated to the green octagon.
Find the centre of rotation and the angle of rotation.

. . . .

Use a trial and improvement approach to find the centre of rotation and the angle of rotation.

The transformation is an anticlockwise rotation of 90° about the point (-1,0).

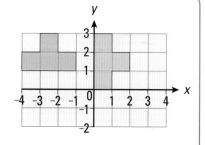

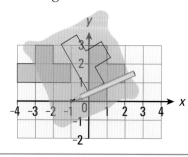

Use tracing paper to try possible centres of rotation and different angles of rotation.

Exercise 9a

1 reflection rotation translation

Use these description cards to describe the transformations
that move the pink shape to

a shape A
b shape B
c shape C
d shape D
e shape E.

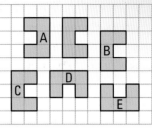

2 Copy the diagram.

a Reflect the two squares in one of the mirror lines.
b Reflect the four squares in the other mirror line.

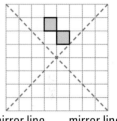

mirror line   mirror line

3 **a** The pink triangle is rotated to the green triangle.
   Find the centre of rotation and the angle of rotation.
b The green triangle is rotated to the orange triangle.
   Find the centre of rotation and the angle of rotation.
c Describe fully the transformation that moves
   i the orange triangle to the pink triangle
   ii the pink triangle to the orange triangle.

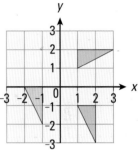

4 **a** Rotate a scalene triangle through 180° about
   the midpoint of a side.
b Mark the equal angles and the equal sides on the
   completed quadrilateral.
c Show that the completed quadrilateral is a parallelogram.

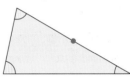

a Draw the 4 by 4 grid and copy this outline.
b Draw the reflection of the outline in the mirror line.
c Can you see a vase or two faces in your completed drawing?
d Colour either the vase or the faces.

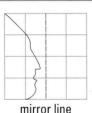

mirror line

activity

- Transform 2-D shapes using combinations of transformations

Keywords
Equivalent   Tessellation
Reflection   Translation
Rotation

You can transform 2-D shapes using repeated **reflections**, **rotations** and **translations**.

example

a Reflect the pink triangle in the line $x = 2$.
Call the image I_1.
b Reflect the image in the line $y = 0$.
Call the image I_2.
c Describe a single transformation that moves the pink triangle to I_2.

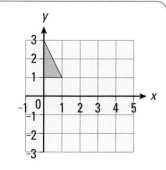

....

a, b

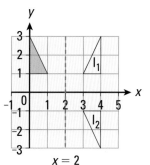

$x = 2$

c A rotation of $180°$ about $(2, 0)$.
This means these two reflections are **equivalent** to one half-turn rotation.

Use tracing paper to find the centre of rotation.

- A **tessellation** is a tiling pattern with no gaps or overlaps.

You can tessellate shapes by repeating the same transformation.

example

a Tessellate a scalene triangle using repeated rotations of $180°$ about the midpoints of the sides.
b Colour the equal angles in your tessellation.
c Which angle properties are shown in the tessellation?

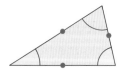

....

a, b

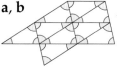

Use the colours of the angles to spot the angle properties.

c Vertically opposite angles are equal.
The exterior angle of a triangle is equal to the sum of the two opposite interior angles.
Alternate angles are equal for parallel lines.
Corresponding angles are equal for parallel lines.
Sum of internal angles in a triangle equals the angle on a straight line, $180°$.

Exercise 9a²

1 Draw this isosceles trapezium on isometric paper.
The shape is rotated clockwise through 120° about the black dot.
The image is again rotated clockwise through 120° about the dot.
Name the shape that is formed by the object and the images.

2 a Tessellate a quadrilateral using repeated rotations
of 180° about the midpoint of the sides.
b Colour the equal angles in your tessellation.
c What angle properties are shown in the tessellation?

3 Two mirrors M_1 and M_2 are 4 units apart.
A pink flag is placed halfway between the mirrors.
a Draw the flag after a reflection in the mirror M_1.
Label this image I_1.
b Draw the reflection of I_1 using the mirror M_2.
Label this new image I_2.
c Describe the single transformation that moves the pink flag to I_2.

4 The green triangle is rotated clockwise through
180° about (0,0).
a Draw the image and label it I_1.
b The triangle I_1 is reflected in the x-axis.
Draw the new image and call it I_2.
c Describe the single transformation that
moves the green triangle to I_2.

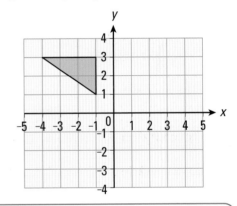

---

activity

Use three squares to draw a hexagon.

Remove a triangle and rotate the shape through 180°.

Show that this shape tessellates using repeated rotations.

Colour your tessellation.

- Recognise reflection symmetry and rotation symmetry of 2-D shapes

Keywords
Line of symmetry
Order of rotation symmetry
Reflection symmetry
Regular
Rotation symmetry

- A **line of symmetry** divides a shape into two identical mirror images.

- A shape has **reflection symmetry** if it has at least one line of symmetry.

- A shape has **rotation symmetry** if it rotates onto itself more than once in a full turn.

- The **order of rotation symmetry** is the number of times a shape looks exactly like itself in a complete turn.

The starfish has 5 lines of symmetry and rotation symmetry of order 5.

- A shape with rotation symmetry of order 1 has no rotation symmetry.

You should know the symmetrical properties of these quadrilaterals.

p. 84

Square	**Rectangle**	**Rhombus**	**Parallelogram**
4 lines of symmetry	2 lines of symmetry	2 lines of symmetry	0 lines of symmetry
Rotation symmetry of order 4	Rotation symmetry of order 2	Rotation symmetry of order 2	Rotation symmetry of order 2

Trapezium	**Isosceles trapezium**	**Kite**	**Arrowhead**
0 lines of symmetry	1 line of symmetry	1 line of symmetry	1 line of symmetry
No rotation symmetry	No rotation symmetry	No rotation symmetry	No rotation symmetry

example

a Draw a shape using five squares that has 4 lines of reflection symmetry and rotation symmetry of order 4.
b Draw the 4 lines of symmetry.

a

b

Exercise 9b

1 These symbols are on Abdi's mobile phone.
  Draw each symbol and draw any lines of symmetry.
  State the order of rotation symmetry in each case.
  a #   **b** ▭   **c** *   **d** ☎   **e** ⇧

2 Draw each of these shapes and draw any lines of symmetry.
  State the order of rotation symmetry in each case.
  a an equilateral triangle
  b a square
  c a regular pentagon
  d a regular hexagon
  e a regular octagon

> A **regular** shape has equal sides and equal angles.

3 Draw three copies of a 3 by 3 square.
  Colour three of the squares as shown in each diagram.
  a Draw the lines of symmetry and state the order of rotation
    symmetry for your first diagram.
  b Add one coloured square to your second diagram so that the
    shape has one line of symmetry, but no rotation symmetry.
    Draw the line of symmetry.
  c Add two coloured squares to your third diagram so that the
    shape has no lines of symmetry, and rotation symmetry
    of order 2.

4 This diagram has a vertical and a horizontal line of symmetry.

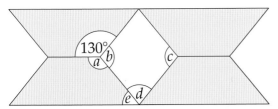

  The angle shown is 130°.
  Calculate the angles *a*, *b*, *c*, *d* and *e*.

Did you know?

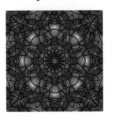

A kaleidoscope uses mirrors and repeated reflections to create symmetrical patterns.

The number 1001 has 2 lines of reflection symmetry
and rotation symmetry of order 2.

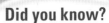

Are there any other numbers between 1000 and 2000 that have both reflection and
rotation symmetry?

* Enlarge a 2-D shape using a centre of enlargement and a positive whole number scale factor

Keywords
Centre of enlargement
Enlargement
Image
Object
Scale factor
Similar
Transformation

You enlarge a shape by multiplying the lengths by the **scale factor**.

 × 3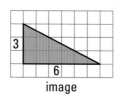

object

image

All the lengths in the object are multiplied by 3.

$1 \times 3 = 3$ $2 \times 3 = 6$

All the angles stay the same.

* An **enlargement** is a type of **transformation** that alters the size of the shape.

  The angles of the shape do not change.

* The **object** and the **image** are **similar**.

  They are the same shape, but a different size.

The position of the image is fixed if you use a **centre of enlargement**.

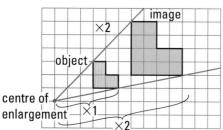

Draw lines from the centre of enlargement through the vertices of the object.

Multiply distances to each vertex by the scale factor to find the distance to the image's vertices.

This enlargement is scale factor 2.

* You describe an enlargement by giving
  – the scale factor
  – the centre of enlargement.

example

Draw the enlargement of the shape using a scale factor of 3 and the marked centre of enlargement.

centre of enlargement

centre of enlargement

Check that each side of the small triangle has been multiplied by 3, for example $2 \times 3 = 6$

Exercise 9c

1 A photograph measuring 10 cm by 15 cm is enlarged to make mathematically similar photographs.
Calculate the scale factor of each enlargement.

a 20 cm by 30 cm **b** 30 cm by 45 cm **c** 25 cm by 37.5 cm

2 Copy these diagrams on coordinate axes.
The blue shapes are enlarged to give the green shapes.
Calculate the scale factor and find the coordinates of the centre of enlargement.

a 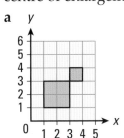 **b** 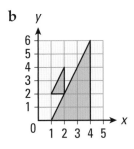 **c**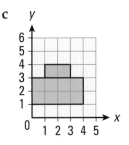

3 Copy these shapes on square grid paper.
Draw the enlargement of each shape using the dot as the centre of enlargement and the given scale factor.

a   **b**   **c**

scale factor 2   scale factor 3   scale factor 4

4 The pink rectangle is enlarged to give the green rectangle using (0,5) as the centre of enlargement.
Part of the green rectangle is shown.
The point (1,5) moves to (4,5).

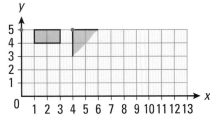

Find **a** the scale factor of the enlargement
      b the four coordinates of the green rectangle.

An equilateral triangle is enlarged by scale factor 2.
Four small triangles will fit inside the image.

The small triangle is enlarged by scale factor 10.
a How many small triangles will fit inside the image?
b Draw the enlarged shape on isometric paper.

scale factor 2

- Enlarge a 2-D shape using a centre of enlargement and a positive fractional scale factor

Keywords

Centre of   Object
enlargement   Scale
Enlargement   factor
Image   Similar

An **enlargement** with a **scale factor** of $\frac{1}{2}$ results in an **image** that is smaller than the **object**.

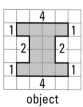

All the lengths in the object are multiplied by $\frac{1}{2}$.

$4 \times \frac{1}{2} = 2$ $2 \times \frac{1}{2} = 1$

$1 \times \frac{1}{2} = \frac{1}{2}$

All the angles stay the same.

- The object and the image are **similar** – the lengths change in proportion – the angles stay the same.

- If the scale factor is greater than 1, the image is larger than the object.

- If the scale factor is less than 1, the image is smaller than the object.

The position of the image is fixed, if you use a **centre of enlargement**.

This enlargement has scale factor $\frac{1}{3}$.

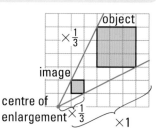

Draw lines from the centre of enlargement through the vertices of the object.

Multiply distances to each vertex by the scale factor to find the distance to the image's vertices.

example

Draw the enlargement of the orange triangle using a scale factor of $\frac{1}{2}$ using the origin as centre of enlargement.

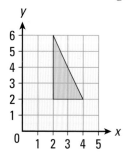

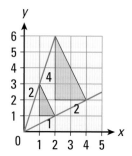

Check that each side of the large triangle has been multiplied by $\frac{1}{2}$.

$4 \times \frac{1}{2} = 2$ $2 \times \frac{1}{2} = 1$

Exercise 9c²

1 Copy the shapes on square grid paper. Enlarge each shape by the given scale factor.
There is no centre of enlargement.

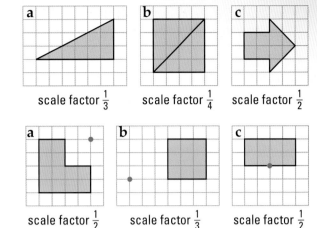

scale factor $\frac{1}{3}$　　scale factor $\frac{1}{4}$　　scale factor $\frac{1}{2}$

2 Copy these shapes on square grid paper. Enlarge each shape using the dot as the centre of enlargement and the given scale factor.

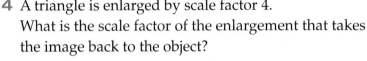

scale factor $\frac{1}{2}$　　scale factor $\frac{1}{3}$　　scale factor $\frac{1}{2}$

3　**a** Copy this coordinate grid and plot the points A(2,2), B(8,0), C(12,8) and D(4,6).
　b State the mathematical name of quadrilateral ABCD.
　c Using (2,4) as the centre of enlargement, enlarge ABCD by scale factor $\frac{1}{2}$.
　d Write the coordinates of the vertices of the image.

4 A triangle is enlarged by scale factor 4.
What is the scale factor of the enlargement that takes the image back to the object?

5 The smaller triangle is an enlargement of the larger triangle.
Calculate　**a**　the scale factor of the enlargement
　　　　　b　the value of x
　　　　　c　the perimeter of each triangle.

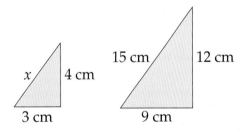

Draw a large triangle.
Mark a point O outside the triangle.
Draw lines from O to the vertices of the triangle.
Find the midpoint of each line and join the three midpoints to form a triangle.

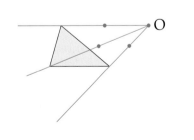

Is this triangle similar to the first triangle?
What is the scale factor of the enlargement?

• Interpret scale drawings and maps using ratios

Keywords
Ratio
Represents
Scale
Scale drawing

You can use **scale drawings** to **represent** real-life objects.

Length 17 m
Height 5 m

Real-life lengths are reduced or enlarged in proportion using a **scale**.

The scale allows you to interpret the scale drawing.

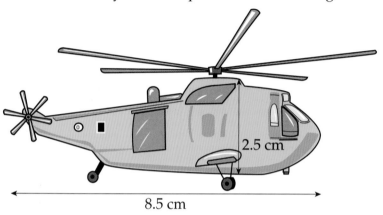

2.5 cm

8.5 cm

Scale: 1 cm represents 200 cm

The real-life lengths are 200 times larger than in the scale drawing.

$8.5 \times 200 = 1700$
$2.5 \times 200 = 500$

The real-life lengths are an enlargement scale factor 200 of the scale drawing.

• The scale can be written as a **ratio**.

1 : 200 means 1 cm on the scale drawing represents 200 cm, or 2 m, in real life.

The scale for a map is often given as a ratio.

example

Jamie is using a map with a scale of 1 : 25 000.
a What does 5 cm on the map represent in real life?
b What distance would represent 4 km on the map?

Dartmoor
Map
1 : 25 000

a 1 cm on the map represents   25 000 cm in real life.
5 cm on the map represents $5 \times 25\,000$ cm in real life.

$5 \times 25\,000$ cm $= 125\,000$ cm $= 1250$ m $= 1.25$ km

b 4 km $= 4000$ m $= 400\,000$ cm
400 000 cm in real life is represented by $400\,000 \div 25\,000$
$= 16$ cm on the map

The real-life lengths are 25 000 times larger than on the map.

The map's lengths are 25 000 times smaller than in real life.

Exercise 9d

1 This is a scale drawing of a bicycle.

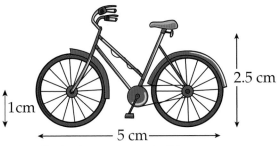

2.5 cm

1cm

5 cm

Scale: 1 cm represents 35 cm

Calculate a the diameter of the wheel

           b the length of the bicycle

           c the height of the saddle above the ground.

2 The diagram represents a full-size sailing dinghy.
Jenny decides to draw a scale drawing of the dinghy using
a scale of 1:50.

Calculate the length in the scale drawing of

a the mast

b the length of the boat

c the horizontal beam.

3 A rectangular field measures 40 m
by 30 m.
Use a scale drawing to calculate
the length of the diagonal of the field.
Remember to state the scale of your
drawing.

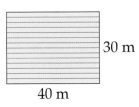

30 m

40 m

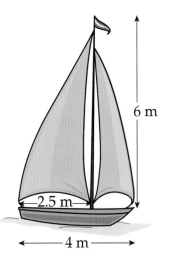

6 m

2.5 m

4 m

The Kennet and Avon Canal has two right-angled bends at the Avoncliff aqueduct.
Boats find it difficult to pass through this part of the canal and in fact some boats
are too long and cannot pass through the bends.

The width of the canal is 5 metres.

a Draw a scale drawing of this part of the canal.
   Use a scale of 1 cm to represent 2.5 m.

b What is the longest boat that can pass through the bends?

   Start by assuming that the boat has no width.

5 m

15 m

5 m

15 m

5 m

1 Copy the diagram on square grid paper.
Describe fully the transformation that moves the pink shape to
  a shape A
  b shape B
  c shape C.

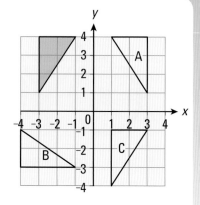

2 Copy the diagram on square grid paper.
  a Reflect the green hexagon in the line $y = x$.
    Colour the image orange.
  b Describe a different transformation that moves the green hexagon to the orange hexagon.

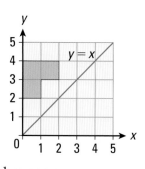

3 a Tessellate a regular hexagon using repeated translations.
  b Which other repeated transformations can you use to tessellate a regular hexagon?

4 The pink triangle is rotated clockwise through 90° about (0,0).
  a Draw the image and label it I_1.
  b The triangle I_1 is reflected in the y-axis.
    Draw the new image and call it I_2.
  c The triangle I_2 is reflected in the x-axis.
    Draw the new image and call it I_3.
  d Describe the single transformation that moves the pink triangle to I_3.

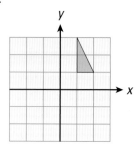

5 Draw these currency symbols.
Draw any lines of reflection symmetry and state the order of rotation symmetry for each symbol.
  a €   **b** $ **c** S   **d** ¥   **e** ₦

6 This triangle has one vertical line of symmetry.
  a State the values of a and b.
  b Explain your reasoning.

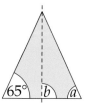

7 Copy the shapes on square grid paper.

Draw the enlargement of each shape using the dot as the centre of enlargement and the given scale factor.

a

scale factor 3

b

scale factor 2

c

scale factor 4

8 a Plot the points A (4,0)' B (7,0) and C (4,6) on the coordinate axes.

  b State the mathematical name of the shape ABC.

  c Using (1,3) as the centre of enlargement, enlarge the shape ABC by scale factor $\frac{1}{3}$.

  d Write down the coordinates of the image A'B'C'.

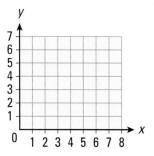

9 The Naze Tower in Essex is 26 metres high and 6 metres wide.

  a Draw a scale drawing of the tower using a scale of 1:500.

    Show your calculations for the height and the width of the tower in a scale drawing.

  b Estimate the height of the person in the photograph.

  c Calculate the height of the person in the scale drawing and draw the person on your scale drawing.

10 Jules is using a map with a scale of 1:50 000.

What is the actual distance in kilometres, if the length on the map is

  a 1 cm   **b** 5 cm   **c** 1.5 cm   **d** 3.5 cm   **e** 4.8 cm?

Maths life

Patchwork

Patchworks are made by sewing together several small pieces of fabric, often polygons that are chosen because they fit together to make the desired design.

YOUR FREE PATCHWORK TEMPLATES!

square

rectangle

right angled triangle

equilateral triangle
60°

rhombus
60°

trapezium
120°

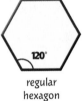
regular pentagon
108°

regular hexagon
120°

regular octagon
135°

Here's some ideas to use with your templates:

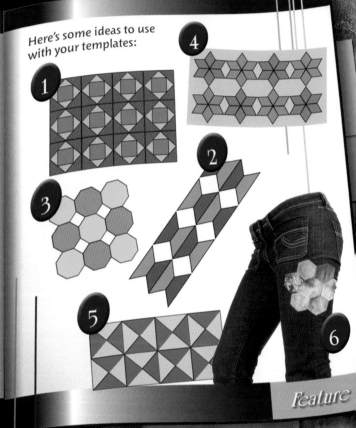

1 2 3 4 5 6

Feature

Mix tunes

- Which templates have been used in each patchwork?
- Which patchworks only use one template? Which patchworks use more than one?
- What can you say about the angles of the shapes where they meet at any point in a patchwork?

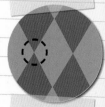

Look at the angles in the templates:

- Can you explain why regular hexagons tessellate but regular pentagons do not?
- Why do regular octagons tessellate when combined with squares but not on their own?
- Thinking about angles, and without drawing anything, what other combinations of the templates might tessellate? You can combine two or more templates.
- Try some of the combinations to see if they do tessellate – you might want to make your own templates to help with this.

Some patchworks do not seem to use recognisable polygons:

In fact, this patchwork is based on a tessellation of squares:

To make a template for a patchwork like this, start with a shape that you know will tessellate, in this case a square:

Draw a new shape inside the square, along one of the sides or from a corner:

Draw exactly the same shape on the opposite side, but this time outside the original shape:

Repeat the process as much as you like, always copying the shape from one side to the outside of the opposite side:

Draw around the new outline and rub out any unwanted lines and you have a template ready to cut out and use for your own patchwork design:

You don't have to start with a square

You don't have to draw straight lines (as long as you can repeat any curves accurately!)

VENICE

ART & ARCHITECTURE

As with this church floor in Venice, tessellation can be used to create 3-D effects

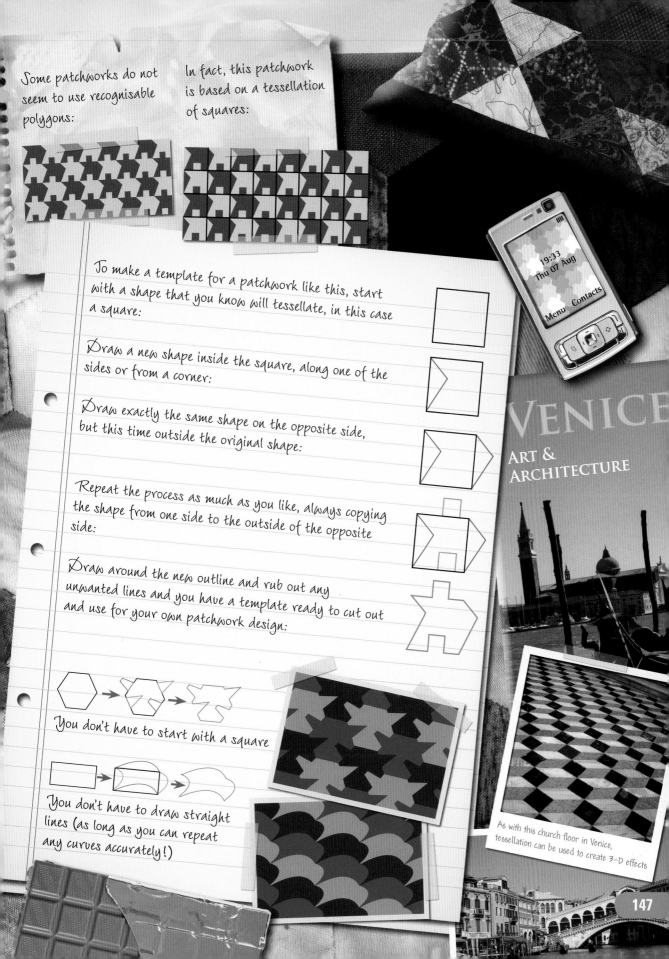

9 Summary

Assessment criteria
- Know that translations, rotations and reflections map objects to congruent images **Level 6**
- Enlarge 2-D shapes using a positive integer scale factor **Level 6**
- Enlarge 2-D shapes using a positive fractional scale factor **Level 7**

Level 6

1 The two triangles are congruent.
Write down the values of a, b and c.

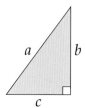

5 cm 3 cm
4 cm

Mel's answer ✔

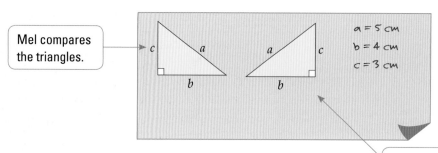

Mel compares the triangles.

$a = 5$ cm
$b = 4$ cm
$c = 3$ cm

Mel rotates, then reflects the second triangle.

Level 6

2 a The grid shows an arrow.
On the grid, draw an enlargement of scale factor 2 of the arrow.
Use C as the centre of enlargement.

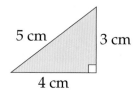

You will need a large sheet of square grid paper.

Level 7

b The sketch shows two arrows.
The bigger arrow is an enlargement of scale factor 1.5 of the smaller arrow.
Write down the three missing values.

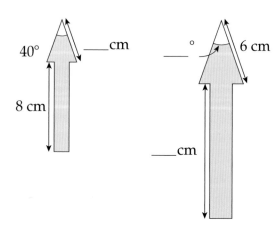

40° ___ cm
8 cm
___° 6 cm
___ cm

KS3 2002 5–7 Paper 2

Sequences and roots

The Italian mathematician Fibonacci believed he could model a population of rabbits using a special sequence. His rule for the number of pairs of rabbits was 'add the two previous terms to get the next term'

1, 1, 2, 3, 5, 8, …

(2 = 1 + 1, 3 = 1 + 2, 5 = 2 + 3, …)

What's the point? Sequences of numbers occur everywhere: stock market prices, daily temperatures, population sizes, … Being able to identify their pattern and predict future numbers is a very valuable skill.

Check in

1 Continue each of these sequences for two more terms.
    a 6, 12, 18, 24, 30, …   **b** 3, 8, 13, 18, 23, …
    c 90, 81, 72, 63, 54, … **d** 720, 360, 180, 90, 45, …

2 Write the first five terms of the sequences described by each rule.
    a The first term is 4.   Each term is 5 more than the previous term.
    b The first term is 1.   Each term is three times the previous term.
    c The first term is 10. Each term is half the previous term.

3 Find the value of each of these. You may use your calculator.
    a 8^2 **b** 14^2 **c** 7^3 **d** 12^3

4 Find the value of each of these. You may use your calculator.
    a $\sqrt{256}$ **b** $\sqrt{441}$ **c** $\sqrt[3]{1728}$ **d** $\sqrt[3]{5832}$

- Generate terms of a sequence given a term-to-term or position-to-term rule
- Find the term-to-term rule of a sequence

Keywords
Difference   Rule
Linear   Sequence
Position   Term
    -to-term Term-to-term

- A **sequence** is an ordered set of numbers, called **terms**. Sequences often follow **rules**.

- A sequence can be described by its **term-to-term** rule.
  The term-to-term rule of the sequence 1, 10, 100, 1000, 10 000 is 'The first term is 1. Each term is 10 times the previous term.'

- A sequence is **linear** if it increases or decreases in equal steps. The increase or decrease is known as the **difference** between terms.

example

Write the first five terms of these sequences.
a The first term is 1. Each term is double the previous term.
b The first term is 90. Each term is 9 less than the previous term.

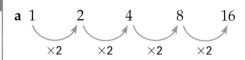

a 1   2   4   8   16
      ×2   ×2   ×2   ×2

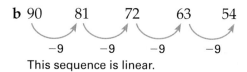

b 90   81   72   63   54
        −9   −9   −9   −9
This sequence is linear.

- A sequence can be described by its **position-to-term** rule.

Sequence 1, 4, 7, 10, 13, …

Position-to-term rule is
in words   'Multiply the position number by 3 and subtract 2'
as a formula $T(n) = 3n - 2$

n is the position number and $T(n)$ is the nth term.

example

Generate the first term and the 100th term of each sequence.
a $T(n) = 4n + 3$ **b** $T(n) = 105 - 5n$

a $T(1) = 4 \times 1 + 3 = 7$ **b** $T(1) = 105 - 5 \times 1 = 100$
    $T(100) = 4 \times 100 + 3$ $T(100) = 105 - 5 \times 100$
        $= 403$ $= -395$

To substitute into $T(n)$, replace n with the position number of the term that you are looking for.

Replace n with 1
Replace n with 100

Exercise 10a

1 Continue each of these sequences for two more terms.

   a 1, 6, 11, 16, 21, …   **b** 2, 4, 8, 16, 32, …   **c** 5, 4.5, 4, 3.5, 3, …

   d 15, 12, 9, 6, 3, …   **e** 243, 81, 27, 9, 3, …   **f** 1, -2, 4, -8, 16, …

2 Generate the first five terms of each of these sequences.

First term	Term-to-term rule
1	Add 4 to the previous term
20	Subtract 3 from the previous term
5	Double the previous term

First term	Term-to-term rule
10 000	Divide the previous term by 10
2	Add $\frac{1}{4}$ to the previous term
100	Halve the previous term

3 **i** Write the term-to-term rule for each of these linear sequences.

   ii Fill in the missing numbers.

   a 4, 8, ☐, 16, 20, …   **b** 2, ☐, 8, 11, 14, …   **c** 3, ☐, ☐, 24, 31, …

   d ☐, ☐, 19, 16, 13, …   **e** 10, ☐, 22, ☐, 34, …   **f** 8, ☐, -2, ☐, -12, …

4 A sequence has term-to-term rule 'add 4'. Write a possible first term for this sequence if all the terms of the sequence are

   a even numbers   **b** multiples of 4   **c** odd numbers   **d** not whole numbers.

5 Generate the first five terms of each of these sequences given by their position-to-term rules in words.

   a Add 10 to the position number   **b** Multiply the position number by 5

   c Double the position number   **d** Multiply the position number by 3

     and add 5   and add 1

6 Generate the first five terms of each of these sequences given by their position-to-term rules.

   a $T(n) = n + 3$ **b** $T(n) = n - 1$ **c** $T(n) = 8n$ **d** $T(n) = 10n + 1$

   e $T(n) = 2n + 3$ **f** $T(n) = 50 - n$ **g** $T(n) = \frac{1}{2}n$ **h** $T(n) = n^2$

Four friends have each written the nth term of a sequence on a card.

In what order should the friends stand if they are to arrange themselves in descending order according to the value of

a T(1)   **b** T(10)   **c** T(100)?

$T(n) = 4n + 3$ — Sarah $T(n) = 100 - n$ — Jamie $T(n) = 2(n + 1)$ — William $T(n) = 20 - 3n$ — Tilly

- Find the position-to-term rule of a sequence
- Justify the form of the position-to-term rule of a sequence

Keywords
nth term
Position-to-term rule

---

example

Find the **position-to-term** rule of the sequence 4, 7, 10, 13, 16, …

a 4　　7　　10　　13　　16

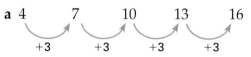

+3　　+3　　+3　　+3

The difference between consecutive terms is 3.
The position-to-term rule involves the 3 times table.

Position number, n	1	2	3	4	5
3 times table	3)+1	6)+1	9)+1	12)+1	15)+1
nth term, $T(n)$	4	7	10	13	16

To get from the 3 times table to the sequence 4, 7, 10, 13, 16, … you add on 1.

Position-to-term rule is in words　'Multiply the position number by 3 and add on 1'

as a formula　$T(n) = 3n + 1$

- All linear sequences have position-to-term rules of the form　$T(n) = an + b$

  5, 10, 15, 20, 25, …　difference = 5　$T(n) = 5n$

a = the difference between consecutive terms.

---

example

Find a rule that relates the number of triangles, n, to the number of straws, m.
Explain why the rule works by referring to the diagrams.

1 triangle　　　2 triangles　　　3 triangles　　　4 triangles

The number of straws forms a sequence 3, 5, 7, 9, …

Number of triangles, n	1	2	3	4
2 times table	2)+1	4)+1	6)+1	8)+1
Number of straws, m	3	5	7	9

The difference between consecutive terms = 2.
Therefore look at the 2 times table. The sequence is 1 more than the 2 times table.

The rule is in words　'To find the number of straws, m, multiply the number of triangles, n, by 2 and add 1'

in symbols　$m = 2n + 1$

The rule works because every new triangle requires 2 straws, plus 1 straw is needed to close the first triangle.

Plus one straw to close the first triangle

2 straws for the first triangle

2 straws for the second triangle

Exercise 10b

1 **a** Find the difference between consecutive terms in the sequence 5, 7, 9, 11, 13, …
  b Use part **a** to help you copy and complete the table.

Position number	1	2	3	4	5
☐ times table					
Term	5	7	9	11	13

  c Write the position-to-term rule of this sequence
  i in words   **ii** in symbols.

2 Match these sequences with one of the nth terms on the cards.

  a 10, 20, 30, 40, 50, …   **b** 1, 4, 9, 16, 25, …
  c 0, 1, 2, 3, 4, …   **d** 4, 8, 12, 16, 20, …
  e 1, 8, 27, 64, 125, …   **f** 3, 5, 7, 9, 11, …

3 Find the nth term of each of these sequences.
  a 3, 6, 9, 12, 15, …   **b** 11, 12, 13, 14, 15, …
  c 7, 9, 11, 13, 15, …   **d** 4, 9, 14, 19, 24, …

4 Find the nth term of each of these sequences.
  a -5, -2, 1, 4, 7, …   **b** $1\frac{1}{2}$, 2, $2\frac{1}{2}$, 3, $3\frac{1}{2}$, …
  c 9, 8, 7, 6, 5, …   **d** 3, 1, -1, -3, -5, …

5 **a** Find a rule that relates the number of pentagons, n, to the number of straws, m.

1 pentagon   2 pentagons   3 pentagons   4 pentagons

  b Use your formula to find the number of straws in a pattern of 50 pentagons.
  c Explain why the rule works by referring to the diagrams.

Hint: construct a table of values.

6 For this pattern of tiles, find a formula that connects the number of red tiles, r, to the number of white tiles, w. Justify your formula.

7 The formula that connects the pattern number, n, to the number of dots, d, is $d = 2(n + 1)$.
Explain why this formula works.

Pattern 1   Pattern 2   Pattern 3   Pattern 4

Isobel, a party-planner, needs to seat 54 people at a formal dinner. She has the option of two configurations of tables.

Advise Isobel on the number of tables required for both options.

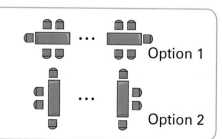

Option 1

Option 2

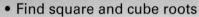

10c Powers and roots

- Find square and cube roots
- Use the x^y button on a calculator to evaluate indices

- A number raised to the power 2 is a **square** number.
  To square a number, you multiply it by itself.

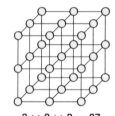

$$1 \times 1 = 1 \qquad 2 \times 2 = 4 \qquad 3 \times 3 = 9$$

- To undo a square number, you find the **square root**.

The symbol for the positive square root is $\sqrt{}$; you write $\sqrt{9} = 3$.

You can only find the square root of a positive number.

$3 \times 3 = 9$
so 3 is a square root of 9.
$-3 \times -3 = 9$
so -3 is a square root of 9.

- A number raised to the power 3 is a **cube** number.
  To cube a number, you multiply it by itself twice.

$$1 \times 1 \times 1 = 1 \qquad 2 \times 2 \times 2 = 8 \qquad 3 \times 3 \times 3 = 27$$

- To undo a cube number, you find the **cube root**.

The symbol for the cube root is $\sqrt[3]{}$; you write $\sqrt[3]{8} = 2$.

$2 \times 2 \times 2 = 8$ so 2 is the cube root of 8.

- In **index notation**:
  a square root is a number raised to the power $\frac{1}{2}$.
  a cube root is a number raised to the power $\frac{1}{3}$.

The $\boxed{y^x}$ key may be $\boxed{\wedge}$ on your calculator.

- You can use the $\boxed{y^x}$ button on a calculator to evaluate indices.

example

Evaluate

a $81^{\frac{1}{2}}$

b $125^{\frac{1}{3}}$

a $81^{\frac{1}{2}} = \sqrt{81} = 9$
 or type

$\boxed{8}\ \boxed{1}\ \boxed{y^x}\ \boxed{(}\ \boxed{1}\ \boxed{\div}\ \boxed{2}\ \boxed{)}\ \boxed{=}$

b $125^{\frac{1}{3}} = \sqrt[3]{125} = 5$
 or type

$\boxed{1}\ \boxed{2}\ \boxed{5}\ \boxed{y^x}\ \boxed{(}\ \boxed{1}\ \boxed{\div}\ \boxed{3}\ \boxed{)}\ \boxed{=}$

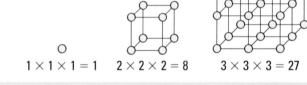

Exercise 10c

1 Evaluate these without a calculator.

a 3^2　　**b** 7^2　　**c** 10^2　　**d** $\sqrt{36}$　　**e** $\sqrt{81}$

2 Evaluate these without a calculator.

a 2^3　　**b** 4^3　　**c** 10^3　　**d** $\sqrt[3]{27}$　　**e** $\sqrt[3]{125}$

3 Use the $\boxed{x^2}$ and $\boxed{\sqrt{\ }}$ buttons on your calculator to evaluate these.

a 15^2　　**b** 28^2　　**c** $\sqrt{441}$　　**d** $\sqrt{1225}$　　**e** $\sqrt{2209}$

4 Use the $\boxed{x^3}$ and $\boxed{\sqrt[3]{\ }}$ buttons on your calculator to evaluate these.

a 9^3　　**b** 16^3　　**c** $\sqrt[3]{1728}$　　**d** $\sqrt[3]{3375}$　　**e** $\sqrt[3]{9261}$

5 Pair these cards together if they show equivalent numbers.
Which is the odd card out?

6^2　　　64　　　$4^{\frac{1}{2}}$　　　36　　　$216^{\frac{1}{3}}$

4　　　$16^{\frac{1}{2}}$　　　6　　　4^3

6 Arrange these algebraic expressions in ascending order of size if

a $x = 2$　　　　**b** $x = -1$

x^3　　$3x^2$　　$x^2 - x$　　$(x+1)^3$　　$(2x-1)^2$

7 Find the value of x that satisfies each of these equations.

a $x^{\frac{1}{2}} = 8$　　**b** $x^3 = -8$　　**c** $\left(\frac{1}{2}\right)^x = \frac{1}{8}$　　**d** $2^x = x^2$

It is always true that, $\sqrt{a \times b} = \sqrt{a} \times \sqrt{b}$.
You can use this rule to help you evaluate the square roots of large numbers.
For example $\sqrt{196} = \sqrt{4 \times 49}$

$$= \sqrt{4} \times \sqrt{49}$$
$$= 2 \times 7$$
$$= 14$$

> $4 \times 49 = 196$

> Check that $\sqrt{196} = 14$ on your calculator

Use this method to evaluate these square roots without a calculator.
a $\sqrt{225}$　　**b** $\sqrt{256}$　　**c** $\sqrt{324}$　　**d** $\sqrt{441}$

Index laws

- Use index notation
- Use simple instances of the index laws

Keywords
Base   *Indices*
Index   *Power*

- **Indices** are a useful way of writing long products.

  $3^5 = 3 \times 3 \times 3 \times 3 \times 3 = 243$

3 is the **base** and 5 is the index or **power**.

The **index** tells you how many times to multiply the base by itself.

---

example

Evaluate   **a** $2^3 \times 3^2$ **b** $3^5 \div 9^2$

a $2^3 \times 3^2 = (2 \times 2 \times 2) \times (3 \times 3)$

          $= 8 \times 9$

          $= 72$

b $3^5 \div 9^2 = \dfrac{3 \times 3 \times 3 \times 3 \times 3}{9 \times 9}$

            $= \dfrac{243}{81}$

            $= 3$

---

example

Evaluate   **a** $3^5 \times 3^2$ **b** $7^5 \div 7^3$

a $3^5 \times 3^2 = (3 \times 3 \times 3 \times 3 \times 3) \times (3 \times 3)$

                 $= 3^7$

    $5 + 2 = 7$

b $7^5 \div 7^3 = \dfrac{7 \times 7 \times 7 \times 7 \times 7}{7 \times 7 \times 7}$

             $= 7^2$

    $5 - 3 = 2$

- When multiplying indices involving the same base number, add the indices.
- When dividing indices involving the same base number, subtract the indices.

When possible always leave your answer as an index number.

---

example

Simplify   **a** $\left(4^3\right)^2$ **b** $\left(a^2\right)^4$

a $\left(4^3\right)^2 = 4^3 \times 4^3$

          $= 4^6$

    $3 \times 2 = 6$

b $\left(a^2\right)^4 = a^2 \times a^2 \times a^2 \times a^2$

          $= a^8$

    $2 \times 4 = 8$

Indices in algebra follow the same rules as in arithmetic.

- When raising an index to an index, using brackets, multiply the indices.

Exercise 10d

1 Write these in index form.

  a $2 \times 2 \times 2$ **b** $5 \times 5 \times 5 \times 5 \times 5$

  c $8 \times 8 \times 8 \times 8 \times 8 \times 8$ **d** $x \times x \times x \times x \times x$

  e $k \times k$ **f** $(-3) \times (-3) \times (-3) \times (-3)$

  g $4 \times 4 \times 4 \times 7 \times 7$ **h** $a \times a \times a \times a \times a \times b \times b \times b$

2 Evaluate these without a calculator.

  a 4^2 **b** 2^5 **c** 3^4 **d** 10^6

  e 5^3 **f** 12^0 **g** $(-2)^3$ **h** $(-1)^8$

3 Simplify these multiplications, leaving your answer in index form.

  a $3^2 \times 3^4$ **b** $6^5 \times 6^3$ **c** $2^8 \times 2^3$ **d** 9×9^7

  e $x^4 \times x^5$ **f** $y^4 \times y^6$ **g** $p^2 \times p^3 \times p^4$ **h** $q \times q^3 \times q^5 \times q^7$

  i $2a^3 \times 3a^7$ **j** $5b^{10} \times 6b^{11}$

4 Simplify these divisions, leaving your answer in index form.

  a $5^8 \div 5^5$ **b** $\dfrac{10^6}{10^4}$ **c** $7^{10} \div 7$ **d** $4^5 \div 4^5$

  e $\dfrac{x^{12}}{x^5}$ **f** $\dfrac{y^6}{y^5}$ **g** $20m^5 \div 4m^2$ **h** $18n^8 \div 6n^8$

5 Simplify these, leaving your answer in index form.

  a $(4^3)^5$ **b** $(10^2)^9$ **c** $(a^4)^6$ **d** $(2k^3)^2$ **e** $(3t^5)^4$

6 The number of diagonals in a polygon with n sides is given by the formula

  $\frac{1}{2}(n^2 - 3n)$.

  Work out the number of diagonals in

  a a pentagon

  b a square

  c a heptagon

  d a decagon.

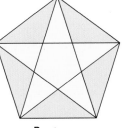

Pentagon

> The diagonals of a shape are found by joining each vertex to another non-adjacent vertex.

Copy and complete.

  a $8^6 \times \square = 8^{10}$ **b** $\square \div 3^2 = 3^5$ **c** $(6^3)^{\square} = 6^{15}$ **d** $x^4 \div \square = x^6$

  e $y^6 \times \square = y^8$ **f** $k^5 \div \square = k$ **g** $3p^{\square} \times \square p^3 = 6p^5$ **h** $(5q^3)^{\square} = 25q^{\square}$

10e Identities

- Distinguish between an equation, an identity and a formula
- Transform and simplify an algebraic expression

Keywords
Equation   Identity
Formula   Unknown
Identically   Variable
    equal

- To solve an **equation** you find the value of the **unknown**.

---

example

Solve
$3(2a + 5) = 4(5 - a)$

$3(2a + 5) = 4(5 - a)$ Expand the brackets.
$6a + 15 = 20 - 4a$ + 4a to both sides.
$10a + 15 = 20$ − 15 to both sides.
$10a = 5$ ÷ 10 on both sides.
$a = \frac{1}{2}$

- An **equation** is true for *particular* values of the unknown.
  $5(x - 1) = 2x + 7$ is true when $x = 4$

- An **identity** is true for *all* values of the unknown.
  $5(x - 1) \equiv 5x - 5$ is true whatever value is
      substituted for x

> The expressions on each side of the equation are said to be **identically equal**.
>
> A $\equiv$ sign is used in place of the = sign.

---

example

Prove that these are identities.

a $3(x - 5) = 3x - 15$ **b** $2(y + 4) + 3(y - 4) = 5y - 4$

· ·

a $3(x - 5) = 3 \times x - 3 \times 5$ **b** $2(y + 4) + 3(y - 4)$ Expand the left-hand side (LHS).
$3(x - 5) \equiv 3x - 15$ $= 2y + 8 + 3y - 12$ Collect like terms.
      $= 5y - 4$ The LHS is identically equal to
      $2(y + 4) + 3(y - 4) \equiv 5y - 4$ the right-hand side (RHS).

- A **formula** connects two or more **variables**.
  The formula for the perimeter of a rectangle is $P = 2l + 2w$.
  The variables are P = perimeter, l = length and w = width.

> When numerical values are given for two of these variables, the third can be found.

---

example

Use the formula $V = lwh$ where V = volume, l = length, w = width and h = height, to find the volume of a 5 cm by 3 cm by 4 cm cuboid.

· ·

$V = 5 \times 3 \times 4 = 60 \text{ cm}^3$.

Exercise 10e

1 Copy this table. Place each of these cards under the correct heading in your table.

Equation	Identity

$3x + 8 = 14$

$5(a + 3) = 5a + 15$

$7(p + 1) + 2p = 9p + 7$

$4(2k - 1) = 8k - 4$

$2t + 6 = 5t - 3$

$3(y + 2) - 2(y + 3) = y$

2 Solve these equations to find the value of the unknown.

  a $4n + 3 = 19$ **b** $13 = 5a - 2$

  c $3(b + 7) = 24$ **d** $10 - 3x = 4$

  e $8 = 9 - 2y$ **f** $3(8 - y) = 9$

  g $5m + 5 = 2m + 8$ **h** $7p - 20 = 2(p + 10)$

  i $3(2q + 1) = 17 - q$ **j** $8(5 - 2t) = 5(7 - 3t)$

3 Find the value of the required variable in each of these formulae.

  a $S = 6l^2$ Find S when $l = 5$

  b $A = \frac{1}{2} bh$ Find A when $b = 8$ and $h = 5$

  c $v = u + at$ Find v when $u = 0$, $a = 1.5$ and $t = 15$

  d $F = \frac{9}{5}(C + 40) - 40$ Find F when $C = 20$

4 Prove that these are identities by transforming the LHS.

  a $3(x + 9) \equiv 3x + 27$ **b** $7(y - 6) \equiv 7y - 42$

  c $5(p + 3) + 2p \equiv 7p + 15$ **d** $8q + 4(q - 2) \equiv 12q - 8$

  e $2(m + 1) + 9(m + 3) \equiv 11m + 29$ **f** $7(n - 2) + 2(3n + 7) \equiv 13n$

  g $3(2a + 1) + 2(5a - 3) \equiv 16a - 3$ **h** $4(3b - 2) - 3(b + 4) \equiv 9b - 20$

5 Prove that these are identities by transforming both sides.

  a $12(x + 2) - 8x \equiv 4(x + 6)$ **b** $3(y - 6) \equiv 2(y - 9) + y$

  c $4(p + 1) + 6(p + 2) \equiv 2(5p + 8)$ **d** $6(2q - 4) + 2(3q + 6) \equiv 6(3q - 2)$

  e $7(m - 1) - 3(2m + 1) \equiv 2(m - 5) - m$ **f** $6(n + 2) - 4(n - 2) \equiv 2(n + 10)$

  g $5(3 - k) + 3(1 - 5k) \equiv 2(9 - 10k)$ **h** $2(t + 5) - 4(3 - 2t) \equiv 2(t - 1) + 8t$

Use factorisation to copy and complete these identities.

$3a + 21 \equiv 3(a + \square)$

$4x - 20 \equiv 4(\square - \square)$

$t^2 + 3t \equiv t(\square + \square)$

$10p + 15 \equiv \square(2p + \square)$

$ab + \square \equiv \square(b + 7)$

$\square - 12k \equiv \square(2k - 3)$

1 Continue each of these sequences for two more terms.
 a 3, 6, 9, 12, 15, …   b 2, 5, 8, 11, 14, …
 c 1, 10, 100, 1000, 10 000, …   d 50, 44, 38, 32, 26, …
 e 1, $1\frac{1}{2}$, 2, $2\frac{1}{2}$, 3, …   f 1024, 512, 256, 128, 64, …
 g 2, 1.8, 1.6, 1.4, 1.2, …   h 1, 8, 27, 64, 125, …

2 i Write the term-to-term rule for each of these linear sequences.
 ii Fill in the missing numbers.
 a 4, □, 14, 19, 24, …   b 2, □, □, 14, 18, …
 c □, □, -1, -4, -7, …   d 5, □, 19, □, 33, …

3 Generate the first five terms of each of these sequences given by their position-to-term rules.
 a $T(n) = n + 10$ b $T(n) = 2n$
 c $T(n) = n - 5$ d $T(n) = \frac{n}{3}$
 e $T(n) = 2n + 1$ f $T(n) = 10 - n$
 g $T(n) = 5n - 2$ h $T(n) = 23 - 3n$

4 Find the nth term of each of these sequences.
 a 5, 10, 15, 20, 25, …   b 1, 4, 7, 10, 13, …
 c -2, 0, 2, 4, 6, …   d 5, 4, 3, 2, 1, …

5 a For this pattern of tiles, find a rule that relates the pattern number, n, to the number of tiles, t.
 b Use your formula to find the number of tiles in pattern number 100.
 c Explain why your rule works by referring to the diagrams.

  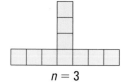
$n = 1$ $n = 2$ $n = 3$

6 a For this pattern of tiles, find a rule that relates the number of red tiles, r, to the number of white tiles, w.
 b Use your formula to find the number of tiles in pattern number 100.
 c Explain why your rule works by referring to the diagrams.

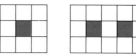 

7 Evaluate these without a calculator.

    a 4^2 **b** 3^3 **c** 8^2 **d** 5^3 **e** 12^2

8 Evaluate these without a calculator.

    a $\sqrt{25}$ **b** $\sqrt{49}$ **c** $\sqrt[3]{8}$ **d** $\sqrt{121}$ **e** $\sqrt[3]{64}$

9 Find the value of x that satisfies each of these equations.

    a $x^{\frac{1}{2}} = 6$ **b** $64^x = 4$ **c** $x^{0.5} = 10$ **d** $\left(\frac{1}{4}\right)^x = \frac{1}{16}$

10 Simplify these, giving your answer in index form.

    a $2^3 \times 2^5$ **b** $4^8 \times 4^2$ **c** 7×7^4 **d** $5^7 \times 5^2$

    e $a^4 \times a^6$ **f** $b^3 \times b^2 \times b$ **g** $2x^7 \times 5x^2$ **h** $3y^3 \times 4y^8$

11 Simplify these, giving your answer in index form.

    a $6^7 \div 6^4$ **b** $10^6 \div 10$ **c** $\dfrac{8^4}{8^3}$

    d $\dfrac{p^{10}}{p^3}$ **e** $16k^8 \div k^6$ **f** $12t^8 \div 6t^8$

12 Simplify these, giving your answer in index form.

    a $\left(3^5\right)^2$ **b** $\left(12^3\right)^5$ **c** $\left(m^4\right)^9$ **d** $\left(n^2\right)^7$ **e** $\left(4d^5\right)^3$

13 Prove that these are identities by transforming the LHS.

    a $4(x + 7) \equiv 4x + 28$ **b** $6(2y - 5) \equiv 12y - 30$

    c $2m + 5(m - 3) \equiv 7m - 15$ **d** $10(n + 1) + 3(n - 4) \equiv 13n - 2$

    e $4(3k - 5) + 5(k + 4) \equiv 17k$ **f** $8(2t - 1) - 5(3t + 2) \equiv t - 18$

14 Prove that these are identities by transforming both sides.

    a $3(x + 5) + 7x \equiv 5(2x + 3)$ **b** $8(2y - 1) \equiv 12y + 4(y - 2)$

    c $15a - 3(a - 4) \equiv 12(a + 1)$ **d** $4(b + 1) + 2(3b + 4) \equiv 2(5b + 6)$

    e $3(3p + 4) - 2(4p - 1) \equiv 2(p + 7) - p$ **f** $4(3 - q) - 10(1 - 2q) \equiv 2(8q + 1)$

10 Summary

Assessment criteria

- Generate terms of a sequence **Level 6**
- Describe the *n*th term of an arithmetic sequence **Level 6**
- Multiply and divide numbers in index form **Level 7**

Level 7

1 Work out the values of p, q and r.

   a $3^2 \times 3^5 = 3^p$

   b $\dfrac{3^6}{3^2} = 3^q$

   c $(3^4)^2 = 3^r$

Graham's answer ✔

Graham knows 3^5 means $3 \times 3 \times 3 \times 3 \times 3$

a $3^2 \times 3^5 = (3 \times 3) \times (3 \times 3 \times 3 \times 3 \times 3) = 3^7 = 3^p$

   $p = 7$

b $\dfrac{3^6}{3^2} = \dfrac{3 \times 3 \times 3 \times 3 \times 3 \times 3}{3 \times 3} = 3^4 = 3^q$

   $q = 4$

c $(3^4)^2 = (3 \times 3 \times 3 \times 3) \times (3 \times 3 \times 3 \times 3) = 3^8 = 3^r$

   $r = 8$

Graham knows $(a)^2$ means $a \times a$

Level 7

2 **a** Draw lines to match each *n*th term rule to its number sequence.

*n*th term	Number sequence
$4n$	4, 7, 12, 19, …
$(n + 1)^2$	4, 8, 12, 16, …
$n^2 + 3$	4, 9, 16, 25, …
$n(n + 3)$	4, 10, 18, 28, …

  b Write the first four terms of the number sequence using the *n*th term rule below.

      $n^3 + 3$ — ——, ——, ——, ——

KS3 2007 5–7 Paper 1

Algebra Sequences and roots

Collecting and representing data

Red Wine Stops Heart Attacks

Alcohol Related Deaths Rise Steeply

CRIME ON THE INCREASE

Poll Lead For Tories

Streets Have Never Been Safer

Labour Win By Election

Many organisations now collect data and carry out surveys to inform their decisions.

Examples include: what policies a political party should endorse, which products a company should bring to market, what facilities a local council should provide, ...

What's the point? Unless a data collection is properly planned and executed the results may be worse than useless!

 **Check in**

1 A survey asked how often people went to the cinema and gave options of
   a a lot   **b** regularly   **c** not very often   **d** never
   Suggest better response options.

2 Andrea was going to ask people coming out of the cinema to fill out the survey in question **1**.
   Explain why this will give biased results.

163

- Know the stages of the data handling cycle
- Be able to plan the outline of a statistical investigation

Keywords
Data handling cycle

- The **data handling cycle** (or problem solving approach) breaks a statistical investigation down into stages.

Why do some road junction have roundabouts, some traffic lights and others none?

This is the most important stage. If you don't collect all the data that you need it may be difficult or expensive or even impossible to collect it later.

Think critically, how you could improve things if you had to repeat the investigation.

evaluate results

Specify the problem and plan

Interpret and discuss data

Collect data from a variety of sources

Process and represent data

How do the police estimate the speed of a car involved in an accident?

example

a Traffic lights and roundabouts allow traffic coming from different directions to have priority at different times. What data would you want to collect if you were planning a junction coming out of a new housing estate?

b What data would the police want to collect from the scene of a road accident?

. . . .

a The critical factor is the traffic flow at different times of the day. So important factors will include
  - The number of houses
  - The profile of the community
  - What direction cars are likely to turn at the junction
  - How busy is the road the traffic wants to get out onto?

b To reconstruct the accident useful information will include
  - The condition of the road
  - The weather
  - The presence of any skid marks on the road
  - The point of impact
  - The final positions of the cars.

Do cars need to go across the traffic flow? If most cars want to turn left there is not as big a problem.

Exercise 11a

1 A psychologist wants to look at factors affecting memory. She thinks gender is likely to be a factor, that is, males and females might be different.

  a How could the psychologist test her theory?

  b Write down any other factors which you think might make a difference to memory.

2 A road safety organisation is concerned about the speeds of cars on the road. They want to plan an advertising campaign to target groups of drivers. They plan to do some research to find out what types of drivers, or types of cars, are particularly bad about speed on the roads.
Suggest categories of people or types of cars which you think they should look at.

3 A medical student is doing some research into the effects of alcohol on people's reaction times. He plans to measure their reaction times without taking any alcohol, and also after taking 1, 2 and 3 units of alcohol. A friend tells him that alcohol affects women more.
Suggest other factors which might make a difference to the effect of the alcohol.

4 A transport manager has to estimate how long it will take his drivers to make deliveries to clients so he can plan the work.
Apart from the distance to the client, what other factors should he take into consideration in estimating the time for each delivery?

discussion

Look back at the different factors you have suggested in each of the investigations. Would you be able to collect data on each of them easily?

- Be able to state a hypothesis in a statistical investigation

- A **hypothesis** is a testable statement that can be investigated by statistical evidence.

It is just the formal name for a claim to be investigated.

First, make a statement:

> Students who are living away from home are more likely to suffer mental health problems than those who live at home.

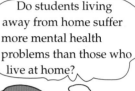

Do students living away from home suffer more mental health problems than those who live at home?

Second, think what data would provide evidence to help decide if the claim is reasonable or not.

> What will I use to measure health?
>   – How will I combine them into a single measure?
> What factors might make a difference to the conclusion?
> • the student's gender?
> • the student's family background?
> • the student's age?

- The more factors that are included in an investigation the more data is needed so that each category has a reasonable sample size.

For the above hypothesis
a How would you measure a student's mental health.
b Your sample size is limited to 60 students.
   Who would you sample and which factors does this allow you to investigate?

. . . .

a In the last year, has the student seen their doctor about feeling depressed.
b Sample boys and girls in their final year.
   This allows you to investigate the effect of gender.

This gives about 30 students in each category.

Family background and age cannot be investigated with this (small) sample.

Exercise 11b

1 For each of the following situations, write a formal hypothesis.

  a Do males have better memories than females?

  b Does memory get worse as you get older?

  c Do people under 22 drive faster than older people?

  d Do drivers of performance cars drive faster than drivers of family cars?

  e Does the same amount of alcohol have a bigger effect on people who do not normally drink alcohol?

  f Does the time of day affect how long it will take to make a delivery to a client?

2 Look back at the factors you considered in questions **1–4** in the previous spread. If your sample will only be large enough to allow you to consider two factors in each case, write down the factors you think should be taken.

3 Look at the data collection sheet below, which shows the first three records in a large set. Write down three hypotheses which could be investigated using this data set.

> The legal limit for alcohol level when driving is 80 mg/100 millilitres of blood.

Subject	Speed	Age	Gender	Type of car	Colour of car	Speed limit on road	Time of day	Alcohol level of driver
1	48	26	F	sports	red	50	08:35	0
2	35	49	M	4 x 4	silver	30	08:40	0
3	61	22	M	family	black	50	01:15	75
...	...	...	...	...	...	...	....	....

discussion

A More males smoke than females.

B There is no difference in smoking between males and females.

Both the above hypotheses relate to the numbers of males and females who smoke.
Is there any difference between them?
Is one better than the other?

- Plan what data to collect for an investigation

Keywords
Factor
Variable

- In a statistical investigation a **variable** is a quantity that you can attach a value to.

Examples include

Body mass index (BMI)	A quantity you can measure
Gender	A **factor** that defines a group: men or women
Year of degree course	A factor you can hold constant: only final year

When planning a statistical investigation, the choice of variables is very important as they will provide the only information available.

- It is important to consider how simple it is to collect the data you want.
    Will it be costly in terms of time, money or effort?

---

example

A university wants to carry out a survey to investigate the mental health of its students. It plans to collect the following information.
a name   **b** gender
c place of residence   **d** general health.
How easy will it be to collect the data?

. . . .

a This will be hard, many students will wish to remain anonymous.

b Straightforward.

c This will be made easier if 'tick boxes' are provided:
   ☐ hall of residence   ☐ family home
   ☐ shared, private house   ☐ other

d This is too vague; it needs to specify actual variables
   i   BMI   **ii** blood pressure
   iii liver function   **iv** kidney function.

> It might require an expert — a nurse or doctor — which will be expensive and time consuming but reliable. Or it may, if allowed, involve searching students' existing medical records.

---

example

Can you think of any other factors which might affect a student's health?

. . . .

- How much exercise they take
- Whether they smoke
- How much alcohol they drink.

Exercise 11c

1 For the following situations, say whether you think data could be collected on each of the variables, and if so how.

> Some data is easy to collect. Some is very difficult or expensive to collect. Some requires special powers, such as only the police have.

  a Volunteers are being used to investigate the effects of alcohol on reaction times. The variables being considered are

    i   age

    ii gender

    iii weight

    iv how used to drinking alcohol is the person

    v   are they taking medication

    vi how tired the person feels.

  b A large teaching hospital is planning to conduct a study on the factors leading to increased risk of heart disease. The variables being considered are

    i   age   **ii** gender

    iii weight   **iv** blood pressure

    v   amount smoked **vi** alcohol consumption

  c A major study into the mental health of students is commissioned by the government. The variables being considered are

    i   age   **ii**   gender

    iii whether living at home   **iv** amount of student debt

    v   in a stable relationship   **vi** family economic circumstances

    vii general health   **viii** academic performance.

2 A botanist wants to investigate the best conditions for growing a particular species. Make a list of variables which you think are factors he should consider and say how each might be measured.

- Design and use appropriate record sheets to collect data for a statistical investigation
- Understand the effect of sample size on an investigation

Keywords
Data logging Record sheet
Population   Sample
Questionnaire Sample size

Using a **questionnaire** results in data in different places.

> - A **record sheet** is used to collect together all the data from different sources.

A record sheet should include the information that is relevant to the hypothesis.

example

Design a record sheet to collate the data from questionnaires used in the student health investigation.

Name	Gender	Living at home?	Stage of course	health score	Age
Helen K.	F	Y	last year	36	22
Amir F.	M	Y	last year	32	21
Javier G.	M	N	last year	35	22
...					

In a statistical investigation
– the **population** is the full set of people or objects being studied.
– a **sample** is a subset of the whole population.

> - A sample is used when it is too expensive to use the whole population

Expense can include time, money or effort.

The **sample size** determines how many hypotheses can be *reliably* tested.

100 students: 'students are healthier if they live at home'

200 students: { 'male students are healthier if they live at home'
               { 'female students are healthier if they live at home'

In each case this gives about 50 students in each group.

> - The larger a sample size the more reliable are the conclusions based on it.
>   Two samples will almost always show differences even if there is no real underlying difference.

Sometimes you can automate data collection and obtain much larger data samples. This is known as **data logging**.
Putting data onto a computer often makes it easier to investigate.

Exercise 11d

1 Katie wants to investigate how long pupils sleep on nights before schooldays. She thinks that there may be differences between boys and girls, that it may change with age and that it may be different for single children and those with brothers or sisters.

   a Design a short questionnaire she could use to collect the information she is interested in from each person.

   b Design a record sheet to show all the data together.

Questionnaire reminders

- Ask relevant questions.
- Avoid biased questions.
- Make questions and answer options unambiguous.
- Make it easy to complete: use 'tick boxes' and include an 'other' option.
- Avoid personal questions.

2 For the investigation into sleep in question **1**, give three hypotheses which Katie can test.

3 Christiano is investigating how long pupils spend on homework. He thinks that there may be differences between boys and girls, that it may change with age and that it may be different for single children and those with brothers or sisters.

He draws up a list of his friends to ask how long they spend on homework. The table shows how many friends he can ask in each category

	Age 12	Age 13	Age 14	Age 15
Boys, only child	7	8	2	1
Girls, only child	5	5	0	1
Boys with siblings	12	16	5	2
Girls with siblings	10	13	3	3

   a Make one criticism of how Christiano plans to collect the data other than some sample sizes.

   b The small numbers in some of the groups means that Christiano will not be able to answer all of the questions he was interested in. What would he have enough information to investigate?

task

How could Christiano improve the survey described in question **3**?

- **Construct and use frequency and grouped frequency tables**

Keywords
Class interval
Frequency table
Grouped frequency table

- Using **frequency tables** and graphs often makes data easier to interpret.

If data takes a small number of discrete values you can individually list each value.

example

Data has been collected on the general health, as measured by a 'health score', for university students who live at home or away from home.

Health score	30	31	32	33	34	35	36	37	38	Total
Home	0	1	0	2	4	16	14	8	2	47
Away	3	5	6	15	11	7	5	4	0	56

Compare the two groups of students.

. . . .

Median = 36   home   24th student's score   Range = 7   home   38 − 31
       = 33   away   middle of 28th and 29th students' scores   = 7   away   37 − 30

On average, the students who live at home have a higher health score than those who don't. Whilst the range of health scores is the same for the two groups, the health scores of those who live at home generally lie closer to their median than do those of students who live away from home.

If the data takes many values or is continuous it should be grouped into suitable **class intervals** in a **grouped frequency table**.

- Use 6−10 intervals.
- Take care that intervals do not overlap or leave gaps.

  $1 < x \leq 2$, $2 < x \leq 3$ ✓
  $1 \leq x \leq 2$, $2 \leq x \leq 3$ ✗
  $1 < x < 2$, $2 < x < 3$ ✗

- Class intervals can be of unequal widths.

Care must be taken when interpreting some aspects of tables and graphs when intervals are unequal.

example

The whole of Year 8 sat a test. The lowest score was 42 and the highest was 94; most of the scores lie between 65 and 85.
Suggest suitable class intervals for a grouped frequency table.

. . . .

40−49, 50−59, 60−64, 65−69, 70−74, 75−79, 80−84, 85−94

This gives more detailed information where there is a lot of data without creating a very large number of intervals.

Exercise 11e

1 The speeds of 60 cars on a single carriageway are recorded by a police mobile speed camera. The speeds are shown below in miles per hour.

61, 63, 58, 55, 73, 84, 61, 53, 67, 59, 63, 78, 57, 43, 58,
62, 62, 69, 55, 46, 79, 58, 51, 59, 62, 67, 58, 49, 64, 111,
63, 48, 57, 59, 60, 57, 59, 63, 61, 89, 61, 64, 58, 59, 56,
52, 59, 61, 63, 74, 81, 56, 56, 70, 58, 61, 60, 57, 75, 62

a Summarise this information in a grouped frequency table. Use the intervals ≤ 54, 55–59, 60–64, 65–69, 70–74, 75–84 and ≥ 85.

b In which interval does the median lie?

Did you know?

60

The speed limit on a single carriageway is 60 mph.

2 After a permanent speed camera and warning signs were installed on the single carriageway in question **1**, the speeds of another 100 cars are recorded.

Speed, v (mph)	≤ 54	55–59	60–64	65–69	70–74	75–84	≥ 85
Frequency	15	49	26	8	1	1	0

a In which interval does the median lie?

b Compare the speeds recorded before and after the permanent speed camera and warning signs were installed.

3 a There are very few observations in the last three intervals in the set of data in question **2**. Explain why it would not be a good idea to combine them into a single interval ≥ 70.

b Police do not usually prosecute motorists if they are less than 5 mph over the speed limit. What proportions of the drivers are likely to be prosecuted for speeding both before and after the traffic calming measures were introduced?

- Construct and use stem-and-leaf diagrams
- Identify which diagrams are most useful for a problem

Keywords
Bar chart
Pie chart
Stem-and-leaf diagram

- A **stem-and-leaf diagram** gives the shape of a distribution in the same way as a bar chart does.
  However unlike a bar chart they also keep every detail available.

Turned on its side, a stem-and-leaf diagram is effectively a bar chart.

p. 244

example

Draw a stem-and-leaf diagram for the following data on the heights of plants, in cm, and use it to find their median height.

61, 74, 59, 61, 82, 59, 64, 57, 63, 77, 71, 67, 78

```
5 | 9 9 7              5 | 7 9 9           Key
6 | 1 1 4 3 7   order  6 | 1 1 3 ④ 7       5 | 7 means 57 cm
7 | 4 7 1 8     ───▶   7 | 1 4 7 8
8 | 2                  8 | 2
```
                        stem   leaf

There are 13 plants, so the median height is the 7th value, 64 cm.

Statistical graphs allow particular aspects of the data to be visualised.

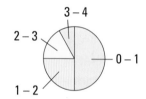

3 – 4

2 – 3

0 – 1

1 – 2

Group sizes are proportional to the angles.

	Advantage	Disadvantage
Pie chart	• Quite easy to compare relative sizes of groups. • Easy to compare their proportion of the whole sample.	• Cannot tell the actual sizes of the groups. • Lose individual data values.
Bar chart	• Shows the shape of a distribution. • Easy to compare relative sizes of groups. • Comparative bar charts make it easy to compare multiple data sets.	• Not so easy to compare a group's proportion of the whole sample • Lose individual data values.
Stem-and-leaf diagram	• Shows the shape of a distribution. • Keep all the individual data values.	• Takes a lot of effort to produce.

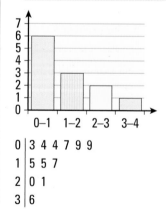

```
0 | 3 4 4 7 9 9
1 | 5 5 7
2 | 0 1
3 | 6
```

Exercise 11f

1 Car speeds recorded on a motorway are shown below.

61, 63, 72, 78, 73, 84, 68, 53, 74, 83, 79, 58, 77, 82, 91,
67, 58, 77, 89, 68, 61, 64, 68, 59, 73, 71, 81, 61, 63, 74

Show this information in a stem-and-leaf diagram.

2 The gender and age of the 36 members of a golf club who
expressed interest in taking part in a charity golf event are
shown below.

M35, F37, M41, M39, F55, M44, F47, M31, M41, F61, M29, M46,
F42, F49, M36, M32, F39, M46, M61, M35, M51, F38, F57, M43,
F52, F47, M37, M49, M45, F41, F49, M34, F63, M57, F34, M60

> M35 means a man
> aged 35

  a Draw a stem-and-leaf diagram to show the ages of the males.
  b Draw a stem-and-leaf diagram to show the ages of the females.
  c Find the median age of each group.
  d Make any comparisons you can between the males and
    females who express interest.

3 The table below gives data on the number of pupils in four schools
who achieve different levels in Intermediate Maths Challenge.

School	No award	Bronze	Silver	Gold	Total
A	53	22	12	4	91
B	37	28	18	9	92
C	44	21	16	7	88
D	41	25	17	5	88

For the following draw a pie chart, a bar chart or a comparative
bar chart, choosing whichever is most appropriate.
  a To compare the numbers at different levels in schools A and D.
  b To see the proportions at different levels in school B.
  c To see the numbers at different levels in school C.

discussion

> If you drew a comparative bar chart to show the data on all four schools, you would
> have 16 bars. If there was data on 10 schools you would have 40 bars. How many
> schools do you think you can draw on a comparative bar chart and still make sense
> of the graph?

- Interpret time series and comparative bar charts

Keywords
Sample
Time series
Trend

- **Time series** can be used to investigate **trends** shown by sets of data.

example

How could you investigate the hypothesis: 'women live longer than men'?

Secondary data on life expectancy at birth is available from the Office for National Statistics. This can be plotted as a time series.

The two graphs show strong similarities in their shape – a generally upward trend (reflecting improving living standards and medical expertise) with occasional irregularities, for example, at the times of the two world wars.

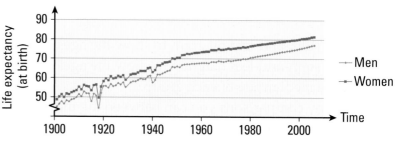

- When using a **sample** you must be convinced that any patterns cannot be explained by natural variation between samples.

The graph shows the level of support for UK political parties.

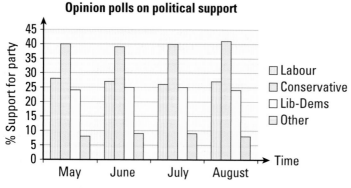

Opinion polls typically use a sophisticated sample of around 1000 people. This gives a margin of error of about 3%.

Would your conclusion hold if you altered the data up or down within the margin of error?

For each party, the month-to-month differences in popularity are small: levels of support remain constant.

The Conservatives maintain a clear lead over Labour.

The Labour lead over the Lib-Dems is much smaller.

Based on one poll it is not safe to say that Labour is ahead.

However since all polls show a small lead the data suggests that there is a real difference between the two parties.

Exercise 11g

1 The chart shows the proportions of boys of different ages who said they had drunk alcohol in the week before a series of surveys were carried out.

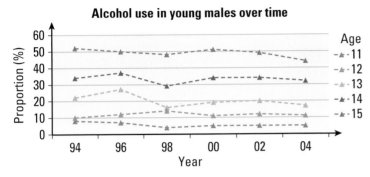

Describe any trends you see over time in the proportions of young boys drinking alcohol.

2 The chart shows the proportions of boys and girls of different ages who said they had drunk alcohol in the week before the survey was done in 1994.

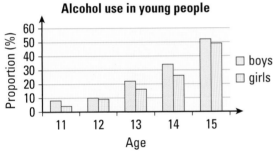

a Describe any trends you see in the data as pupils get older.
b Is there any difference between boys and girls?

The chart below shows the same data as in question **1**, but now showing all the ages together for each year in turn. Is one of the graphs easier to interpret than the other, or is it equally easy to see the patterns in both cases?

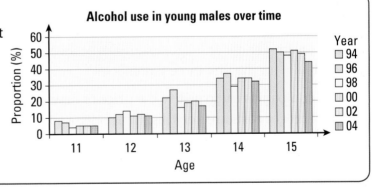

11a

1 A drug company wants to test the effectiveness of different doses of a new drug and whether the drug will affect some groups of people differently.

Suggest at least six ways to group people you think might react differently to the drug, for example, by gender if you think males and females might react differently.

> A patient's general health is important when taking medication.
> You may wish to consider factors affecting general health.

11b

2 For each of the groups you suggested in question **1**, write down a hypothesis which could be investigated.

11c

3 a Make a list of the variables the company will need to collect data on in order to investigate these hypotheses.

b If the initial trials are to be done with groups of volunteers, say how easy you think it will be to get the information for each variable.

c Are there any of the variables you think will be harder to get information on when the people involved are not volunteers?

11d

4 Part of the data record sheet for the drug trial might look like this.

Patient identifier	Gender	Age	......	......	Dosage	Treatment outcome
0001	M	56			XXXX	XXXX
0002	M	24			XXXX	XXXX
0003	F	37			XXXX	XXXX

Create a record sheet for the variables you have chosen to consider, and fill in (as for gender and age) examples of the values those variables might take for the first three patients.

5 Drug companies try to justify the price of new drugs by saying that the development costs are very high and only a small proportion of drugs they test end up with approval to go on the open market.

For the initial trials the company say they will only consider a maximum of four variables by which to group people. Which four of the variables you chose in question **1** would you recommend they consider?

6 The ages of a group of patients in a nursing home who were given the drug are given below.

67, 63, 52, 49, 71, 82, 71, 59, 61, 57, 64, 72, 56, 48, 59,64, 70, 53, 49, 67,
81, 80, 56, 53, 59, 63, 67, 64, 47, 51, 60, 76, 70, 61, 53, 52, 59, 72, 86, 49,
73, 71, 59, 62, 57, 46, 62, 70, 49, 57, 62, 70, 49, 80, 66, 47, 55, 90, 53, 61

a Summarise this information in a grouped frequency table using intervals ≤ 54, 55–59, 60–64, 65–69, 70–74, 75–84, ≥ 85.

b In which interval does the median lie?

c Give two reasons, apart from the size of the group, why this group of patients would not be a good sample on its own to investigate the effectiveness of the drug.

7 A sample of half the population used in question **6** is taken.

a Draw a stem and leaf diagram to show the ages of these patients.

b Hence find the median of this group.

> 67, 63, 52, 49, 71, 82, 71, 59,
> 61, 57, 81, 80, 56, 53, 59, 63,
> 67, 64, 47, 51, 73, 71, 59, 62,
> 57, 46, 62, 70, 49, 57

8 a The left hand chart shows the recorded rates of treatment (per 1000 people) of different age groups of females between 1994 and 1998.

   i Describe any trends you see over the period 1994 to 1998.

   ii Describe any differences you see between the different age groups.

b The right hand chart shows the same data for males, using the same scale for comparison.

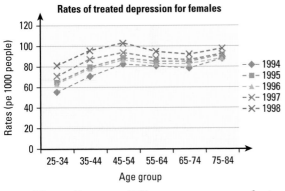

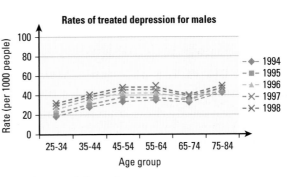

Describe any differences you see between males and females

11 Summary

Assessment criteria
- Design suitable collection sheets **Level 6**
- Interpret charts, graphs and diagrams **Level 6**

Level 6

1 Zana wants to find out how far the student in her class travel to school and their method of transport.
Design a data collection sheet for Zana.

Zana's answer ✔

Distance(km)	Walk	Car	Bus	Tram	Other
$0 < d \leq 1$					
$1 < d \leq 2$					
$2 < d \leq 3$					
$3 < d \leq 4$					
$4 < d \leq 5$					
5+					

Zana makes sure the intervals do not overlap.

Zana allows for students who travel more than 5 km.

Zana decides to a two-way table

Zana remembers include 'Other'.

Level 6

2 A newspaper wrote an article about public libraries in England and Wales. It published this diagram.

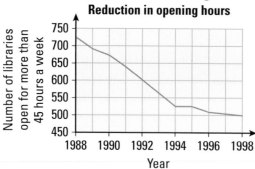

Reduction in opening hours

Number of libraries open for more than 45 hours a week (y-axis: 450, 500, 550, 600, 650, 700, 750)

Year (x-axis: 1988, 1990, 1992, 1994, 1996, 1998)

Use the diagram to decide whether each statement below is true or false, or whether you cannot be certain.

a The number of libraries open for more than 45 hours per week fell by more than half from 1988 to 1998.

☐ True ☐ False ☐ Cannot be certain

Explain your answer.

b In 2004 there will be about 450 libraries open in England and Wales for more than 45 hours a week.

☐ True ☐ False ☐ Cannot be certain

Explain your answer.

KS3 2002 4–6 Paper 2

Ratio and proportion

Cartographers use exact proportion to reduce the size of actual features to fit on a map. Different maps use different scales to show different levels of detail.

When you zoom in on a map you are changing the scale.

What's the point? Proportional reasoning is used to convert sizes and distances on a map into real life sizes.

✔ Check in

1 Write each of these ratios in their simplest form.
   a 12:20   **b** 42:28
   c 144:108   **d** 250 cm : 3.5 m

2 Divide 60 cakes in the ratio 2:3.

3 4 kg of pears cost 145p. Use direct proportion to find the cost of 12 kg of pairs.

4 An alloy is made from copper and zinc in the ratio 4:5.
  How much copper needs to be mixed with 60 kg of zinc?

5 In a running club there are 25 beginners, 35 intermediate and
  10 advanced runners.
   a What proportion of the running club members are intermediate?
   b What is the ratio of beginners to advanced runners at the club?

6 Mark wants to buy a pair of trainers. The normal price of the trainers is £90.
  In a sale all prices are reduced by 20%. What is the sale price of the trainers?

12a) Ratio

- Write a ratio using ratio notation
- Simplify a ratio expressed in fractions or decimals
- Compare ratios by changing them to the form 1 : *n*

- You **simplify** a ratio by dividing or multiplying all parts of the ratio by the same number.

> **example**
>
> Write these ratios in their **simplest form**.
>
> **a** 12 : 9 : 3   **b** 48 cm : 180 mm   **c** 0.4 : 3
>
> -
>
> **a**
> $$12 : 9 : 3$$
> $\div 3 \big(\quad \big) \div 3$
> $$4 : 3 : 1$$
>
> **b**
> $$48 \text{ cm} : 180 \text{ mm}$$
> $$480 \text{ mm} : 180 \text{ mm}$$
> $$480 : 180$$
> $\div 60 \big(\quad \big) \div 60$
> $$8 : 3$$
>
> **c**
> $$0.4 : 3$$
> $\times 5 \big(\quad \big) \times 5$
> $$2 : 15$$
>
> Divide all the parts of the ratio by the HCF, 3.
>
> Change both quantities to the same units, mm.
>
> Multiply all parts of the ratio by 5 to make all numbers whole.

- You can **compare ratios** by expressing them in the form **1 : *n*.**

   This means that one of the parts of the ratio has to be 1, and the other part may be a decimal.

> **example**
>
> Statto is looking at the ratio of goals scored to shots taken by the two strikers who play in the school football team. He finds that the ratio of goals : shots is 7 : 40 for Ree Bok and 4 : 25 for Ade Idas. Which striker is more accurate?
>
>
>
> -
>
> Express both ratios in the form 1 : *n*.
>
> Ree Bok   Ade Idas
> goals : shots   goals : shots
>
> $\div 7 \big(\, 7 : 40 \, \big) \div 7$ $\div 4 \big(\, 4 : 25 \, \big) \div 4$
>
> $1 : 5.71$ (2 dp) $1 : 6.25$
>
> Ree Bok scores 1 goal every 5.71 shots.
> Ade Idas scores 1 goal every 6.25 shots.
> So Ree Bok is the more accurate striker.

Exercise 12a

1 Write each of these ratios in its simplest form.

    a 8:20   **b** 32:28   **c** 12:15:24   **d** 45:60:135

    e 80:112:176   **f** 4m:205cm   **g** 5kg:2800g   **h** £3.50:80p

2 Write each of these ratios in its simplest form.

    a 0.5:2   **b** 0.3:8   **c** 1.5:5   **d** 1.6:2.4

    e 4.5:6:7.5   **f** 0.4m:240cm   **g** 2.5kg:1800g   **h** £6.25:75p

3 Express each of these ratios in the form 1:n.

    a 5:10   **b** 3:12   **c** 5:25   **d** 8:112   **e** 5:9   **f** 3:14

    g 5:17   **h** 8:116   **i** 3:8   **j** 7:18   **k** 6:11   **l** 3:41

4 Here are the shots taken and goals scored for six football players.

Name of striker	Goals scored	Shots taken	Goals : Shots	Goals : Shots
Ade Byor	17	43	17 : 43	1 : 2.53
Frank Tores	21	50		
Ricardo Cruz	16	35		
Warren Roone	13	34		
Javed Chokes	19	53		

    a Copy and complete the table.

    b Use the ratios you have worked out to put the players in
        order from most to least accurate. Explain your reasoning.

5 The ratios of cotton to other materials in two T-shirts are
3:8 and 5:14. Which T-shirt has the greater proportion
of cotton?

> Simplify the ratios by writing
> them in the form 1:n.

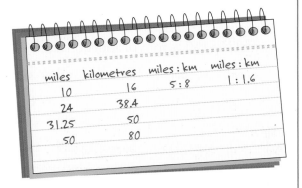

Brian has made a table using some measurements
of distances given in miles and kilometres.

    a Copy and complete the table.

    b What do you notice about the results?
        What is the significance of the ratio in
        the form 1:n?

    c Investigate some more quantities in
        the same way, such as

            pounds:dollars   £35:$68.25

        model bus:real-life bus   62.5cm:15m

    d Comment on the meaning of the
        ratio 1:n in each case.

miles	kilometres	miles : km	miles : km
10	16	5 : 8	1 : 1.6
24	38.4		
31.25	50		
50	80		

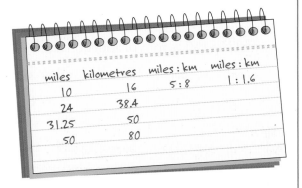

- Divide a quantity into two or more parts in a given ratio
- Solve ratio problems in a range of contexts

Keywords
Proportion
Ratio
Unitary method

- **Ratios** can be used to divide a quantity into unequal sized pieces. This process is called division in a given ratio.

- You can divide a quantity in a given ratio by using a **unitary method**.

  In this method you always find the value of one equal share of the quantity.

example

Naheeda is 7 years old, Marie is 10 years old and Evie is 13 years old.
Their gran gives them £450 to share in the ratio of their ages.
How much money do they each receive?

....

Dividing the money in the ratio 7 : 10 : 13 requires 30 equal parts.

$$\div 30 \left(\begin{array}{cc} 30 \text{ parts} & £450 \\ 1 \text{ part} & £15 \end{array} \right) \div 30 \quad \text{Each part is £15.}$$

You calculate the size of each part by division.

Naheeda gets 7 parts.   Marie gets 10 parts.   Evie gets 13 parts.

$$\times 7 \left(\begin{array}{cc} 1 \text{ part} & £15 \\ 7 \text{ parts} & £105 \end{array} \right) \times 7 \quad \times 10 \left(\begin{array}{cc} 1 \text{ part} & £15 \\ 10 \text{ parts} & £150 \end{array} \right) \times 10 \quad \times 13 \left(\begin{array}{cc} 1 \text{ part} & £15 \\ 13 \text{ parts} & £195 \end{array} \right) \times 13$$

Naheeda receives £105.   Marie receives £150.   Evie receives £195.

- A quantity can be divided in a given ratio using the relationship between ratio and **proportion**.

example

Carole, Sarah and Monty share 5 kilograms of strawberries in the ratio 1 : 2 : 4.
How much compost do they each receive?

....

Convert the ratios into proportions and take these fractions of the total.

Carole : Sarah : Monty

Ratio   1 : 2 : 4

Proportion $\frac{1}{7}$ $\frac{2}{7}$ $\frac{4}{7}$

1 + 2 + 4 = 7 equal parts

Carole receives
$\frac{1}{7}$ of 5 kg = 0.71 kg (2 dp)
Sarah receives
$\frac{2}{7}$ of 5 kg = 1.43 kg (2 dp)
Monty receives
$\frac{4}{7}$ of 5 kg = 2.86 kg (2 dp)

This method involves the same steps of multiplying and dividing as the unitary method.

Exercise 12b

1 Divide these quantities in the ratios given.
 a 80 cakes in the ratio 2:3 b 156 km in the ratio 5:7
 c £384 in the ratio 4:5   d £1.62 in the ratio 1:2:3

2 Divide these quantities in the ratios given.
 Give your answers to 2 dp as appropriate.
 a £13 in the ratio 3:5   b 200 m in the ratio 7:9
 c 4 GB in the ratio 2:5   d £40 in the ratio 2:3:4

3 a In a school the ratio of boys to girls is 15:16. There are
   1085 pupils at the school. How many girls are there at
   the school?
 b A cake mixture contains flour, sugar and margarine in the
   ratio 4:3:2. How much sugar is needed to make 630 g of
   cake mixture?

4 Solve these problems.
 a A metal alloy is made from tin, iron and nickel in the ratio 3:7:1.
   How much iron is needed to mix with 150 kg of tin?
 b 3 parts of yellow paint are mixed with 4 parts of red paint to
   make orange paint. Zahid has 75 ml of yellow paint and 120 ml
   of red paint.
   What is the maximum amount of orange paint he can make?

5 a The ratio of KS3 to KS4 pupils in Weregood School is 7:5.
   Are there more pupils in Year 11 than in Year 7?
   Explain and justify your answer.
 b Last year Jameela was 110 cm tall. This year she has increased in
   height by 25%.
   What is the ratio of her height last year to her height this year?

Great-grandad Vernon dies. He had three great-grandchildren, 6-year-old Zoe,
9-year-old Breeze and 15-year-old Jenny. Each year his will gives £1000 to the girls,
which must be shared in the ratio of their ages.

 a Work out the amount each girl receives in the first year.
 b Work out the amount each girl receives for the next 10 years.
 c Write down what you notice.
   Try to use the ratios to explain what is happening.

- Recognise when two quantities are in direct proportion
- Use scaling and the unitary method to solve direct proportion problems
- Identify when direct proportion is needed to solve a problem

- Two quantities are in **direct proportion** if when one of them increases, the other one increases by the same proportion.

- You can use a **scaling** method to solve problems involving direct proportion.
    In this method you multiply or divide both quantities by the same number.

example

Two litres of orange juice cost £2.60.
What is the cost of 5 litres of orange juice?

×2.5 (2 litres   £2.60) ×2.5   5 litres of orange juice
        5 litres   £6.50   costs £6.50.

Work out the multiplier using division $\frac{5}{2} = 2.5$

- You can use the **unitary method** to solve problems involving direct proportion.
    In this method you always find the value of one unit of a quantity.

example

a 15 voice minutes cost 48p.
What is the cost of 23 voice minutes?

b There are 46 calories in a jaffa cake that weighs 12 g. How many calories are there in a 100 g of jaffa cakes?

a
÷15 (15 mins   48p) ÷15
     1 min   3.2p
×23 (23 mins   73.6p) ×23

b
÷12 (46 calories   12 g) ÷12
     3.8333... calories   1 g
×100 (383.33... calories   100 g) ×100

23 voice minutes cost 74p.

100 g of jaffa cakes contain 383 cal.

Round the final answers to the nearest whole penny or calorie, but do not round any intermediate steps.

Exercise 12c

1 Use direct proportion to solve each of these problems.

   a 5 kg of pears cost 195p. What is the cost of 15 kg of pears?

   b 40 g of breakfast cereal contain 128 calories.
     How many calories are there in 100 g of breakfast cereal?

   c A recipe for six people uses 750 ml of stock.
     What amount of stock is needed for four people?

2 Solve each of these problems, giving your answers to an
  appropriate degree of accuracy.

   a 5 litres of oil cost £4.79. What is the cost of 18 litres of oil?

   b There are 12 biscuits in a packet. The packet weighs 200 g.
     What is the weight of 23 biscuits?

   c A car's petrol tank when full holds 48 litres of petrol. On a
     full tank of petrol Jake can drive 650 km.

     i How far could Jake's car travel on 20 litres of petrol?

     ii How much petrol would he need to travel 130 km?

   d £10 is worth 92.27 Croatian kuna.

     i How much is £325 worth in Croatian kuna?

     ii How much is 1000 Croatian kuna worth in pounds?

3 Here are three offers for text
  messages on a mobile phone.
  In which of these offers are the
  numbers in direct proportion?
  In each case, explain and justify
  your answers.

A

texts	cost (p)
15	
40	36
70	96
	168

B

texts	cost (p)
15	
40	33
70	84
	140

C

texts	cost (p)
15	
40	33.75
70	90
	157.5

Use **direct proportion** to copy and complete this conversion table for kilograms and
pounds. Write the ratio in its simplest form.

   a Write anything you notice.
     What do these results tell
     you about the relationship
     between pounds and
     kilograms?

   b How could you quickly
     change from kilograms to
     pounds using what you've
     found out?

Kilograms (kg)	Pounds (lb)	Pounds ÷ Kilograms	Ratio Pounds : Kilograms
1			
	4.4		
5	11		
10			
23			
	110		

   c What about changing from pounds to kilograms?

12d Ratio and proportion

- Understand the relationship between ratio and proportion
- Solve problems involving ratio and proportion

Keywords
Proportion
Ratio

- You can compare the size of two quantities using a **ratio**.

example

Dax the cat weighs 6 kg. Tess the dog weighs 7.5 kg.
What is the ratio of Dax's weight to Tess' weight?
What fraction of Tess' weight is Dax?
How many times heavier than Dax is Tess?

Dax's weight : Tess' weight = 6 : 7.5
$= 12 : 15$
$= 4 : 5$

Dax's weight is
$\frac{4}{5}$ of or 80% of or
0.8 of Tess' weight

Tess' weight is
$\frac{5}{4}$ of or 125% of or
1.25 times Dax's weight

The ratio tells you how many times bigger one part is compared to the other part.

- You can compare two or more parts of the same quantity using ratio and **proportion**.
  The ratio compares the size of the parts.
  The proportion compares the size of the part with the whole.

example

In a skiing club there are 20 beginners, 16 intermediate and 8 advanced skiers.
a What proportion of the skiing club members are intermediate skiers?
b What is the ratio of beginners to advanced skiers at the club?

a Total number of skiers = 20 + 16 + 8 = 44
Proportion of intermediates $= \frac{16}{44}$
$= \frac{4}{11}$ (= 36.4% to 1 dp)

b beginners : advanced = 20 : 8
$= 5 : 2$

The ratio compares how many skiers there are in each category.
number of beginners $= \frac{5}{2} \times$ number of advanced skiers
number of advanced skiers $= \frac{2}{5} \times$ number of beginners

Exercise 12d

Write all ratios and fractions in their simplest forms.

1 For each of these two diagrams
   i   Find the ratio of pink : yellow : blue
   ii Find the proportion of the shape shaded each colour (as a fraction)
   iii Copy and complete these two sentences.

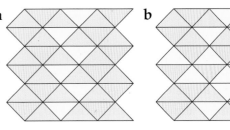

a   b

$$\text{pink section} = \frac{\square}{\square} \times \text{yellow section}$$

$$\text{pink section} = \frac{\square}{\square} \text{ of the whole shape}$$

2 In a bag of mixed fruit and nuts there are 75 g of raisins, 30 g of currents and 95 g of nuts.
   a Write the ratio of raisins : currants : nuts in the bag.
   b How many times more raisins than currants are there?
   c Write the proportion of the bag that is nuts.

3 a An alloy is made from copper and iron in the ratio 2 : 5.
     How much copper needs to be mixed with 45 kg of iron?
   b The length and width of a football pitch are in the ratio 8 : 5.
     The length of the pitch is 110 m. What is the width of the pitch?
   c A cake is made using flour, margarine, ground almonds and sugar in the ratio 4 : 3 : 4 : 5. How many grams of ground almonds are needed to mix with 180 g of margarine?
   d The ratio of protein to carbohydrate in a tin of tomatoes is 12 : 35. If the tin contains 7 g of carbohydrate, how many grams of protein are there in it?

4 a $\frac{4}{7}$ of the pupils at a school are girls.
     What is the ratio of boys : girls at the school?
   b Benni McShot scores $\frac{3}{5}$ of the time he shoots at the goal.
     What is Benni's ratio of goals to shots taken?
   c Josh is 1.5 m tall. Gary is 20% taller than Josh.
     What is the ratio of Josh's height to Gary's height?
   d Cinema tickets for an adult and a child cost £9.80.
     The adult ticket is $1\frac{1}{3}$ times the price of the child's ticket.
     How much does each ticket cost?

Challenge

A square and a rectangle have the same area.
The sides of the rectangle are in the ratio 4 : 3.
The perimeter of the rectangle is 294 cm.
What is the length of side of the square? Give your answer to 1 dp.

Percentage change

- Calculate a percentage increase or decrease
- Use percentage change to solve problems

It is important to set out a problem involving a **percentage change** in a consistent way.

example

In a sale, all prices are reduced by 15%.

a A pair of jeans normally cost £50.
What is the sale price of the pair of jeans?

b A pair of trainers now cost £76.50.
What was the original price of the trainers?

· ·

a In the sale the prices decrease by 15%.

original price $\times 0.85$ sale price
£50   decrease by 15%   £☐

Sale price of jeans = $(100 - 15)\%$ of the original price
= 0.85×50 $85\% = 0.85$
= £42.50

b $\times 0.85$
original price   decrease by 15%   sale price
£☐   £76.50
    $\div 0.85$

Sale price of trainers = $(100 - 15)\%$ of the original price
= $0.85 \times$ original price

Original price of   = sale price $\div 0.85$
trainers   = £76.50 $\div 0.85$
= £90

> The inverse of multiplying by 0.85 is dividing by 0.85.

- You should always check your answer after a percentage change calculation by working out the percentage **increase** or **decrease** of your answer.

example

On 1st April, Sam is promoted and his wage is increased by 10% to £352 per week. What was Sam's wage on the 31st March?

Jonah has worked out the answer to be £316.80. Is his answer correct?

· ·

10% of £316.80 = £316.80 $\div 10$ = £31.68
New wage   = £316.80 + £31.68 = £348.48 $\neq$ £352
This is not Sam's wage given in the question so Jonah's answer must be wrong.

Exercise 12e

Give answers to 2 dp where appropriate.

1 Calculate these percentage changes.
   a Increase £60 by 15%.   b Decrease £270 by 8%.
   c Increase 350 km by 12%.   d Decrease 530 m by 55%.
   e Increase 25 kg by 3%.   f Decrease £450 000 by 2.5%.

2 Samina decides to increase the prices of all the items in her shop by 10%. Copy and complete her new price list.

Item	Original price	New price
Greeting card	£2.40	
Wrapping paper(per roll)		£3.19
Tape roll	78p	
Mug		£1.76

3 a Kelvin weighs 65 kg. He decides to go on a diet and 1 month later his weight has decreased by 7%. What is Kelvin's new weight?
   b In a sale, all prices are reduced by 21%. A DVD costs £11.50 before the sale.
   What is the sale price of the DVD?
   c A computer costs £340. At the checkout, VAT is added at 17.5%. What is the total price of the computer including the charge for VAT?

4 a Melvin decides to go on a diet and 1 month later his weight has decreased by 5%. Melvin now weighs 57 kg.
   What was Melvin's weight before the diet?
   b In a sale all prices are reduced by 15%. A CD costs £10.20 in the sale. What was the cost of the CD before the sale?
   c A computer costs £329 including VAT at 17.5%. What was the price of the computer before VAT was added?

5 a This week Shabana scored 54 marks in a geography test. Her teacher said that this was a 12.5% improvement on her last score. What was Shabana's score in her last geography test?
   b A packet of biscuits is increased in size by 20%. The new packet weighs 216 g. What was the weight of the original packet?

The population of Mathstown in the year 2008 was 88 400.

a If the population of the town has increased by approximately 3% a year, what was the population of the town in   i 2007   ii 2006?
b What would you expect the population of Mathstown to be in   i 2009   ii 2010?
c In what year did the population of Mathstown reach 50 000?
d In what year will the population of Mathstown reach 100 000?
e Investigate the population of Mathstown in different years.

* Use percentages or fractions to compare proportions and solve problems
* Write one number as a percentage of another number

* You can compare **proportions** by converting them to **percentages**.

---

example

Linda is looking at the nutritional information of beef and pork sausages.

a Which type of sausage has the lower proportion of fat?

b How much fat is there in 150 g of beef sausages?

(Give your answer to the nearest gram.)

Pork sausages

NUTRITION INFORMATION	
Typical values	Per sausage
Energy	276 kJ/66 kcal
Protein	2.2 g
Carbohydrate	7.5 g
Weight	24 g
Fat	5.7 g

Beef sausages

NUTRITION INFORMATION	
Typical values	Per sausage
Energy	450 kJ/108 kcal
Protein	12.3 g
Carbohydrate	4.7 g
Weight	55 g
Fat	11.1 g

....

a Pork sausage contains 5.7 g of fat in every 24 g

$= 5.7 \div 24$

$= 0.2375$

$= 23.75\%$

$= 23.8\%$ (1 dp)

Beef sausage contains 11.1 g of fat in every 55 g

$= 11.1 \div 55$

$= 0.201\,818...$

$= 20.1818\%$

$= 20.2\%$ (1 dp)

Write the proportion as a **fraction** and convert this into a decimal and then a percentage.

The beef sausage contains a lower proportion of fat.

b Beef sausages are 20.2% fat.

In 150 g of beef sausages there are 20.2% of 150 g of fat

$= 0.202 \times 150$

$= 30.3\,g$

$= 30\,g$ (nearest gram)

---

* You can express the change in an amount as a percentage of the original amount.

If a packet of biscuits increases in weight from 180 g to 210 g the percentage increase is

$$\frac{(210 - 180)}{180} \times 100 = \frac{\cancel{30}^{1}}{\cancel{180}_{6}} \times 100 = 16.7\% \text{ (1 dp)}$$

Exercise 12f

1 Express each of your answers
   i as a fraction in its simplest form **ii** as a percentage (to 1 dp).
   a Four out of every 500 drawing pins produced by a machine
     are rejected. What proportion of drawing pins are rejected?
   b In a survey, 23 out of 40 cats preferred chicken flavour cat
     food. What proportion of the cats surveyed preferred
     chicken flavour cat food?
   c In class 8X1 there are 35 pupils. 21 of these pupils are boys.
     What proportion of the class are girls?

2 This table shows the number of grams of fat
   in different chocolate bars.
   a Copy and complete the table.
   b Which is the least healthy bar to eat?
     Explain and justify your answer.
   c How many grams of fat would there be in
     150 g of each chocolate bar?
     (Give your answers to the nearest gram.)

Chocolate	Weight (grams)	Fat content (grams)	% fat
Kit Kit	21	5.5	
Malties	37	8.5	
Venus bar	65	11.4	
Cream egg	39	6.2	
Twicks	62	14.9	

3 Many food labels give the proportion
   of energy, protein, carbohydrate, fat,
   fibre and salt that the product contains.
   a Which cereal contains the least
     amount of fat?
     Explain and justify your answer.
   b Which is the healthiest cereal to eat?
     Explain your answer.
   c How much fat is there in a 40 g serving
     of each cereal?

In 1997 about 45% of the tropical rain forests had been destroyed around the world.
Since then about 175 000 square kilometres have been destroyed every year, which
represents about 1.1% of the remainder.

a Estimate the original area of rain forest.
b Estimate the current area.
c Estimate when the rain forest will disappear.

12a

1 Write each of these ratios in its simplest form.

    a 0.4:3   **b** 0.6:5   **c** 1.2:4   **d** 2.5:4

    e 1.8:2.8   **f** 3.2:4:4.8   **g** 2:3:4.5   **h** 1.6:2.4:6.4

    i 0.6 m:360 cm **j** 2.2 kg:1100 g   **k** £3.75:90p   **l** 440 ml:1.4 litres

2 Express each of these ratios in the form $1:n$.

    a 3:15   **b** 8:12   **c** 10:25   **d** 9:12

    e 15:21   **f** 5:19   **g** 6:21   **h** 15:100

    i 7:12   **j** 26:9100   **k** 3.4:68 000 **l** 2.5 cm:75 m

12b

3 Divide these quantities in the ratios given.

    a Divide 140 km in the ratio 2:5   **b** Divide £640 in the ratio 3:5

    c Divide $728 in the ratio 6:7   **d** Divide 30 cm in the ratio 4:3

    e Divide 7 MB in the ratio 8:7   **f** Divide €3000 in the ratio 4:2:1

4 **a** In a school, the ratio of boys to girls is 7:9. There are 371 boys at the school. How many girls are there at the school?

  b A metal alloy is made from zinc and iron in the ratio 7:2. How much iron is needed to make 792 kg of the alloy?

  c Gina draws a pie chart to show how the pupils in her school travel home. The pupils travel home by walking, bus or car in the ratio 7:3:2. How big are the angles she needs to draw for each of the three sectors?

12c

5 **a** 7 litres of petrol cost £7.91. What is the cost of 35 litres of petrol?

  b There are 15 cakes in a box. The cakes weigh 420 g. What is the weight of 25 cakes?

  c Rene's mobile phone contract means she pays £3.60 for 150 text messages.

    i How much would Rene pay for 500 text messages?

    ii How many text messages could she have for £2?

12d

6 **a** An alloy is made from lead and iron in the ratio 4:7. How much lead needs to be mixed with 8.4 kg of iron?

  b The length and width of a netball court are in the ratio 9:5. The length of the court is 40.5 m. What is the width of the court?

  c The ratio of pop music to rock music CDs in Jermal's collection is 4:11. If there are 28 pop music CDs, how many rock music CDs does Jermal have in his collection?

7 a $\frac{2}{9}$ of the pupils at a school gym club are boys.
What is the ratio of boys to girls at the gym club?

b Roldova scores $\frac{7}{11}$ of the time he shoots at the goal.
What is Roldova's ratio of goals to missed shots?

c Hannah is 1.75 m tall. Ursula is 20% shorter than Hannah.
What is the ratio of Hannah's height to Ursula's height?

d A bow and set of arrows costs £40.50. The bow is $1\frac{1}{4}$ times the price of the arrows. How much did the bow cost?

8 a Sam weighs 84 kg. He decides to go on a diet for three months. At the end of the three months his weight has decreased by 8%.
What is Sam's new weight?

Give your answers to 2 dp where appropriate.

b In a sale, all prices are reduced by 22%. A sofa costs £1349 before the sale. What is the cost of the sofa during the sale?

c A car costs £7300. On the bill, VAT is added at 17.5%.
What was the total price of the car including VAT?

9 a Steve decides to go on a diet but unfortunately three months later his weight has increased by 3.5%. Steve now weighs 74.52 kg.
What was Steve's weight before the diet?

b In a sale, all prices are reduced by 12%. A sofa costs £1188 in the sale.
What was the cost of the sofa before the sale?

c A car costs £19 328.75 including VAT at 17.5%.
What was the price of the car before VAT was added?

10 a Copy and complete the table.

b Which is the least healthy food to eat? Explain and justify your answer.

c Which is the most healthy food to eat? Explain and justify your answer.

d How many grams of fat would there be in 250 g of each food?
(Give your answers to the nearest gram.)

Type of food	Weight (grams)	Fat content (grams)	%fat
Lamb chops	28	5	
Chocolate bar	26	4.3	
Crisps	35	11.6	
Burger and bun	215	23	
Peas	60	0.4	

Maths Life

Food crops

There is widespread concern that a change in the type of crops being grown is causing shortages and increased prices of the cereal crops grown for human consumption and feed for livestock.

What do you think are some possible causes for the demand for wheat to be outstripping its production?

World wheat production, consumption and stocks (million tonnes)						
1		02/03	03/04	04/05	05/06	06/07 estimated	07/08
2				628	620		608
3	produced	566	556	616		611	612
4	consumed	601	596		137	123	
5	stocks	169	129				

▶ Complete the missing entries in the spreadsheet.

▶ In how many years does consumption of wheat exceed production?

▶ What is happening to the stocks of wheat that are held in reserve?

▶ Roughly what fraction are the estimated 07/08 stocks of the 02/03 stocks?

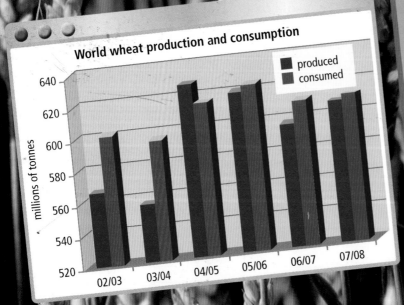

World wheat production and consumption

Here is a bar chart generated from the spreadsheet

▶ Roughly how tall is the 'produced' bar compared with the 'consumed' bar for the first two years?

▶ How does that compare with the figures in the spreadsheet for those years?

▶ Do you think that the chart is a good representation of the actual figures?

Wheat prices continue to rise

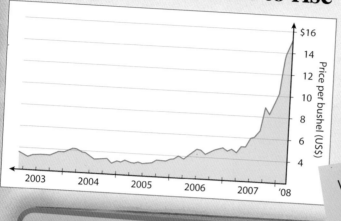

The past few [...]
of [...]
re[...]
30[...]
the[...]
prov[...]
In th[...]
fallen[...]
of dro[...]
winter[...]
class [...]

What is a bushel?

- Roughly what is the lowest price a bushel of wheat has cost since 2003?
- When was the price at its lowest?
- How long did the price take to double from its lowest value?
- How long did it take to double again?

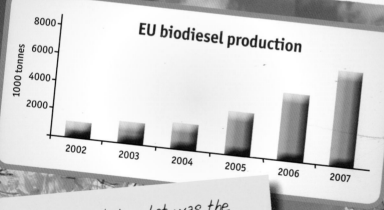

How is biodiesel made?

Diesel

- Approximately what was the average annual production from 2002 to 2005?
- Approximately what was the average annual production from 2006 to 2007?
- What percentage increase is that?

- Why do you think that biodiesel is becoming more widely used?
- Do you think that there is any way that the increase in biofuel production could have an influence on wheat prices?

197

12 Summary

Assessment criteria
- Divide a quantity in a given ratio **Level 6**
- Use proportional reasoning to solve problems, choosing the correct number to take as 100% **Level 6**

1 A supermarket sells 5 different sorts of bread.
The table shows the sales of bread for one day.

Type of bread	Number of loaves sold	Takings (£)
Brown	53	50.88
Whole grain	36	42.48
White	93	73.47
Granary	47	60.63
Soda	25	28.75

a What percentage of the total loaves sold was Granary bread?
b What percentage of the total takings was for Soda bread?
c Which bread is more expensive, White or Brown?
Show your working.

Rose's answer ✔

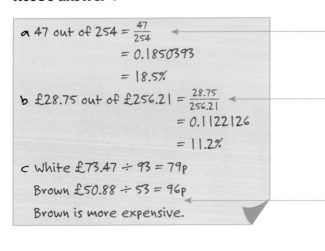

Rose adds 53 + 36 + 93 + 47 + 25 = 254 to find the total of loaves sold.

Rose adds 50.88 + 42.48 + 73.47 + 60.63 + 28.75 = 256.21 to find the total of the takings.

Rose remembers to answer the question, White or Brown?

2 A dessert has both fruit and yoghurt inside.

Altogether, the mass of the fruit and yoghurt is 175 g. The ratio of the mass of fruit to the mass of yoghurt is 2:5.

What is the mass of the yoghurt?

KS3 2008 4–6 Paper 2

13 Algebra

Algebra

Computers help to run the modern world.

They work by solving problems using logic and mathematics.

When you solve a problem, you take some numbers and perform a calculation.

Computers are programmed to do this in such a way that they don't need to know the actual values of the numbers in advance.

What's the point? Algebra allows you to give general solutions to problems even when you don't know the actual input values.

✓ Check in

1 Find the value of the required variable in each of these formulae.

　　a $P = 3l$　　Find P when $l = 12$　　　　　　　**b** $k = \dfrac{m}{1000}$　　Find k when $m = 3200$

　　c $V = \dfrac{1}{3}b^2h$　Find V when $b = 3$ and $h = 4$

2 Evaluate these calculations.

　　a $\dfrac{1}{5} + \dfrac{2}{5}$　　　　**b** $\dfrac{8}{9} - \dfrac{1}{9}$　　　　**c** $\dfrac{3}{4} - \dfrac{3}{8}$　　　　**d** $\dfrac{4}{5} - \dfrac{1}{15}$

　　e $\dfrac{2}{3} + \dfrac{2}{9}$　　　　**f** $\dfrac{5}{6} - \dfrac{1}{4}$　　　　**g** $\dfrac{3}{4} + \dfrac{2}{5}$　　　　**h** $\dfrac{7}{12} + \dfrac{3}{8}$

3 Expand the brackets and simplify.

　　a $8(3a + 2)$　　　　**b** $4(5b - 1)$　　　　**c** $k(k - 4)$　　　　**d** $x(5 - y)$

　　e $5p(2p - 3)$　　　　**f** $12(1 - 2q)$　　　　**g** $-3(7 - m)$　　　**h** $-n(10 - n)$

4 Solve these equations.

　　a $8x + 3 = 5x + 9$　　　　　　　　　　**b** $3(2y + 1) = 4y + 11$

　　c $4(3m - 1) = 7(m + 3)$　　　　　　　**d** $5(4n - 3) = 3(6n - 1)$

- Simplify expressions by collecting like terms
- Multiply a single term over a bracket
- Use algebra in context

Keywords
Brackets   Like terms
Expand   Simplify

- An algebraic expression can be **simplified** by collecting **like terms**.

example

Write a simplified expression for the missing length in this rectangle.

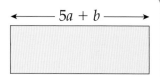

$\square = 5a + b - 3a$

$= 5a - 3a + b$ Keep the sign in front with the term.

$= 2a + b$ Collect like terms.

- To simplify an expression involving **brackets, expand** each pair of brackets and then collect like terms.

example

Find the perimeter of this rectangle. Fully simplify your answer.

$4x - y$

$2y$

Perimeter $= 2(\text{length} + \text{width})$

$= 2(4x - y + 2y)$

$= 2(4x + y)$ Collect like terms.

$= 8x + 2y$ Multiply each term inside the bracket by 2.

example

a Write an algebraic expression using brackets for the shaded area of this rectangle.

b Expand the brackets.

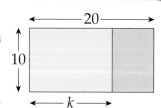

a The shaded area has length $= 10$
and width $= 20 - k$
Shaded area $= 10(20 - k)$

b $10(20 - k) = 200 - 10k$ Multiply each term inside the bracket by 10.

Exercise 13a

1 Guide Xavier along the grid of Milton Keynes streets to his office building.

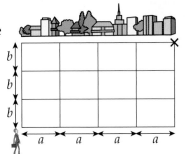

Going three blocks right and two block up becomes:
$+ a + a + a + b + b = 3a + 2b$

One block right $= +a$
One block left $= -a$
One block up $= +b$
One block down $= -b$

a Devise three different routes that Xavier can take to work and write these as algebraic expressions.

b For each expression, simplify by collecting like terms. Write what you notice.

2 In a magic square, the sum of each row, column and diagonal is the same.
Show that this is a magic square.

$b - a$	$3a + 2b$	a
$3a$	$a + b$	$2b - a$
$a + 2b$	$-a$	$3a + b$

3 Write a simplified expression for the missing lengths on each of these rectangles.

a ← 5k + 3 →

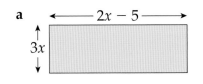

← 2k + 1 →← ☐ →

b ← 4t + 5 →

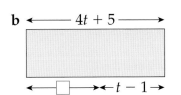

← ☐ →← t − 1 →

4 i Write an algebraic expression using brackets for each of these shaded areas.

ii Expand the brackets.

a ← 2x − 5 →

3x

b ← p →

q

← 8 →

c ← 10 →

3

← k → ← k →

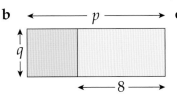

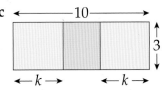

In this rectangle, length $= y + 3$ and width $= y + 2$.
The area of this rectangle $= (y + 3)(y + 2)$.
By writing an expression for the area of each of the four small rectangles, summing and collecting like terms, find an expression equivalent to $(y + 3)(y + 2)$.

Can you use this method to expand $(x + 1)(x + 4)$?

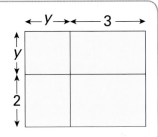

← y → ← 3 →

y

2

13b Algebraic fractions

- Know that algebraic expressions follow the same conventions as arithmetic operations
- Add and subtract simple algebraic fractions

Keywords
Algebraic fractions
Common denominator
Equivalent fractions

p.52

- Fractions can be added and subtracted if they have a **common denominator**.

$$\frac{2}{7} + \frac{3}{7} = \frac{5}{7}$$

7 is the *common* denominator as it is common to all the fractions that you want to add.

- When the fractions have different denominators, find a common denominator and use **equivalent fractions**.

$$\frac{3}{5} - \frac{1}{2} = \frac{6}{10} - \frac{5}{10}$$

The lowest common multiple (LCM) of 5 and 2 is 10.

$$= \frac{1}{10}$$

Using equivalent fractions
$$\overset{\times 2}{\underset{\times 2}{\frac{3}{5} = \frac{6}{10}}} \text{ and } \overset{\times 5}{\underset{\times 5}{\frac{1}{2} = \frac{5}{10}}}$$

- **Algebraic fractions** have algebraic expressions in the numerator or denominator or in both.

  Algebraic fractions follow the same rules as numerical fractions.

$$\frac{x}{2} + \frac{x}{3} = \frac{3x}{6} + \frac{2x}{6}$$

The LCM of 2 and 3 is 6.

$$= \frac{5x}{6}$$

Using equivalent fractions
$$\overset{\times 3}{\underset{\times 3}{\frac{x}{2} = \frac{3x}{6}}} \text{ and } \overset{\times 2}{\underset{\times 2}{\frac{x}{3} = \frac{2x}{6}}}$$
You can add the numerators as they are like terms.

Take extra care when the algebraic terms are in the denominators.

example

Calculate

a $\dfrac{2}{x} + \dfrac{5}{y}$

b $\dfrac{4}{x^2} - \dfrac{3}{x}$

. . . .

a $\dfrac{2}{x} + \dfrac{5}{y} = \dfrac{2y}{xy} + \dfrac{5x}{xy}$

The LCM of x and y is xy.

$$= \frac{5x + 2y}{xy}$$

$5x$ and $2y$ are not like terms so cannot be added.

b $\dfrac{4}{x^2} - \dfrac{3}{x} = \dfrac{4}{x^2} - \dfrac{3x}{x^2}$

The LCM of x and x^2 is x^2.

$$= \frac{4 - 3x}{x^2}$$

4 and -3x are not like terms so cannot be added.

Exercise 13b

1 Work these out, simplifying your answer as necessary.

a $\dfrac{1}{7} + \dfrac{3}{7}$ **b** $\dfrac{5}{9} - \dfrac{1}{9}$ **c** $\dfrac{3}{5} + \dfrac{1}{5}$ **d** $\dfrac{8}{11} - \dfrac{4}{11}$

e $\dfrac{3}{4} - \dfrac{1}{4}$ **f** $\dfrac{5}{6} + \dfrac{1}{6}$ **g** $\dfrac{7}{8} - \dfrac{5}{8}$ **h** $\dfrac{7}{12} + \dfrac{11}{12}$

2 Simplify these.

a $\dfrac{x}{3} + \dfrac{x}{3}$ **b** $\dfrac{x}{4} + \dfrac{y}{4}$ **c** $\dfrac{2a}{5} + \dfrac{a}{5}$ **d** $\dfrac{4}{7}t - \dfrac{3}{7}t$

e $\dfrac{1}{6}p + \dfrac{5}{6}q$ **f** $\dfrac{1}{x} + \dfrac{2}{x}$ **g** $\dfrac{8}{k} - \dfrac{3}{k}$ **h** $\dfrac{5}{x^2} - \dfrac{2}{x^2}$

3 Sort these cards into pairs of equivalent fractions.

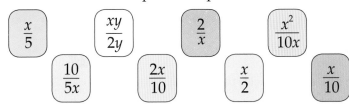

$\dfrac{x}{5}$ $\qquad$ $\dfrac{xy}{2y}$ $\qquad$ $\dfrac{2}{x}$ $\qquad$ $\dfrac{x^2}{10x}$

$\dfrac{10}{5x}$ $\qquad$ $\dfrac{2x}{10}$ $\qquad$ $\dfrac{x}{2}$ $\qquad$ $\dfrac{x}{10}$

4 Work these out using equivalent fractions.

a $\dfrac{1}{3} + \dfrac{1}{9}$ **b** $\dfrac{2}{3} + \dfrac{1}{6}$ **c** $\dfrac{7}{10} - \dfrac{2}{5}$ **d** $\dfrac{5}{8} - \dfrac{1}{4}$

e $\dfrac{1}{2} + \dfrac{1}{3}$ **f** $\dfrac{4}{5} - \dfrac{2}{3}$ **g** $\dfrac{3}{4} - \dfrac{1}{5}$ **h** $\dfrac{5}{6} + \dfrac{3}{4}$

5 Simplify these fractions.

a $\dfrac{x}{2} + \dfrac{x}{4}$ **b** $\dfrac{p}{3} - \dfrac{p}{6}$ **c** $\dfrac{2a}{3} + \dfrac{a}{4}$ **d** $\dfrac{4}{5}b - \dfrac{1}{2}b$

e $\dfrac{4}{x} + \dfrac{5}{y}$ **f** $\dfrac{5}{m} - \dfrac{3}{n}$ **g** $\dfrac{1}{x} + \dfrac{1}{x^2}$ **h** $\dfrac{3}{k^2} - \dfrac{2}{k}$

A box of chocolate chunks contains c chocolates. Ashim and Aesha share a box of chocolate chunks. This is how much they eat.

I have eaten $\dfrac{c}{3}$ chocolates

I have eaten $\dfrac{2c}{7}$ chocolates

a Write and simplify an algebraic expression to show the fraction of the box of chocolate chunks that Ashim and Aesha have eaten.

b Ashim and Aesha have eaten 26 chocolate chunks.
Work out the number of chocolate chunks, c, in a box.

- Find an unknown when it is not the subject of a formula
- Change the subject of a formula

Keywords
Subject
Substitute
Variable

p.74

- You can **substitute** into a formula to find an unknown **variable**.

  If the unknown variable is not the **subject** of the formula, substitute the values of the given variables and solve the equation.

example

Fabienne uses the formula $C = 100 - 12n$ to calculate the change, £C, from £100 for n DVDs at £12 each.
Fabienne has £28 change.
Work out the number of DVDs that she has bought.

· ·

$$C = 100 - 12n$$
$$28 = 100 - 12n \quad \text{Substitute 28 for } C \text{ and then solve the equation.}$$
$$12n + 28 = 100 \qquad +12n \text{ to both sides.}$$
$$12n = 72 \qquad -28 \text{ from both sides.}$$
$$n = 6 \qquad \div 12 \text{ on both sides.}$$

Fabienne has bought 6 DVDs.

- Alternatively, you can change the subject of the formula before substituting the values of the given variables.

example

a Rearrange $y = m(x + a)$ to make x the subject.

b Hence find x when $y = 9$, $m = 3$ and $a = 2$.

· ·

a
$$y = m(x + a) \qquad \text{Multiply out the brackets.}$$
$$y = mx + am \qquad \text{Write variables in alphabetical order. } m \times a = am$$
$$y - am = mx \qquad -am \text{ from both sides.}$$
$$\frac{y - am}{m} = x \qquad \div m \text{ on both sides.}$$
$$x = \frac{y - am}{m}$$

Read the formula, starting with the variable that you want to make the subject. 'Start with x, multiply by m and then add am to get y'. Undo each operation in turn.

b Substituting $y = 9$, $m = 3$ and $a = 2$ gives
$$x = \frac{9 - 2 \times 3}{3} = \frac{9 - 6}{3} = \frac{3}{3} = 1$$

So $x = 1$

Exercise 13c

1 By substituting the given values to form an equation, find the required variable in each of these formulae.

a $m = \dfrac{c}{100}$ Find c when $m = 3.2$

b $A = \dfrac{1}{2}bh$ Find h when $A = 27$ and $b = 6$

c $P = 2(l + w)$ Find w when $P = 22$ and $l = 8$

d $s = \left(\dfrac{u + v}{2}\right)t$ Find t when $s = 180$, $u = 0$ and $v = 24$

2 The area, A, of a trapezium is given by the formula

$A = \dfrac{1}{2}(a + b)h$ where a, b and h are the lengths as shown on the diagram.

  a By forming and solving an equation, find h when
       $A = 12$, $a = 2$ and $b = 6$.

  b By forming and solving an equation, find a when
       $A = 24$, $b = 7$ and $h = 4$.

3 The surface area, S, of a cuboid is given by the formula
$S = 2lw + 2hw + 2hl$ where l is the length, w is the width and h is the height.

  a By forming and solving an equation, find w when
       $S = 76$, $l = 4$ and $h = 5$.

  b Find the length of a cuboid with a surface area of 94,
       a width of 3 and a height of 4.

  c Explain why this formula works.

4 Make x the subject of each of these formulae.

  a $a = b(x + y)$ **b** $p(w + x) = q$

  c $t = m(x - n)$ **d** $x(a + b) = c$

  e $k^2 = t(m + x)$ **f** $t = \dfrac{1}{2}(x + y)$

  g $r^2 = \dfrac{1}{3}(x - p)$ **h** $pq(x - p) = r$

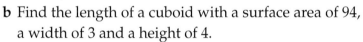

  a Make x the subject of these formulae.

    i $\dfrac{a}{x} = b$ **ii** $p + q = \dfrac{r}{x}$

  b Create some more formulae involving x as the denominator of a fraction and challenge your partner to rearrange your formulae to make x the subject. Discuss your methods.

- Solve linear equations involving fractions

Keywords
Cross-multiply
Equation
Solve

- When **solving equations**, a fraction can be thought of as a division.

$$\frac{x + 5}{3} = 2$$ reads 'Start with x, add 5, and then divide by 3 to get 2'

The fraction is read as 'divide by 3'

- You can undo a division by multiplying.

Multiplying by 3 on both sides of $\frac{x + 5}{3} = 2$ gives $x + 5 = 6$

> Multiplication and division are inverse operations.

example

Solve these equations.

a $\dfrac{3x + 4}{5} = 2$ **b** $\dfrac{x}{3} - 6 = 1$

> The operation that was performed last is −6 so deal with this first.

. . . .

a $\dfrac{3x + 4}{5} = 2$ ×5 on both sides

$3x + 4 = 10$ −4

$3x = 6$ ÷3

$x = 2$

b $\dfrac{x}{3} - 6 = 1$ +6 to both sides.

$\dfrac{x}{3} = 7$ ×3

$x = 21$

- To solve an equation with fractions on both sides, you will need to perform two multiplications.

This is known as **cross-multiplying**.

example

Solve the equation.

$$\frac{3x - 4}{5} = \frac{x + 4}{3}$$

. . . .

$\dfrac{3x - 4}{5} = \dfrac{x + 4}{3}$ ×5 on both sides.

$3x - 4 = \dfrac{5(x + 4)}{3}$ ×3

$3(3x - 4) = 5(x + 4)$ Expand the brackets.

$9x - 12 = 5x + 20$ −5x

$4x - 12 = 20$ +12

$4x = 32$ ÷4

$x = 8$

$$\frac{3(3x - 4)}{5} = \frac{5(x + 4)}{3}$$

Cross-multiplying is performing these two multiplications at the same time.

Exercise 13d

1 Solve these equations involving a fraction on one side.

a $\dfrac{x}{9} = 7$ **b** $5 = \dfrac{a}{8}$ **c** $\dfrac{3y}{4} = 1$ **d** $\dfrac{5k}{3} = 3$

e $\dfrac{n}{5} + 2 = 4$ **f** $3 + \dfrac{p}{4} = 5$ **g** $\dfrac{1}{3}t - 5 = 2$ **h** $5 = \dfrac{2}{3}b - 1$

i $\dfrac{m + 4}{5} = 3$ **j** $\dfrac{q - 8}{3} = 2$ **k** $9 = \dfrac{2d + 5}{3}$ **l** $\dfrac{4(g - 1)}{10} = 2$

2 Solve these equations where the unknown is in the denominator of the fraction.

> Hint: in part **a**, multiply by a on both sides.

a $\dfrac{6}{a} = 3$ **b** $4 = \dfrac{20}{y}$ **c** $\dfrac{2}{k} = 3$ **d** $4 = \dfrac{7}{t}$

e $\dfrac{10}{b} + 3 = 8$ **f** $7 + \dfrac{15}{x} = 10$ **g** $\dfrac{6}{p} - 3 = 1$ **h** $10 - \dfrac{4}{m} = 7$

i $\dfrac{6}{n + 1} = 3$ **j** $\dfrac{9}{2d - 1} = 3$ **k** $\dfrac{20}{6 - g} = 4$ **l** $4 = \dfrac{8}{3(1 - q)}$

3 Solve these equations by cross-multiplying.

a $\dfrac{x}{2} = \dfrac{x + 6}{4}$ **b** $\dfrac{y + 3}{2} = \dfrac{4y}{5}$ **c** $\dfrac{t + 7}{5} = \dfrac{t + 1}{2}$

d $\dfrac{p + 4}{7} = \dfrac{p - 4}{3}$ **e** $\dfrac{3a - 1}{4} = \dfrac{a + 7}{5}$ **f** $\dfrac{2k + 4}{7} = \dfrac{3k - 5}{5}$

g $\dfrac{4m - 1}{3} = \dfrac{3m - 2}{2}$ **h** $\dfrac{2(b + 3)}{5} = \dfrac{3b - 2}{2}$

4

> I add 7 to my Mom's age and then divide by 5. I get the same answer as if I subtract 2 from my Mom's age and then divide by 4. Work out my Mom's age.

5 The rectangle and the triangle have the same area. Write and solve an equation for x and hence find the area of these shapes.

 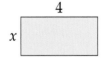

The sum of the external angles of a polygon is 360°.

a Write an algebraic expression for the size of an external angle of a regular n-sided polygon.

b By forming and solving an equation, find the number of sides of a regular polygon with an external angle of

   i 72°   **ii** 36°   **iii** 45°

• Use systematic trial-and-improvement methods to find solutions or approximate solutions to equations

Keywords
Approximate
Trial-and-improvement

p.124

• Equations can be solved using a **trial-and-improvement** method.

example

Solve $x^3 - x = 120$ using a trial-and-improvement method.

Try 4	$4^3 - 4 = 60$	too small
Try 6	$6^3 - 6 = 210$	too large
Try 5	$5^3 - 5 = 120$	correct

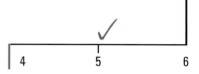

The solution is $x = 5$.

• Trial-and-improvement can be used to find **approximate** solutions to complex equations.

The answer must be bounded from above and below.

example

Find a positive solution of $x^2 + \dfrac{1}{x} = 10$ by trial-and-improvement.
Give your answer to 1 decimal place.

x	x^2	$\dfrac{1}{x}$	$x^2 + \dfrac{1}{x}$	Result
3	9	$\dfrac{1}{3}$	$9\dfrac{1}{3}$	low
4	16	$\dfrac{1}{4}$	$16\dfrac{1}{4}$	high
3.2	10.24	0.3125	10.5525	high
3.1	9.61	0.3225...	9.9325...	low
3.15	9.9225	0.3174...	10.2399...	high

x lies between 3 and 4 but is closer to 3.

x lies between 3.1 and 3.2 but is closer to 3.1.

The solution lies between 3.10 and 3.15.
Any number between 3.10 and 3.15
rounds to 3.1 to 1 dp.
The solution is 3.1 (1 dp).

Exercise 13e

1 Copy and complete this table to find a positive solution of $x^2 + x = 240$.

x	x^2	$x^2 + x$	Result
10	100	110	low

2 Find a positive solution of each of these equations using a trial-and-improvement method.

a $x^2 - x = 90$ **b** $x^2 - 2x = 63$ **c** $x^3 + 3x = 536$ **d** $2^x = 1024$

3 Copy and complete this table to find a positive solution of $x^3 - 2x = 100$.

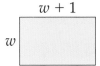

Give answers correct to 1 decimal place.

x	x^3	$2x$	$x^3 - 2x$	Result
4	64	8	56	low
5	125	10	115	high

4 Find a positive solution of each of these equations using a trial-and-improvement method.

a $x^4 = 60$ **b** $x(x - 3) = 25$

c $3^x = 50$ **d** $x + \dfrac{10}{x} = 9$

5 A rectangle has width w cm and length $w + 1$ cm. The area of the rectangle is $100\,\text{cm}^2$. Use trial-and-improvement to find w.

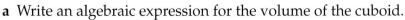

6 A cuboid has a square cross-section. The length of the cuboid is 1 more than a side of this square.

a Write an algebraic expression for the volume of the cuboid.

b Given that the volume of the cuboid is $90\,\text{cm}^3$, find k.

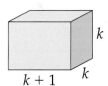

Here is a quadratic equation.

$x^2 + 2x = 20$

Use a spreadsheet to solve this equation by trial-and-improvement.

Start by inputting these formulae.

	A	B	C	D
1	x	x^2	$2x$	$x^2 + 2x$
2	1	= A2^2	= 2*A2	= B2+C2
3	= A2+1	= A3^2	= 2*A3	= B3+C3
4	= A3+1	= A4^2	= 2*A4	= B4+C4
5	= A4+1	= A5^2	= 2*A5	= B5+C5

Choose new values for x based on your results from the spreadsheet above. Continue until you find x.

- Plot the graphs of linear functions given in the form $ax + by = c$

Keywords

Explicit   Rearrange
Implicit   Subject

p.106

- When y is the **subject**, the equation is an **explicit** equation.

  $y = 3x + 2$, $y = 4x$ and $y = \frac{1}{2}x - 1$ are explicit equations.

Equations of the form $y = mx + c$ produce straight-line graphs.

- When y is not the subject, the equation is an **implicit** equation.

  $y - 3x = 2$, $\frac{y}{4} - x = 0$ and $2y - x + 2 = 0$ are implicit equations.

- You can **rearrange** implicit equations to make y the subject.

---

example

For each of these implicit equations, find an equivalent explicit equation.

a $2x + y - 3 = 0$ **b** $4y - 2x = 3$

....

a $2x + y - 3 = 0$ **b** $4y - 2x = 3$

$\quad\quad 2x + y = 3$ $+3$ $\quad 4y = 2x + 3$ $+2x$

$\quad\quad\quad y = 3 - 2x$ $-2x$ $\quad\quad y = \frac{2}{4}x + \frac{3}{4}$ $\div 4$

$\quad\quad\quad\quad\quad\quad\quad\quad\quad\quad\quad\quad\quad\quad\quad y = \frac{1}{2}x + \frac{3}{4}$

You must do the same to both sides of the equation.

- To plot the graph of an implicit function, either
  - rearrange to make the equation explicit, or
  - find the coordinates of the points where the graph cuts the axes.

To find the coordinates of the points where the graph cuts the axes, substitute $x = 0$ and then $y = 0$ into each implicit equation.

---

example

a Plot $x + y = 5$ and $x - 2y = 2$ on the same axes and find their point of intersection.
b Show that the coordinates of the point of intersection satisfy both equations.

....

a $x + y = 5$ $y = 0$, $x = 5$ $\Rightarrow (5, 0)$ $\Rightarrow$ means 'implies'.
$\quad\quad\quad\quad\quad x = 0$, $y = 5$ $\Rightarrow (0, 5)$
$\quad x - 2y = 2$ $y = 0$ $x = 2$ $\Rightarrow (2, 0)$
$\quad\quad\quad\quad\quad x = 0$ $-2y = 2$ $\div -2$
$\quad\quad\quad\quad\quad\quad\quad y = \frac{2}{-2} = -1$ $\Rightarrow (0, -1)$

The coordinates of the point of intersection are $(4, 1)$.

b $x + y = 4 + 1 = 5$ ✓ $x - 2y = 4 - 2 \times 1 = 2$ ✓
Substitute $x = 4$ and $y = 1$ into each equation.

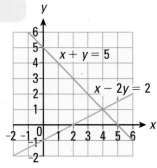

Exercise 13f

1 Rearrange these implicit equations to make y the subject.

  a $x + y = 8$ **b** $2x + y = 1$ **c** $y - 3 = 4x$

  d $3x + y - 2 = 0$ **e** $2y - x = 6$ **f** $3y + 2x = 3$

  g $\dfrac{y}{3} - x = 0$ **h** $12 - 4y + x = 0$

2 For each implicit equation, copy and complete the table of values and hence plot the graph of the function.

  a $x + y = 4$

x	0	2	
y			0

  b $2x + y = 8$

x	0	2	
y			0

  c $x + 3y = 6$

x	0	3	
y			0

3 **a** Using these graphs, write the coordinates of the points of intersection of these pairs of equations.

    i $x + y = 6$ and $2y - 3x = 2$

    ii $x + y = 6$ and $3y - 2x = 3$

    iii $2y - 3x = 2$ and $3y - 2x = 3$

  b Show that the coordinates of each point of intersection satisfy both equations in each pair.

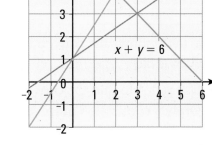

4 Two numbers have a sum of 7 and a difference of 3. Let these numbers be x and y.

  a Write a pair of implicit equations to represent this information.

  b Construct tables of values and plot the graphs of these equations.

  c Write the point of intersection of your graphs and prove that these coordinates satisfy the equations in part **a**.

Two adults and two children visit the zoo at a cost of £50.
One adult and three children visit the zoo at a cost of £45.

  a Write a pair of implicit equations to represent this information.

  b Using graphical software or a graphical calculator, plot the graphs of these equations on the same axes.

  c Work out the cost of an adult's ticket and a child's ticket.

- Solve problems involving direct proportion using algebraic methods
- Construct functions arising from real-life problems and plot their graphs

Keywords
Direct proportion
Ratio

p.186

- Two quantities are in **direct proportion** if, as they vary, they remain in the same **ratio**.

The symble ∝ means 'is directly proportional to '.

example

Here is a recipe for 8 scones.
How much sugar is required to make 12 scones?

Recipe for 8 scones

50g soft margarine
25g sugar
200g self-raising flour

number of scones ∝ amount of sugar

Let x be the amount of sugar for 12 scones.

$$\frac{x}{12} = \frac{25}{8}$$

sugar is the numerator in both fractions.

sugar needed for 12 scones, $x = \dfrac{25 \times 12}{8} = 37.5\,\text{g}$

- The graph of two quantities that are in direct proportion is a straight line that passes through the origin.

example

The table shows the conversion of pounds (£) to New Zealand dollars (NZ$).

£	2	4	6
NZ$	5	10	15

a Use ratios to find the conversion rate between £ and NZ$.
b Draw a conversion graph and use it to estimate how many NZ$ you get for £5.

a £ : NZ$ = 2 : 5 = 1 : 2.5 The conversion rate is £1 = NZ$2.50.

b
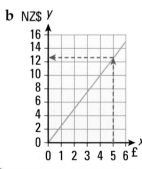

The gradient, $m = 2.5$.
For every 1 unit across you move 2.5 units up.

$c = 0$
The coordinates of the y-intercept are (0, 0).

Using $y = mx + c$, the line is $y = 2.5x$.
This is the conversion rate.

You get NZ$12.50 for £5.

Exercise 13g

1 Write whether these quantities are in direct proportion.
   a The number of euros purchased for an amount of pounds sterling without a commission fee.
   b Temperature in degrees Celsius and temperature in degrees Fahrenheit.
   c The amount you earn and the number of years you have worked.
   d The circumference and the diameter of a circle.
   e The number of hours you spend on your maths homework and the number of marks you receive.

2 For each of these tables, use ratios to work out whether the two quantities are in direct proportion.

a
No. of hours worked	8	12	32
Amount earned in £	72	108	288

b
Length of rectangle, cm	10	15	50
Width of rectangle, cm	8	12	40

3 These are similar triangles.
   This means that corresponding sides are in the same ratio.
   Work out the height of the large triangle.

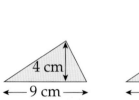 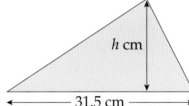

4 The exchange rate for pounds sterling (£) to euros (€) is £1 = € 1.25.
   a Copy and complete this table of values.
   b Draw a conversion graph for £ (x) to € (y) at this exchange rate.

£	1	4		16
€	1.25		10	

   c Use your graph to convert
      i £6 to €   ii €18 to £
   d Write the equation of your line.
   e Use your equation to help you decide whether you would rather accept a gift of £75 or €100.

Two quantities are in inverse proportion when one increases at the same rate as the other decreases.
For example, the time a car journey takes is inversely proportional to the average speed of the car.
List some other pairs of quantities that are inversely proportional.

- Plot and sketch graphs arising from real-life situations
- Interpret graphs arising from real-life situations

Keywords
Distance–time Sketch
   graph   graph
Gradient   Speed
Plot

- A real life situation can be represented by a **sketch graph**.
  You do not need data to sketch a graph but you should make
  sure that the general shape of the graph models the situation.

example

Clare washes up a milk
pan after breakfast.

Sketch a graph to show
the depth of water in the
washing-up bowl over
a period of time.

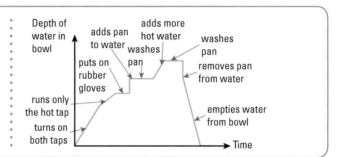

- Data can be **plotted** to represent a real-life situation.

- A **distance–time graph** represents a real-life journey.
  Time is recorded on the horizontal axis and distance travelled on the vertical axis.

example

Jason leaves his home at 07:00 and cycles to work. He cycles a distance of 10 km in half
an hour and then stops for 10 mins to repair a puncture. He cycles the remaining 10 km
to work in 20 mins. Jason spends only 2 hours at work before feeling unwell and being
driven home in a colleague's car. He arrives home 25 mins later.

a Draw a distance–time graph to represent this information.
b Calculate the speed at which Jason's colleague drove him home.

a Distance from home

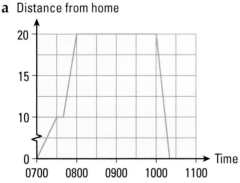

b Jason's colleague drives him
20 km in 25 mins.

$$\text{Speed} = \frac{\text{Distance}}{\text{Time}}$$

$$= \frac{20\,\text{km}}{\left(\frac{25}{60}\right)\text{hours}} \qquad 25\text{ mins} = \frac{25}{60}\text{ hrs}$$

$$= 20 \times \frac{60}{25}$$

$$= 48\,\text{km/h}$$

- The **gradient** of a line on a distance-time graph represents the **speed**.

Exercise 13h

1 The graph represents the depth of tea in Sandeep's cup.

Depth of tea in cup

a Match each section of the graph marked by a letter with one of the statements below.

  i Sandeep drains her cup.

  ii Sandeep adds a splash of cold water from the tap.

  iii Sandeep drinks some tea.

  iv Sandeep solves a sudoku puzzle.

  v Sandeep uses the teapot to top up the tea in her cup.

  vi Sandeep pours a cup of tea from her teapot.

b Draw a sketch graph of the temperature of Sandeep's tea over the same period of time.

2 Water is poured at a constant rate into each container A, B and C. Match each of these containers with one of the graphs.

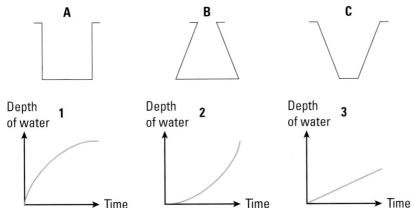

3 Samantha leaves her house at 11 a.m. and walks 3 km in half an hour to 'Atlas' delicatessen. She spends 15 mins buying some groceries and then walks for 15 mins towards home at a speed of 4 km per hour. A passing friend then picks her up on his tandem and together they cycle the rest of the journey in 5 mins.

a Draw a distance–time graph to represent this information.

b At what time does Samantha arrive home?

c What is the average speed of the tandem?

> **task**
>
> Using ideas from question **2**, draw a variety of containers and challenge your partner to sketch a related graph of the depth of the water against time. Make sure you can check their answers!

1 Write an algebraic expression for each missing length on this rectangle.

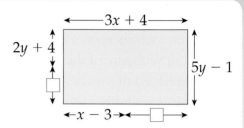

2 i Write an algebraic expression using brackets for the shaded areas in these rectangles.

ii Expand the brackets.

a

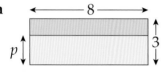

b

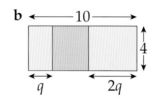

3 Simplify these expressions.

a $\dfrac{x}{5} + \dfrac{2x}{5}$ **b** $\dfrac{p}{8} - \dfrac{q}{8}$ **c** $\dfrac{5}{9}a - \dfrac{1}{9}a$ **d** $\dfrac{10}{t} - \dfrac{3}{t}$

4 Simplify these using equivalent fractions.

a $\dfrac{k}{4} + \dfrac{k}{8}$ **b** $\dfrac{2y}{5} - \dfrac{y}{100}$ **c** $\dfrac{3}{8}m + \dfrac{1}{2}m$ **d** $\dfrac{3}{10}n - \dfrac{1}{8}n$

e $\dfrac{3}{a} + \dfrac{2}{b}$ **f** $\dfrac{6}{p} - \dfrac{1}{q}$ **g** $\dfrac{10}{t} - \dfrac{7}{t^2}$ **h** $\dfrac{5}{xy} - \dfrac{3}{x}$

5 Jolyon decides to spend his £80 birthday money on CDs.

He uses the formula

$$P = 80 - 9x$$

to calculate P, the amount of money that he has left after buying x CDs.

a Write the cost of each CD.   **b** Jolyon has £26 left.
Write and solve an equation to calculate x, the number of CDs that Jolyon has bought.

6 Make x the subject of these formulae.

a $m = 3(x + n)$ **b** $k = \dfrac{1}{10}(c + x)$ **c** $p = q(x - t)$ **d** $k(x - r) = d^2$

7 Solve these equations.

a $\dfrac{a}{3} = \dfrac{a + 4}{5}$ **b** $\dfrac{b - 1}{3} = \dfrac{2b}{7}$ **c** $\dfrac{x + 5}{3} = \dfrac{x + 11}{5}$

d $\dfrac{y + 6}{9} = \dfrac{y - 2}{5}$ **e** $\dfrac{2p - 1}{9} = \dfrac{p - 3}{2}$ **f** $\dfrac{5q - 1}{4} = \dfrac{7q - 5}{5}$

g $\dfrac{3m + 1}{7} = \dfrac{5m - 6}{4}$ **h** $\dfrac{3n - 2}{5} = \dfrac{5n - 8}{6}$

8 Copy and complete this table to find a positive solution of $x^3 - x = 50$, correct to 1 dp.

x	x^3	$x^3 - x$	Result
4	64	60	high
3	27	24	low

9 a Copy and complete the tables and plot the graphs of these implicit functions on the same set of axes.

$x + y = 5$

x	0	1	2
y			

$5x - y = 1$

x	0	1	2
y			

b Write the coordinates of the point of intersection of these graphs.

c Show that the coordinates of the point of intersection satisfy each equation.

10 To convert miles to kilometres, you use the direct proportion relationship

$$5 \text{ miles} = 8 \text{ kilometres}$$

a Copy and complete this table of values.

Miles	5	7.5		20
Kilometres	8		16	

b Draw a graph to convert miles to kilometres.

c Use your graph to estimate how many kilometres are equivalent to 7 miles.

d Write the equation of your line.

11 Patrick leaves his home at 08:00. He jogs 3 km in 20 mins and then stops for 30 mins to have breakfast at a local café. Patrick sprints home in 10 mins. Patrick's wife, Giselle, leaves home at 08:15. She runs to the same café as Patrick in 15 mins and joins her husband for breakfast. Giselle leaves at the same time as Patrick and quickly walks back home, arriving at 09:15.

a Draw each of these journeys on the same distance−time graph.

b How long did Patrick and Giselle spend together over breakfast?

c Calculate the average speed at which

   i Patrick ran home   **ii** Giselle walked home.

13 Summary

Assessment criteria

- Use systematic trial and improvement methods to solve equations **Level 6**
- Interpret graphs arising from real situations **Level 6**

1 Use trial and improvement to solve the equation

$$2x^2 = 87$$

Give your answer to one decimal place.

Joey's answer ✔

x	x^2	$2x^2$	comment
6	36	72	low
7	49	98	high
6.5	42.25	84.5	low
6.6	43.56	87.12	high
6.55	42.9025	85.805	low

6.5   6.55   6.6

Joey narrows the square root to be between 6.5 and 6.6

$x = 6.6$ to 1 decimal place

2 The line on the graph represents a speed of 60 km/hour.

a Draw a line on the graph to represent a speed of 30 km/hour.
Label the line by writing 30 km/hour.

b Now draw a line on the graph to represent a speed of 120 km/hour.
Label the line by writing 120 km/hour.

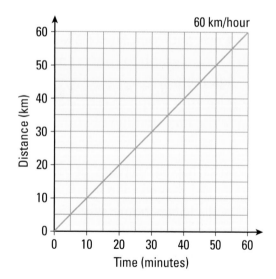

KS3 2007 4–6 Paper 1

Construction and 3-D shapes

Maps are essential for journeys. Surveying the land is the first stage in creating a map. A surveyor takes readings with a theodolite and using these measurements, it is possible to do calculations involving triangles to find the distances and heights of landmarks. This information is then used to make the scale drawing or map.

What's the point? Knowing how to make accurate measurements and drawings allows you to 'triangulate' the position of distant objects.

✓ Check in

1 Use angle properties of parallel lines to calculate the unknown angles.

a

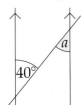

40°

a

b

140°

b

2 The radius of this circle is 8 cm.
Calculate
   a the circumference
   b the area of the circle.

8 cm

a

3 Calculate the volume of these cuboids.
State the units of your answers.

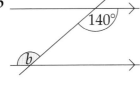

3 cm

4 cm

6 cm

6 m

2 m   2 m

14a Constructing triangles 1

- Use a ruler and a protractor to construct triangles and quadrilaterals accurately

Keywords
Congruent   Ruler
Construct   Triangle
Protractor

You can **construct** a **triangle** using a **ruler** and a **protractor**.
You always construct **congruent** triangles, when you are given either

> Congruent means the same shape and the same size.

| two angles and the included side (ASA) | or | two sides and the included angle (SAS) |

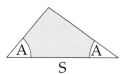 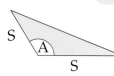

> Included means 'in between'.

example

Construct the triangle ABC so that
AC = 5 cm   angle A = 53°   angle C = 74°.

First draw a sketch of the triangle.

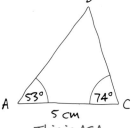 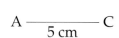 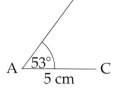 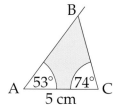

This is ASA.   Draw the base line of 5 cm using a ruler.   Draw an angle of 53° at A using a protractor.   Draw an angle of 74° at C using a protractor to complete the triangle.

example

a Construct the triangle DEF so that
DF = 4 cm   EF = 3 cm   angle F = 40°.
b Measure DE and calculate the perimeter of the triangle.

a
First draw a sketch of the triangle.

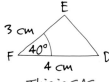 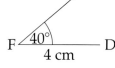 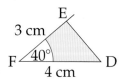

This is SAS.   Draw the base line of 4 cm using a ruler.   Draw an angle of 40° at F using a protractor.   Mark E at 3 cm from F and draw DE to complete the triangle.

b Measuring, DE is 2.6 cm.
Perimeter = 4 + 3 + 2.6 = 9.6 cm

Exercise 14a

1 Construct these triangles.
Measure and calculate the perimeter of each triangle.

a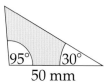

b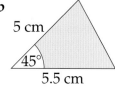

c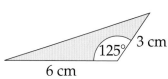

2 Construct these triangles and give the mathematical name of
each triangle.
Draw a sketch first.

a AC = 6.5 cm   angle A = 30°   angle C = 75°
b angle Q = 40°   angle R = 50°   QR = 55 mm
c EF = 7 cm   angle F = 120°   FD = 4 cm

3 Calculate the unknown angles and then construct each triangle.

a

b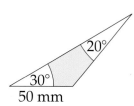

c

4 a Construct the quadrilateral.
  b Measure the four interior angles of the
    quadrilateral.
    Check that the total is 360°.
  c Measure and calculate the perimeter of the
    quadrilateral.

a Construct and cut out two congruent triangles with these dimensions.

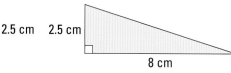

b Fit the triangles together to make a kite.
c Calculate the area of the kite.

- Use a ruler, compasses and protractor to construct triangles and quadrilaterals accurately

Keywords
Compasses Construct
Congruent Hypotenuse

You can **construct** a triangle using a ruler, **compasses** and a protractor.

You always construct **congruent** triangles, when you are given either

the length of all three sides (SSS)

or

a right-angle and the length of one side and the **hypotenuse** (RHS)

> Congruent means the same shape and the same size.

> The hypotenuse is the longest side in a right-angled triangle.

---

example

Construct the triangle ABC so that

AB = 6 cm   AC = 5 cm   BC = 4 cm.

First draw a sketch of the triangle.

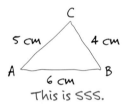

> Do not rub out the construction lines.

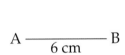

Draw the base line of 6 cm using a ruler.

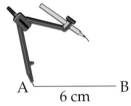

Draw an arc 5 cm from A using compasses.

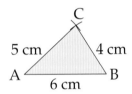

Draw an arc 4 cm from B. Draw AC and BC to complete the triangle.

---

example

Construct the triangle DEF so that

DF = 4 cm   angle F = 90°   DE = 7 cm.

First draw a sketch of the triangle.

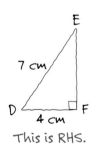

This is RHS.

Draw the base line of 4 cm using a ruler and use a protractor to draw an angle of 90° at F.

Draw an arc 7 cm from D using compasses.

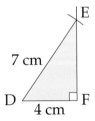

Draw DE to complete the right-angled triangle.

Exercise 14b

1 Construct these triangles, using ruler and compasses.
Measure the angles in each triangle and check that the total is 180°.

a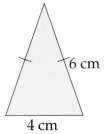
4 cm
6 cm

b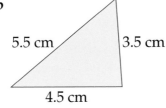
5.5 cm   3.5 cm
4.5 cm

c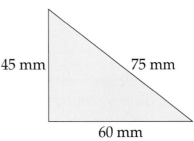
45 mm   75 mm
60 mm

2 Construct these right-angled triangles.
Draw a sketch first.

a angle C = 90°   AB = 6 cm   BC = 4 cm
b angle R = 90°   PR = 3.5 cm   PQ = 6 cm
c angle F = 90°   EF = 25 mm   DE = 55 mm

3 Construct these quadrilaterals.
Measure the length of the diagonals in each quadrilateral.

a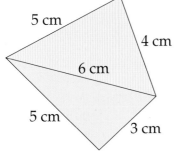
5 cm
4 cm
6 cm
5 cm
3 cm

b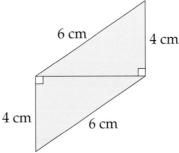
6 cm   4 cm
4 cm   6 cm

4 A 4 metre ladder is put against a wall.
The ladder is 2 metres from the wall at ground level.
a Using a scale of 1 cm to represent 50 cm,
construct a scale drawing of the ladder.
b Measure and calculate the distance of the
ladder up the wall.
c Measure the angle of the ladder to the ground.

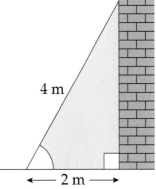
4 m
2 m

Draw a horizontal line measuring 8 cm.
Spread your compasses to a distance of 4 cm.
Use the compasses to construct the regular hexagon.
Explain why this method works.

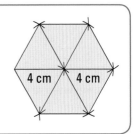
4 cm   4 cm

- Use ruler and compasses to construct the
  perpendiculars
  – from a point to a line
  – from a point on a line

Keywords
Bisector   Perpendicular
Compasses   bisector
Perpendicular

- The **perpendicular bisector** divides a straight line into two equal parts at right angles.

You can use **compasses** to construct an angle **bisector**

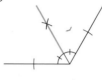

and   a line bisector.

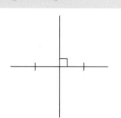

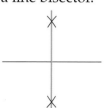

You use compasses to construct a perpendicular from a point to a line.

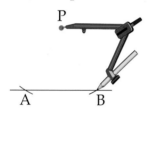

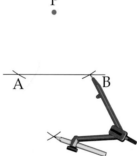

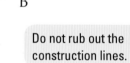

P

Perpendicular means
'at right angles'.

Do not rub out the construction lines.

Use compasses to draw arcs from P on the line.

Draw arcs from A and B that intersect at C.

Draw a line from P to C.

You use compasses to construct a perpendicular from a point on a line.

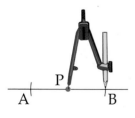

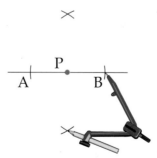

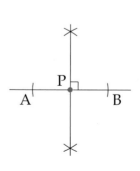

Use compasses to draw arcs from P on the line.

Draw arcs from A and B above and below the line.

Draw a line between the intersections of the arcs.

Exercise 14c

1 Draw and label these lines.

Using compasses, construct the perpendicular bisector of each line.

Use a ruler and protractor to check your answers.

a AB = 5.8 cm   **b** CD = 64 mm   **c** EF = 7.2 cm

2 Draw each angle.

Using compasses, construct the angle bisector of each angle.

Use a protractor to check your answers.

a 124°   **b** 78°   **c** 240°

3 Draw a line AB so that AB = 8 cm.

Mark the point P so that AP = 5 cm and PB = 3 cm.

Construct the perpendicular to AB that passes through the point P.

4 Draw a line AB, with a point P above the line.

  a Construct the perpendicular to AB that passes through the point P.

  b Measure the shortest distance from the point P to the line AB.

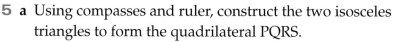

5 a Using compasses and ruler, construct the two isosceles triangles to form the quadrilateral PQRS.

  b State the mathematical name of the quadrilateral.

  c Construct the perpendicular line from P to the line SQ.

  d Extend the line to the point R and explain why the line PR is a line of symmetry.

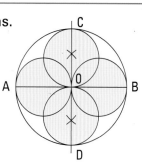

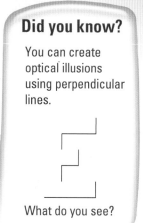
In this construction, you are not allowed to measure any lengths.

Draw a horizontal line AB.

Find the midpoint of AB by constructing the perpendicular bisector of the line.

O is the midpoint of AB.

Draw a circle with centre O passing through A, B, C and D.

Using compasses, construct the perpendicular bisectors of AO, OC, OB and OD to find four new midpoints.

Use these midpoints to draw four more circles.

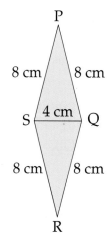

activity

- Describe a locus of a moving point and draw it accurately

Keywords

Angle bisector

Equidistant

Locus

Path

Perpendicular bisector

- The **locus** of an object is its **path**.

The locus of a windmill blade tip is a circle.

- A point that moves according to a rule forms a locus.

The points on the red circle are the same distance from the centre O.

The locus is a circle.

The points on the red line are **equidistant** from A and B.

The locus is the **perpendicular bisector** of AB.

Equidistant means 'equal distance'.

The points on the red line are equidistant from the lines OA and OB.

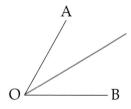

The locus is the angle bisector.

The points on the red lines are 1 cm from the line AB.

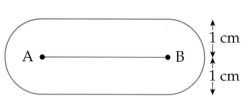

The locus is two lines each parallel to the line AB and two semicircles.

example

Construct the locus of the point that is equidistant from OA and OB.

The locus is the **angle bisector** of the angle AOB.
Use compasses to construct the angle bisector.

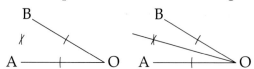

This is the angle bisector construction.

Exercise 14d

1 Draw an angle ROQ of 110°.

Using ruler and compasses, construct the locus
of the point that is equidistant from OR and OQ.

> The locus is the angle
> bisector.

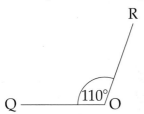

2 Two cones A and B are placed 5 metres apart.
   a Draw a scale drawing, using a scale of 1:100.
   b Using ruler and compasses, construct the locus of the
   point that is equidistant from the cones.

3 Draw the locus of a point that is 35 mm from a fixed point.

4 A straight stream is 2 metres wide.
   a Draw a scale drawing, using a scale of 1:50.
   b Draw the locus of the point that is the centre of the
   stream.

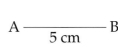

5 A triangle ABC has an area of 10 cm².
   The base of the triangle is 5 cm.
   Draw the line AB and draw the locus of the point C.

Cut out a 2 cm by 2 cm square and place it on a straight line.

The square is rotated clockwise about
the point O through an angle of 90°.

The locus of the red cross is the red curve.

The square is now rotated clockwise about the point Q, through an angle of 90°.

Draw the locus of the red cross, as the square
continues to be rotated about the right-hand
vertex on the straight line.

• Use bearings to specify direction

Keywords
Bearing   Three-figure
Direction   bearing

This indicator board shows the **direction** of places from a hill called Hampsfell in Cumbria.

The numbers are the **bearings** of places from Hampsfell.

Each number is an angle called a **three-figure bearing**.

The three-figure bearing of Wetherlam from Hampsfell is 342°.

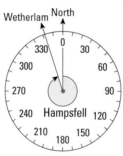

Centre your protractor on Hampsfell.

• When you use bearings
  – measure from North
  – measure in a clockwise direction
  – use three figures.

000° is always North.

---

example

Calculate the bearing of
a P from Q   **b** Q from P

· ·

a Measure the bearing from Q

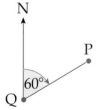

P from Q is 060°

b Measure the bearing from P

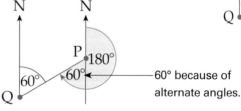

60° because of alternate angles.

Q from P is 240°

This is sometimes called the back bearing.

Notice that   60° + 180° = 240°   and   240° − 180° = 60°

You can either add or subtract 180° to find the reverse bearing.

Exercise 14e

1 Measure these three-figure bearings for towns on the Isle of Wight.

  a Sandown from Newport   **e** Newport from Ventnor

  b Freshwater from Newport   **f** Freshwater from Ventnor

  c Cowes from Newport   **g** Sandown from Ventnor

  d Ventnor from Newport

> Centre your protractor on Ventnor.

> Centre your protractor on Newport.

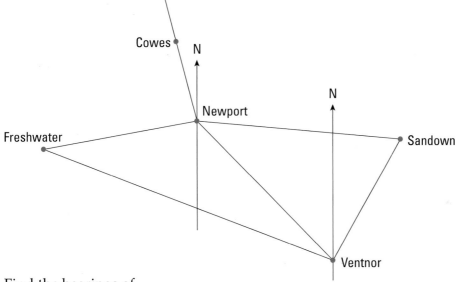

2 Find the bearings of

  a B from A   **b** D from C   **c** F from E   **d** H from G   **e** J from I

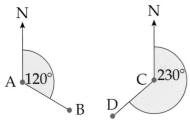 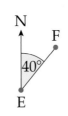 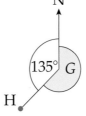 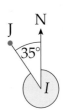

Now use the same diagrams to calculate the bearings of

  f A from B   **g** C from D   **h** E from F   **i** G from H   **j** I from J

Andy walks on a bearing of 020°.
He then turns round and returns on a bearing of 200°.

These three-figure bearings use the same digits 0, 0 and 2.

Can you find any other bearing and return bearing that
uses the same three digits?

> 020° + 180° = 200°

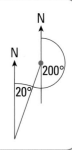

14f Circumference and area of a circle

- Calculate the circumference and area of a circle

The **circumference** (C) is the distance around a circle.

The **radius** (r) is the distance from the centre to the circumference.

The **diameter** (d) is the distance across the centre of a circle.
The diameter is twice the length of the radius: $d = 2 \times r$
You should know these formulae.

- Circumference = π × diameter $C = \pi d$

where π = 3.141 592 653 589 793 228 ...

- Area of a circle = π × radius × radius $A = \pi r^2$

---

example

The circumference of a trundle wheel is exactly 100 centimetres. Calculate the diameter of the wheel.

Take π to be 3.14

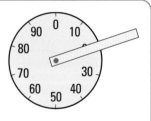

$$C = \pi d$$
$$100 = \pi d \qquad \text{The circumference is 100 cm.}$$
$$\text{and so} \quad d = \frac{100}{\pi}$$
$$d = 31.8 \text{ cm (1 dp)} \quad 100 \div 3.14 = 31.8$$

---

example

The radius of the large circle is 8 cm and the radius of the small circle is 3 cm.

Calculate the blue area.
Take π to be 3.14

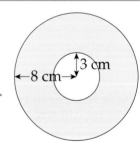

Area of the large circle $= \pi r^2$
$\qquad = 3.14 \times 8 \times 8$
$\qquad = 200.96 \text{ cm}^2$
Area of the small circle $= \pi r^2$
$\qquad = 3.14 \times 3 \times 3$
$\qquad = 28.26 \text{ cm}^2$
Area of the blue annulus = 200.96 − 28.26 = 172.7 cm^2

An annulus is the area between two circles with the same centre.

Exercise 14f

Use π = 3.14 for all the questions on this page.

1 Calculate the circumference and area of these circles.
State the units of your answers.

a
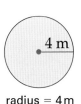
radius = 4 m

b
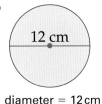
diameter = 12 cm

c

radius = 20 cm

d

diameter = 30 m

2 The minute hand of a clock is 7 cm long.
Calculate the distance the tip of the minute hand travels in
a one hour   **b** one day.

3 Toni is given a 40 centimetre length of string.
She forms a circle with the string.
Calculate
a the diameter
b the radius
c the area of the circle.

4 A square with a diagonal of length 50 cm is placed inside
a circle.
Calculate the green area.

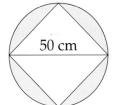

5 The radius of the large circle is 10 cm and the radius of the
small circle is 5 cm.
Calculate pink area in each diagram.

a
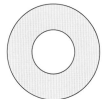

b
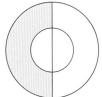

c
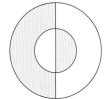

challenge

The word 'circle' is written on 1 centimetre grid paper.
Calculate the combined length of the letters.

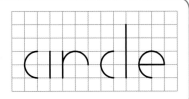

14g Surface area of a prism

- Calculate the surface area of prisms
- Recognise the net of a prism

Keywords
Cross-section   Prism
Face   Surface area
Net

- A **prism** is a solid that has the same **cross-section** throughout its length.

When you unfold a solid, the 2-D shape forms a **net**.

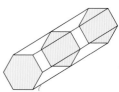

A hexagonal prism.

 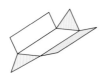

- The **surface area** of a solid is the total area of its **faces**.

The surface area of a cube is 13.5 cm².
Calculate the length of one side of the cube.

· ·

A cube has six square faces.
The area of one face = 13.5 ÷ 6 = 2.25 cm²
Length of one side = $\sqrt{2.25}$ = 1.5 cm

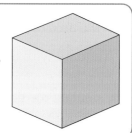

---

a Calculate the surface area of the triangular prism.
b Draw the net of the solid.

· ·

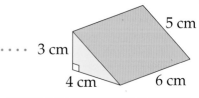

a Area of the pink rectangle = 5 × 6   = 30 cm²

Area of the green rectangle = 4 × 6   = 24 cm²

Area of the blue rectangle = 3 × 6   = 18 cm²

Area of the yellow triangle = $\frac{1}{2}$ × 3 × 4 = 6 cm²

Area of the other triangle   = $\frac{1}{2}$ × 3 × 4 = <u>6 cm²</u>

Surface area = 84 cm²

b

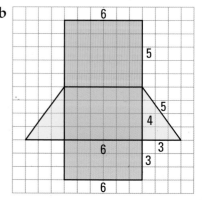

Exercise 14g

1 Calculate the surface area of each cuboid.
State the units of your answers.

a

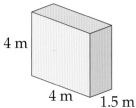

4 m

4 m   1.5 m

b

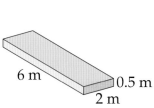

6 m

0.5 m

2 m

c

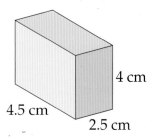

4 cm

4.5 cm   2.5 cm

2 Calculate the length of one side of a cube, if the surface
area of the cube is
   a 1350 cm^2 **b** 121.5 cm^2 **c** 6 m^2

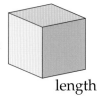

length

3 a Calculate the surface area of the triangular prism.
   b Draw a sketch of the net of the prism.

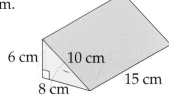

6 cm   10 cm   15 cm

8 cm

4 a Calculate the surface area of the prism.
   b Draw a sketch of the net of the prism.

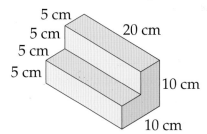

5 cm
5 cm
5 cm
5 cm

20 cm

10 cm

10 cm

5 A cube has a length of *l*.
Calculate the surface area of the cube in terms of *l*.

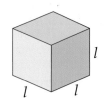

l

l   *l*

The surface area of each cuboid is 78 cm^2.

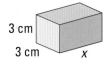

3 cm
3 cm   *x*

1 cm
4 cm   *y*

1 cm
3 cm   *z*

Find the values of *x*, *y* and *z*.

Clues:
x, *y* and *z* form a
mathematical sequence.

x, *y* and *z* are all less
than 10.

- Calculate the volume of simple right prisms

Keywords
Cross-section Prism
Cubic Volume
centimetre
(cm^3)

- The **volume** is the amount of space inside a 3-D shape.

You measure volume in cubic units: a cubic millimetre (mm^3)
a **cubic centimetre (cm^3)**
a cubic metre (m^3).

- Volume of a cuboid = length × width × height

This is the same as Volume = width × height × length
= area of **cross-section** × length

- Volume of a **prism** = area of cross-section × length

---

example

The area of cross-section of a prism is $14\,m^2$.
The length of the prism is 3.5 metres.
Calculate the volume of the prism.

. . . .

Volume of a prism = area of cross-section × length
= 14 × 3.5
= $49\,m^3$

The units of volume are cubic metres.

---

example

Calculate **a** the area of cross-section
b the volume of the prism.

. . . .

a Area of the red triangle = $\frac{1}{2}$ × 6 × 5 = $15\,cm^2$
b Volume of the prism = area of cross-section × length
= 15 × 8 = $120\,cm^3$

The units of volume are cubic centimetres.

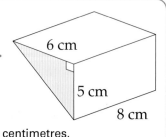

Exercise 14h

1 A cuboid container has dimensions 12.2 m by 2.4 m by 2.6 m.

   a Calculate the volume of the container.

   A container ship carries 5000 of these containers.

   b Calculate the volume of all the containers.

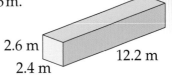

2.6 m

2.4 m

12.2 m

2 Two steps are made in the shape of a prism.

   a Calculate the area of the green shape

   b Calculate the volume of the prism.

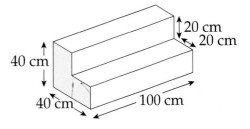

20 cm
20 cm
40 cm
40 cm
100 cm

3 A door wedge is shown.

   a State the mathematical name of the shape.

   b Calculate

     i the area of the triangle

     ii the volume of the wedge.

5 cm

8 cm

6 cm

4 The nets of two prisms are shown.
Calculate the volume of each prism.

   a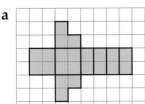

   b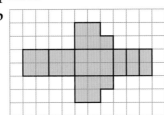

5 A step-up is made in the shape of a prism.
The cross-section is an isosceles trapezium.

   a Calculate the area of the trapezium.

   b Calculate the volume of the prism.

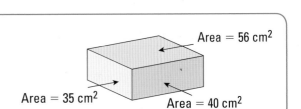

20 cm
15 cm
60 cm
40 cm

6 A cylinder has a length of 15 cm and a radius of 5 cm.
Calculate

   a the area of the circle   Use π = 3.14

   b the volume of the cylinder.

5 cm

15 cm

---

puzzle

A cuboid has faces with areas of
35 cm², 40 cm² and 56 cm².
Find the volume of the cuboid.

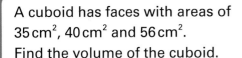

Area = 56 cm²

Area = 35 cm²

Area = 40 cm²

14a

1 Construct these triangles.

a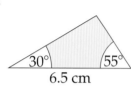

b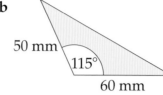

c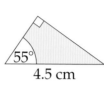

14b

2 Construct these nets, using ruler and compasses.
Each triangle is equilateral.
State the name of the 3-D shape formed by the net.

a
b

14c

3 Draw a horizontal line and a point P above the line.

a Using compasses, construct the perpendicular to the line passing through P.
b Label your diagram A, B, P and C as shown.
c What is the mathematical name of the quadrilateral APBC?
d Explain why this construction gives a perpendicular line.

14d

4 A goat is tethered to a post with a 3 metre length of rope.

a Using a scale of 1:100, draw a scale drawing showing all the grass the goat can reach to eat.
b The goat is now tethered with the same rope to a wall.
Draw another scale drawing with the same scale, showing all the grass the goat can now eat.

3 m

5 The map shows three villages in Derbyshire.
Measure the bearing of

a Baslow from Bakewell

b Ashford from Bakewell
Centre your protractor at Bakewell.

c Baslow from Ashford
Centre your protractor at Ashford.

d Bakewell from Baslow

e Ashford from Baslow.
Centre your protractor at Baslow.

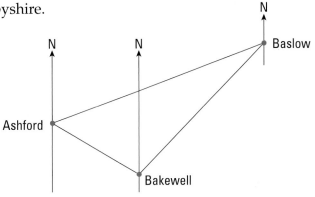

6 A circle has a circumference of 3 metres.
Calculate the diameter of the circle.
Give your answer to a suitable degree of accuracy.

Use π = 3.14

7 Calculate the shaded areas.

a

b

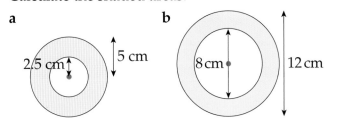

2.5 cm   5 cm

8 cm   12 cm

8 a Find the nine possible cuboids that can be made using 48 one-centimetre cubes.

b Calculate the surface area of each cuboid.

c Which cuboid has the largest surface area?

d Which cuboid has the smallest surface area?

9 A chocolate box has a cross-section of an equilateral triangle.

a State the mathematical name of the solid.

b Draw a sketch of the net, showing the dimensions.

c Calculate

  i the surface area

  ii the volume of the solid.

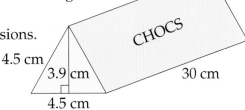

4.5 cm

3.9 cm

4.5 cm

30 cm

Assessment criteria
- Know and use the formulae for the circumference and area of a circle **Level 6**
- Calculate the surface area and volume of a prism **Level 7**

Level 7

1 Calculate the volume of the triangular prism.

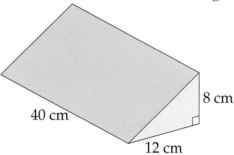

40 cm 12 cm 8 cm

Sarah's answer ✔

| Sarah knows area is measured in cm². | Area of the triangle $= \frac{1}{2} \times$ base $\times$ perpendicular height $= \frac{1}{2} \times 12 \times 8$ $= 48\ cm^2$ | Sarah first calculates the area of the cross-section. |

Volume of the prism $=$ area of cross-section $\times$ length
$=$ area of triangle $\times$ length
$= 48 \times 40$
$= 1920\ cm^3$

She knows volume is measured in cm³.

Level 7

2 The diagram shows two circles and a square, ABCD.
A and B are the centres of the circles.
The radius of each circle is 5 cm.

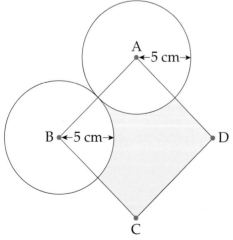

A ←5 cm→

B ←5 cm→ D

C

Calculate the area of the shaded part of the square.

KS3 2005 5–7 Paper 2

Analysing and interpreting data

Every ten years, since 1801, the government has carried out a census of everybody in England and Wales. In it people are asked about where they live, their family, ethnicity, religion, job, health, etc.

This generates a huge amount of data that is used by government to plan for the future.

What's the point? You cannot hope to look at each individual piece of data. Instead you must use statistics to summarise the data and to draw sensible conclusions from it.

✔ Check in

1 For the data below, find the
   a mean   **b** median   **c** mode   **d** range.
      5, 7, 6, 5, 9, 4

2 For the data in the table, draw
   a a bar chart   **b** a pie chart.

Number of children in family	One	Two	Three
Frequency	3	9	6

1 person = 20°

- Find the median, modal class and range for grouped
  frequency tables

p. 172

Keywords
Grouped   Modal class
frequency   Mode
table   Range
Median

For large data samples, summary statistics are used to
investigate the overall picture of what is happening.

Examples include averages and measures of spread.

- The **mode** is the data value that occurs most often.
- The **median** is the middle value when the data are
  arranged in order.
- The **range** is the difference between the highest and
  lowest data values.

The range is sensitive to
unusual values and so
only provides a rough
idea of the data's spread.

example

Find the mode, median
and range of this data on
the price of chocolate bars.
50p, 56p, 30p, £1.20, 60p,
45p, £1.10, 60p, 30p, 60p

Order the list   Convert all prices to pence.
30, 30, 45, 50, 56, 60, 60, 60, 110, 120
Mode = 60p
Median = $\frac{(56 + 60)}{2}$ = 58p
Range = 120 − 30 = 90p

An even number of data
values, therefore use the
middle of the two central
values for the median.

- For large data sets, a **grouped frequency table** is used to
  organise the data into more manageable intervals.

By doing this we lose
detail but make the data
easier to understand.

example

The table shows the resting pulse rates of a number of Year 8 students.

Pulse rate, p	$60 \leq p < 65$	$65 \leq p < 70$	$70 \leq p < 75$	$75 \leq p < 80$	$80 \leq p < 85$
Frequency	6	14	35	22	8

For this data, what can you say about the   **a** median   **b** mode   **c** range?

a Number of students = 6 + 14 + 35 + 22 + 8 = 85
  The median will be the pulse rate of the 43rd student in an ordered list. $\frac{(85 + 1)}{2}$ = 43
  We don't know this value but we know that it lies in the interval $70 \leq p < 75$.
b It is not possible to say which pulse rate occurs most often
  but we can say that the class interval $70 \leq p < 75$ contains most entries.
c It is not possible to say what are the actual highest and lowest pulse rates
  but we can estimate the range as 85 − 60 = 25; this is its largest possible value.

- The **modal class** is the interval with the highest frequency.
  For the data on resting pulse rates, the modal class is $70 \leq p < 75$.

Exercise 15a

1 Find the mode, median and range of these lengths.
45 cm, 26 cm, 1.11 m, 70 cm, 0.45 m, 0.9 m,
650 mm, 80 cm, 1.2 m, 60 cm, 1.45 m, 145 mm

2 The table shows the times taken, in minutes, for a group
of Year 8 students to complete a Sudoku puzzle.

Time, t	$0 \leq t < 5$	$5 \leq t < 10$	$10 \leq t < 15$	$15 \leq t < 20$
Frequency	2	18	12	3

  a Find the modal class for the time taken to solve the puzzle.
  b Find the class containing the median time taken to solve the puzzle.
  c Find the range of the times taken to solve the puzzle.

3 Louise is going to Africa to do some volunteer work. A number of her friends
decide to do a sponsored walk to raise money for her. The amounts they raised are
listed below (in £).

45, 58, 62, 46, 35, 72, 65, 46, 40, 82, 39, 46, 52
58, 43, 45, 49, 56, 47, 48, 49, 76, 62, 67, 54, 48

  a Construct a frequency table with intervals
    30−39, 40−49, 50−59, 60−69, 70−79 and 80−89.
  b Find the modal class for the amount raised.
  c Find the class containing the median amount raised.
  d Find the actual median from the list of values.

4 The table shows the times taken, in minutes, for people doing a 5 km fun run.

Time, t	$10 \leq t < 15$	$15 \leq t < 20$	$20 \leq t < 25$	$25 \leq t < 30$	$30 \leq t < 35$
Frequency	345	598	2007	865	84

  a Find the modal class for the time taken.
  b Find the class containing the median time.
  c Find the range of the times taken.

A teacher set a maths exam at the end of the year. The marks went from 22 to 80
with a median of 57. She decided that the exam was harder than in previous years
so she would add 10 to each mark. Discuss whether the following statements must
be true, must be false, or could be either.
  a The median does not change but the range increases by 10.
  b The range does not change but the median increases by 10.
  c The highest mark will be 88.

discussion

- Find the mean for a list of numbers
- Find the mean from a frequency table

Keywords
Frequency table
Mean

- The **mean** is the total of the data values divided by the number of values.

example

Calculate the mean of these lengths.

1.05 m, 102 cm, 99 cm, 1050 mm, 0.98 m, 103 cm

. . . .

Number of measurements = 6

Sum of lengths = $105 + 102 + 99 + 105 + 98 + 103 = 612$ cm

Mean = $\frac{612}{6}$ cm

= 102 cm

Use the same units for all measurements.

Sometimes it is easier to do the calculation by subtracting a common value.

Mean = $100 + \frac{(5 + 2 - 1 + 5 - 2 + 3)}{6} = 100 + \frac{12}{6} = 102$ cm

When you have a lot of data it is helpful to organise it using a **frequency table**.

example

The list shows the number of radios that are in the homes of Mrs Bowler's Year 8 form class.

2, 3, 1, 2, 0, 1, 5, 2, 3, 1, 2, 3, 2, 1, 0,

0, 2, 3, 1, 1, 1, 1, 2, 5, 2, 3, 2, 0, 2, 3

Calculate the mean number of radios per household.

. . . .

Number of radios, n	Tally	Frequency, f	$n \times f$
0	||||	4	0
1	卌 |||	8	8
2	卌 ||||	10	20
3	卌 ||	6	18
4		0	0
5	||	2	10
Total		30	56

Mean = $\dfrac{\text{total number of radios}}{\text{total number of households}}$

= $\frac{56}{30}$

= $1.8\dot{6} = 1.9$ (1 dp)

Exercise 15b

1 Calculate the mean of these weights.

813 g, 807 g, 0.81 kg, 796 g, 0.817 kg, 800 g

2 A tailor will not throw away material if there is
at least 20 cm left on the roll. The table shows the
lenghts, to the nearest 5 cm, of the bits thrown away
at the end of 30 rolls.

Length, l	Frequency, n
0	7
5	10
10	6
15	5
20	2

  a Find the mean length thrown away at the end of a roll.
  b Is your calculation of the mean exact or is it an estimate?
    Explain your answer.

3 The list shows the number of televisions that are in the homes
of Mrs Bowler's Year 8 form class.

2, 3, 2, 4, 1, 3, 6, 0, 4, 3, 3, 4, 1, 3, 2,
1, 2, 0, 1, 5, 3, 4, 3, 2, 4, 3, 3, 1, 2, 4

  a Construct a frequency table and hence calculate the mean
    number of televisions per household.
  b Comment on the distributions of radios, from the example,
    and televisions in the households.

4 The table shows the times taken, to the nearest 5 minutes,
for the people taking part in a 5 km fun run.

Time, t	15	20	25	30	35
Frequency	345	598	2007	865	84

You may use a calculator.

Calculate the mean time taken for the fun run.

> Look back at the discussion question on the last spread. There is no information at all
> about the mean mark on the actual examination.
>
> Can you say anything at all about the revised mean after the teacher has changed
> the marks?

- Learn how to interpret comparative graphs of statistical data

- Two sets of data can be **compared** using a back-to-back **stem-and-leaf diagram**.

p. 174

example

The pulse rates of a group of Year 8 students are taken before exercise when they are resting, and again after 5 minutes of brisk exercise.

Before exercise		After exercise	
(2)	9 7 | 6 |		(0)
(6)	8 6 6 3 2 1 | 7 | 8		(1)
(6)	7 7 5 4 1 0 | 8 | 0 3 5 6 6 9		(6)
(2)	0 0 | 9 | 0 1 1 8 8 9		(6)
(0)	| 10 | 0 1 3		(3)

Key
1| 8 |5 means
81 before exercise
85 after exercise

For each data set, find **a** the range **b** the median.
Comment on what you find.

....

a range $= 23 = 90 - 67$ range $= 25$ $= 103 - 78$

b median $= 79 = \dfrac{(78 + 80)}{2}$ median $= 90.5 = \dfrac{(90 + 91)}{2}$

The mode is not defined for either data set.

The pulse rates before exercise are lower on average than the rates after the exercise, and there is a similar spread for the two sets of data.

- **Pie charts** are a good way to compare proportions.

They do not tell you about the actual numbers in a category.

School A, Key Stage 3, Maths

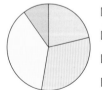

- ☐ Level 4
- ☐ Level 5
- ☐ Level 6
- ☐ Level 7

School B, Key Stage 3, Maths

- ☐ Level 4
- ☐ Level 5
- ☐ Level 6
- ☐ Level 7

School B may have twice as many pupils as school A.

It is important to know what you are and are not allowed to conclude.

True	**Not necessarily true**
School A has larger proportions achieving higher KS3 results.	School A has more level 6s than School B.
	School A is better than school B.

This depends on the school's intake: A may be a grammar school and B an inner city comprehensive school.

Exercise 15c

1 The lists show the times taken, in seconds, to run 100 metres for a men's squad and a ladies' squad at a football club.

Men
13.3, 12.7, 11.7, 14.2, 13.7,
12.7, 13.6, 13.0, 13.6, 13.0,
12.8, 14.1, 12.1, 12.4, 12.2,
11.9

Ladies
14.3, 14.6, 16.0, 13.2, 13.7,
13.7, 14.8, 15.6, 12.8, 15.5,
13.5, 14.5, 14.2, 13.9, 14.0,
13.6

a Draw a back-to-back stem-and-leaf diagram for the two data sets.
b Find the median time for the two squads.
c Compare the times taken by the two squads.

2 The pie charts show the ages of guests at two camp sites.

Ages of guests at camp A

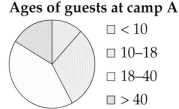

- □ < 10
- □ 10–18
- □ 18–40
- □ > 40

Ages of guests at camp B

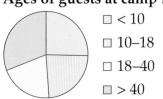

- □ < 10
- □ 10–18
- □ 18–40
- □ > 40

a Compare the proportions of different ages at the two sites.
b Katie has 2 children aged 5 and 7. She decides to send them to camp B because she thinks there will be more young children there. Explain why she cannot be sure of this.

3 Data on the Key Stage 3 Maths results for a school and for the county that it is in are summarised in the table.

	Level 4	Level 5	Level 6	Level 7
School	15	45	25	35
County	254	481	180	134

Hint: for each level, write the number of entries as a fraction of the total and take this proportion of 360°.

a Draw pie charts to show the school's results and the county's results.
b Compare the performance of the school in maths with the general performance in the county.

discussion

The actual numbers for the pie charts in the example on the page opposite are given in the table.

	Level 4	Level 5	Level 6	Level 7	Total
School A	26	38	45	12	121
School B	22	25	19	8	74

Can you think of how you might draw pie charts which would allow you to compare not only the proportions but also the actual numbers at the different levels?

- Compare groups of data on a scatter graph
- Identify regular patterns and long-term trends in time series data

Keywords
Scatter graph *Trend*
Time series *Variation*

- Pairs of variables can be plotted as coordinates in a **scatter graph.**

To plot more than one set of data on the same scatter graph, use different colours or symbols.

This scatter graph shows the times taken to complete the 100 m and 200 m by members of an athletics club and a soccer team.

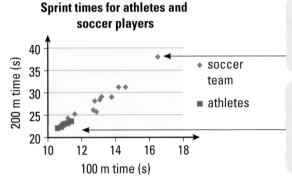

For both groups, the time for the 200 m tends to be just over twice the time for 100 m.

This soccer player ran the 100 m in 16.5 s and the 200 m in 38.0 s. It is plotted at (16.5, 38.0).

The athletes' performances on both events are much more similar than the performances of the players on the soccer team.

- For a variable measured over a period of time a scatter graph, with time as the horizontal axis, is called a **time series** plot.

  p. 176

  Such graphs can be used to identify regular patterns, which repeat over time, and more long-term **trends**.

Describe any patterns in this data for a household's electricity bill.
Comment on
a the short-term (yearly) **variation**
b the long-term variation.

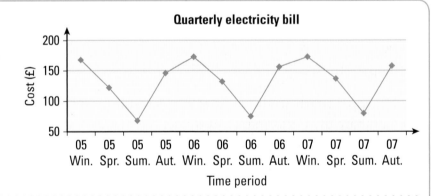

a Electricity bills are highest in Winter, reduce in Spring, are lowest in Summer and rise in Autumn. This is a regular annual pattern.
b Comparing equivalent quarterly electricity bills, the year-on-year trend is upward indicating rising electricity costs.

Exercise 15d

1 A medical student finds some data on the blood pressures, given in mmHg, of a number of men and women, taken in 1993.

	Age (years)	18	22	27	31	33	35	39	41	46	46	48	52	57	64	69
Men	Blood pressure	64	68	67	71	74	73	77	79	85	81	83	81	86	84	87
Women	Age (years)	17	19	23	35	37	39	41	44	47	51	55	61	63	67	70
	Blood pressure	66	67	67	74	75	76	76	79	78	78	80	79	81	82	32

a Plot a scatter graph to show the men's and women's data.

b Describe any trend you see in blood pressures as men get older.

c The medical student thinks that a data pair was misrecorded. Which point do you think it is and what may have happened?

d Do you think there was any difference between the blood pressures of men and women in 1993?

> Use different symbols or colours for the men's and women's data points.

2 The medical student thinks that typical blood pressures are falling. She also has some data for men, taken in 2005.

Age (years)	19	23	25	30	34	36	39	41	44	46	49	53	56	62	66
Blood pressure	65	68	69	73	74	75	74	76	75	76	75	79	75	74	76

Plot this data on a new scatter graph, using the same scales as in question **1** and comment on any differences in blood pressures between 1993 and 2005?

3 The graph below shows the number of minutes Sasha has used her mobile phone for in one billing period, which started on a Tuesday.

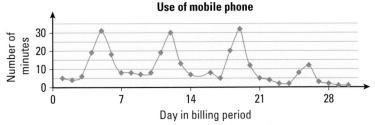

Use of mobile phone

a Describe any patterns you see in the use of her phone.

b Her contract includes 300 free minutes in each billing period. She checks her account online after 20 days and sees that she has used 266 minutes already. Comment on what the graph tells you about her use of the phone for the rest of the month.

> **Did you know?**
>
>
>
> Predicting the future behaviour of time series is very important in business; and profitable for mathematicians.

task

a Can you improve on what the medical student did to investigate if the population's blood pressure had decreased between 1993 and 2005?

b Can you think of any reasons why such an improvement might have taken place?

15e Correlation

• Learn how to identify different forms of correlation

Keywords

Correlation   Positive
Moderate   Scatter
Negative   graph
No correlation

• **Correlation** is a way of describing any linear association there is between the two variables in a **scatter graph**.

    The closer the data is to lying on a straight line, the stronger is the correlation.

> Players who were quick over 100 m also tended to be quick over 200 m.

The 100 m and 200 m sprint times for the soccer team, in spread **15d,** show a **strong positive correlation**.

High values of the two variables occur together as do low values.

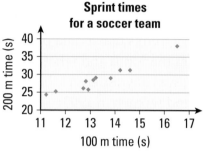

Sprint times for a soccer team

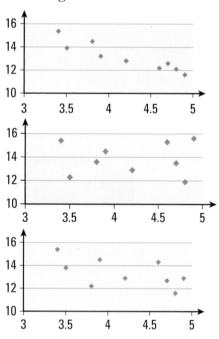

When the trend is decreasing, there is **negative correlation** between the variables.

When no trend is obvious, there is **no correlation** between the variables.

If there is an obvious downward trend, but the values are not so close to a straight line, there is a **moderate** negative correlation.

When there is a strong relationship between two variables, but it is not a straight-line relationship, we do not talk about correlation at all.

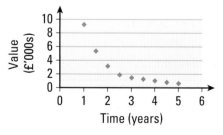

> A car's value will decrease over time, but not in a straight line if you plot value against time.

Exercise 15e

1 The scatter graph shows the age at marriage of a number of married couples.

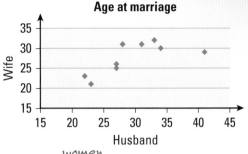

Age at marriage

a Describe the correlation between the ages of the husband and the wife for these married couples.

b Copy and complete this sentence by filling in appropriate words in the blank spaces.

In this group, older men tend to marry _____ women, and younger men tend to marry _____ women.

2 For these diagrams, describe any correlation you see.

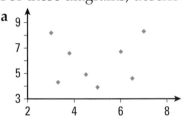

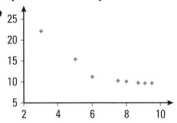

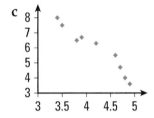

3 The table shows the performances of 10 athletes in three of the events in a decathlon competition.

	A	B	C	D	E	F	G	H	I	J
100 m (s)	11.25	11.30	11.4	11.45	11.50	11.50	11.60	11.7	11.73	11.90
Long jump (m)	6.78	6.67	6.56	6.68	6.40	6.37	6.25	6.38	6.11	6.15
Shot-put (m)	11.20	11.45	11.65	11.80	12.10	11.28	11.90	12.06	11.78	11.93

a Draw a scatter graph showing the times for the 100 m on the horizontal axis, and the distances for the shot-put on the vertical axes.

> Use a vertical scale that starts at 0 and goes up to at least 12.

b On the same scatter graph, using a different colour or symbol, plot the long jump distances against the times for the 100 m.

c Describe the correlation between the times for the 100 m and the distances thrown in the shot-put and the correlation between performances in the 100 m and the long jump.

Use the data and your scatter graphs for question **3** for these questions.

a Which athlete was quickest in the 100 m?

b Taking the 100 m and the long jump together, which athletes do you think were the best and worst over the two events. Give reasons for your answers.

c Taking the three events together who were the best and worst athletes? Give reasons.

• Compare distributions using statistical measures

Keywords
Mean   Range
Median

• You can calculate statistics to summarise and make comparisons for the data.

example

The depth of water (in m) at a number of high tides is measured in early February and in late March.

| Early February | 3.5 | 3.7 | 3.6 | 3.7 | 3.8 | 3.5 | 3.8 | 3.7 | 3.7 | 3.6 |
| Late March | 3.8 | 3.9 | 4.1 | 3.8 | 3.9 | 4.7 | 4.0 | 3.9 | 3.9 | 4.0 |

a For each month, calculate
  i the **mean**   ii the **median**   iii the **range**.
b Use this information to compare the two distributions.
c Comment on the effect of the very high tide (4.7 m) on the results for late March.

a

	i mean	ii median	iii range
Feb.	$3.66 = \frac{36.6}{10}$	3.7	$0.3 = 3.8 - 3.5$
Mar.	$4.0 = \frac{40.0}{10}$	3.9	$0.9 = 4.7 - 3.8$

b The averages show that the tides in late March were generally higher than in early February. The range in late March is much larger than in early February.
c The very high tide has a large effect on the range, which is sensitive to exceptional values.
It also makes a significant contribution to the mean but less so to the median. This causes a noticeable difference between the two averages.

An average should indicate a typical central value for a data set.
If the data contains unusual values or is not symmetrical then the median is more likely to give a more representative value.

• Using summary statistics to make large data sets more manageable means that, possibly important information is lost.
In the example, quoting the range, mean and median does not tell us that every early February tide is lower than every late March tide.

Exercise 15f

	Mean	Range
Before	35.4	15.2
After	48.1	12.3

1 A training programme is designed to improve memory. To assess its effectiveness, tests were carried out before and after the training for 14 participants.

    a Compare the performance on the two tests.

    b Do you think this provides strong evidence that the training is effective in improving memory?

2 A nurse records the LDL cholesterol levels and the gender of all the patients she sees during a morning surgery.

> F3.7 means a female patient with a cholesterol level of 3.7.

  F3.7, M3.2, M2.8, M3.1, F3.6, F3.4, F3.7, M3.1, F3.6, M3.2, M3.7, M3.1, M3.5, M3.1, F3.5, F3.1, F3.7, F3.1, M3.6, M3.1, M 3.1, F3.4

    a Find the median cholesterol levels for male and female patients seen that morning.

    b Compare the cholesterol levels for these male and female patients.

3 The road safety officer in a large town collects information on the speeds of cars when they are 50 m from two sets of traffic lights.

Speed, v (mph)	$20 \leq v < 25$	$25 \leq v < 30$	$30 \leq v < 35$	$35 \leq v < 40$	$40 \leq v < 45$
Frequency at set A	7	28	6	1	0
Frequency at set B	0	12	15	8	4

Set A is on a stretch of road with warnings about the presence of speed cameras.
Set B is on a similar road that does not have speed cameras.

    a Find the intervals which contain the median speed approaching each set of traffic lights.

    b Find the range of the speeds approaching each set of traffic lights.

    c Compare the speeds of the cars approaching the two sets of traffic lights.

---

task

If a local politician visited the surgery and saw the data described in question **2**, why should he not take these medians as estimates of the median LDL cholesterol levels for males and females in his constituency?

1 Two friends wash cars on Saturday mornings, charging £2 for small cars and £3 for larger cars. These are the amounts (in £) they collect over a six-month period.

| 48, 54, 82, 75, 64, 41, |
| 85, 76, 34, 48, 46, 71, |
| 63, 86, 71, 59, 64, 38, |
| 47, 51, 56, 78, 83, 57, |
| 53, 46 |

  a Construct a frequency table with amounts 30−39, 40−49, 50−59, 60−69, 70−79 and 80−89.
  b Find the modal class for the amount they collect.
  c Find the class containing the median amount collected.
  d Find the actual median from the list of values.

2 The table shows the times taken, in minutes, for a group of Year 8 students to complete a cross-country run.

Time, t	$10 \leq t < 12$	$12 \leq t < 14$	$14 \leq t < 16$	$16 \leq t < 18$	$18 \leq t < 20$
Frequency	7	24	15	6	2

  a Find the modal class for the time taken for the run.
  b Find the class containing the median time taken for the run.
  c Find the range of the times taken for the run.

3 Sally sells some raffle tickets. Using the table calculate the mean number sold per person.

Number of tickets	1	2	3	4	5
Frequency	8	5	2	1	9

4 Data is collected on the distances in miles driven in a week by a number of people.

Females
97, 82, 86, 89, 92, 77, 104, 85, 84, 91, 80, 86, 95, 101

Males
102, 121, 93, 86, 112, 100, 107, 109, 109, 103, 117, 94, 93, 114, 91, 98

  a Draw a back-to-back stem-and-leaf diagram for these two data sets.
  b Find the median distance driven for females and males.
  c Compare the distances driven by females and males.

5 100 people in London and in Belfast were asked to choose which food they preferred. The results are shown in the pie charts.

London

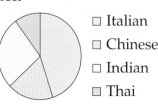

☐ Italian
☐ Chinese
☐ Indian
☐ Thai

Belfast

☐ Italian
☐ Chinese
☐ Indian
☐ Thai

Compare the food preferences of people in London and Belfast.

6 Karim runs a newsagent which sells CDs. The time series graph shows the number sold recently in each quarter. Describe two features of the graph.

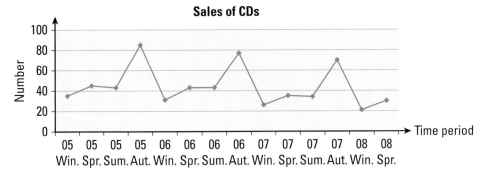

7 Sketch three scatter graphs showing these types of correlation.

   a strong negative   **b** none   **c** weak positive

8 The scatter graph shows the marks scored by a number of pupils in examinations in maths and in biology.

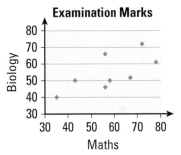

   a Describe the correlation between the marks obtained in the two subjects.

   b Copy and complete the following sentence by filling in appropriate words in the blank spaces.

In this group of pupils, those who score high marks in maths tend to score _____ marks in biology and pupils who score low marks in maths tend to score _____ marks in biology.

9 A training programme is designed to improve a school athlete's technique in the javelin. The table shows a summary of samples of 10 throws taken before and after the athlete follows the training programme.

	Mean	Range
Before	51.3	4.2
After	56.4	3.1

   a Compare his performance before and after the training.

   b Do you think this provides strong evidence that the training is effective in improving his technique?

10 A careers teacher has collected data from some sixth form pupils who left school to start a job on whether they did A-level maths and their starting salary (in £'000s).

   a Find the median starting salaries for the two groups.

   b Is it reasonable to say that on average people with an A-level in maths earn more than those without one?

> Y15.7, N13.7, Y13.5, Y14.2,
> N14.0, Y14.8, Y13.9, N13.7,
> Y13.9, N14.2, Y14.6, Y13.9,
> N13.8, N14.3, Y14.8, Y13.9,
> Y15.1, N13.6, Y14.3, Y14.1

> Y15.7 means yes did A-level maths, starting salary £15.7k.

Energy in the home

With headlines and adverts like the ones here, it's no surprise that people are looking at alternative forms of energy and other ways of saving energy in their homes.

Solar power

Save up to 70% on your yearly hot water bill.
Use an everlasting FRE source of energy!
Save money on you electricity bill forev
Cut your CO_2 emissi

ELECTRICITY PRICE SHOCK!

Oil cost hits new high

Gas price explodes

➡ Look at all the items with the green labels and, for each one, work out roughly how long it would take for the savings in costs to repay the cost of installing the item.

➡ Which things do you think are most cost effective?

➡ Which are not so cost effective?

➡ Would the length of time you are going to live in the same house alter the decisions you might make about any of the items?

➡ What things other than cost might affect your decisions?

Loft insulation
Cost £200 – £350
Save £100 – £200 per year

Lagging hot water tank
Cost £15 – £20
Save £40 – £50 per year

Efficient A rated boiler
Cost £1500 – £2000
Save £100 – £150 per year

New heating controls
Cost £150
Save £30 – £50 per year

Ground based heat pump
Cost £7000 – £12000
Save £400 – £800 per year

Double glazing to replace single glazing
Cost £2500 – £3500
Save £50 – £100 per year

An average house uses about 3.5 MW of electricity averaged over the year.

A 1kWp photovoltaic solar system will generate approximately 750kWh of electricity averaged over a year.

➔ How much would it cost to install photovoltaic panels to meet all the electricity demands of the house?

➔ What would be the cost savings over a year?

➔ How long would it take to recover the cost of the panels? What might happen to make this time shorten?

Small wind generator
Cost £2500 – £5000
Save ???
There is much debate about the effectiveness of small rooftop wind turbines.

Solar water heating
Cost £2500 – £5000
Save £50 – £100 per year

Photovoltaic solar panel to generate electricity
Cost £5000 – £6000 per kWp (kW peak)
Save £120 per kWp

Energy efficient light bulbs

An 18W energy efficient bulb costs £1.49 and gives light equivalent to a 100W standard bulb.

A 100W standard light bulb costs £0.39

Electricity costs 11p per kWh (kW x hours)

➔ How much will one energy efficient bulb save over a year? You will need to decide how many hours on average the light might be on each year.

Cavity wall insulation
Cost £200 – £350
Save £100 – £200 per year

Draught proofing
Cost £80 – £120
Save £25 – £50 per year

1kWh is the amount of electricity to run something that uses 1000W for 1 hour.
100W= 0.1kW so a 100W bulb uses 0.1kWh
1kWh will run a 100W light bulb for 10 hours.
1 Megawatt = 1000 kW

Assessment criteria
- Use scatter graphs to develop further understanding of correlation **Level 6**
- Communicate interpretations and results of a statistical survey **Level 6**

Level 6

1 There are several rose plants in my garden.
Each plant has at least one flower.
Altogether there are 20 flowers on the rose plants.
a Write the missing frequency in the table below.

Number of flowers on one plant	Number of plants
1	
2	3
3	3
4	1

b Calculate the mean number of flowers on each plant.

Pablo's answer ✔

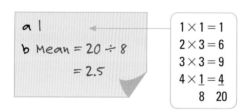

a 1

b Mean = 20 ÷ 8
  = 2.5

$1 \times 1 = 1$
$2 \times 3 = 6$
$3 \times 3 = 9$
$4 \times 1 = \underline{4}$
$\quad\quad 8 \quad 20$

Level 6

2 The scatter graph shows 15 pupils' coursework and test marks.

To find a pupil's total mark, you add the coursework mark to the test mark.
a Which pupil had the highest total mark?
b Look at the statement below. Tick (√) True or False.

> The range of coursework marks was greater than the range of test marks.

☐ True   ☐ False
Explain your answer.

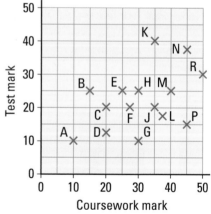

KS3 2006 4–6 Paper 1

16 Number

Calculation plus

Financial markets trade almost everything from commodities, like oil and wheat, through company shares, to money itself.

Individual traders do deals by agreeing how much to buy, when and at what price. They need to be able to think fast to get a good deal.

What's the point? Traders need to be able to calculate quickly and accurately as errors can cost millions.

Check in

1 Calculate these using an appropriate method.
   a 5.42 + 324.9 + 8
   b 44.7 + 198.5 − 38.6
   c 528.38 − 129.7 − 32 − 0.78
   d 456.97 + 99.99 − 1.99

2 Calculate these using a written method.
   Remember to do a mental approximation first.
   a 13 × 4.68   **b** 47 × 4.95   **c** 5.3 × 49.6   **d** 57.3 × 0.85

3 Calculate these using an appropriate method.
   Give your answer as a decimal to 1 dp where appropriate.
   a 563 ÷ 3.8   **b** 922 ÷ 4.8   **c** 722 ÷ 1.9   **d** 697 ÷ 4.1

- Consolidate and extend a range of mental strategies for addition and subtraction
- Make and justify estimates and approximations
- Identify the information necessary to solve a problem

Keywords
Approximate
Estimate
Information

- Always make an **approximation** before you try to solve a problem involving addition and subtraction.

p. 116

example

Barry wins £5000 on the lottery.
He decides to buy these three items.
How much money does he have left?

holiday £3842   jacket £95   photo £8

. . . .

Approximate

Total cost = £3842 + £95 + £8 ≈ £3900 + £100 + £10
= £4010

Money left ≈ £5000 − £4010 = £990

> Approximate by rounding appropriately.

Calculate, using mental methods

Total cost = £3842 + £95 + £8 = £3945

Money left = £5000 − £3945 = £1055

> Check calculation and **estimate** agree.

- Write the **information** you know and the information you are trying to find out when solving a problem.

  This makes it easier to solve the problem by changing it into a calculation.

example

Here are the distances in kilometres between six towns.

Helen walks from Aley to Bright to Deeton to Fite.
Jenny walks from Aley to Ceough to Esville to Fite.
Who walks the furthest distance and by how much?

Aley					
3.17 km	Bright				
5.86 km	6.45 km	Ceough			
3.7 km	4.08 km	1.74 km	Deeton		
6.32 km	5.04 km	2.64 km	1.84 km	Esville	
6.10 km	6.03 km	4.93 km	4.56 km	3.75 km	Fite

. . . .

Write each person's journey and read off the distances from the table.

Helen's journey = Aley−Bright + Bright−Deeton + Deeton−Fite
= 3.17 + 4.08 + 4.56 = 11.81 km

Jenny's journey = Aley−Ceough + Ceough−Esville + Esville−Fite
= 5.86 + 2.64 + 3.75 = 12.25 km

Jenny walks further by 12.25 − 11.81 = 0.44 km

Exercise 16a

1 This is a diagram of a road network.

   a What is the shortest route from Pi to Epsilon?
   Explain your answer.

   b Miss Wilton is a teacher.
   She travels from her home
   in Alpha to her school in Phi
   every day.
   How many kilometres does she travel in a week?

Epsilon
Beta
Alpha
6.02 km   6.45 km   8.32 km
Pi   Delta   Gamma   9.02 km
16.4 km   9.74 km   6.9 km
31.2 km   10.73 km   Phi
Theta

2 Read this information carefully and then answer the questions.
   Ian is 1.63 m tall.
   Kiefer is 0.23 m taller than Ian.
   Hanif is 0.25 m shorter than Jason but 0.08 m taller
   than Guiseppe.
   Liam is 0.51 m taller than Guiseppe.
   Kiefer is 7 cm shorter than Liam.

   a Who is the tallest pupil and what is their height?

   b How much taller than Hanif is Kiefer?

   c Put the boys in order of height from shortest to tallest.

3 Here are some items for sale in a shop.
   The shop is trying out two special offers.

   a Using special offer 2, work out the cost of these orders.

   i Martin buys a memory pen, a DVD, a computer
   game and a book. He pays with a £50 note, how
   much change should he get?

   ii Vincent buys a 2 DVDs and 2 books. Naheeda
   buys 5 identical memory pens. Who spends the
   most and by how much?

   b Does using special offer 1 change the costs for any of
   the people in part **a**?

   c Which is the better offer?
   Explain and justify your answer.

Special offer 1
Buy 3 of the same
item and pay only for 2

Special offer 2
Buy 4 items and get the
cheapest one FREE!

DVD

£9.99

Computer game

£16.39

Memory pen

£5.85

Book

£7.99

- Consolidate written methods for addition and subtraction
- Check by doing the inverse operation
- Break a problem down into smaller steps

Keywords
Inverse operations

- Some problems can be solved by breaking down the working out into smaller steps.

example

Tobias records the weights of all the parts of the space shuttle.

2 booster rockets = 1.186 M kg.   crew + other = 0.00157 M kg

separate fuel tank = 0.7538 M kg   shuttle body = ?

payload = 0.02 M kg   total weight = 2.000 M kg

Use this information to calculate the weight of the shuttle body.

Step 1 Find the weight of all the parts of the space shuttle.

	1.18600
	0.75380
	0.02000
	+0.00157
	1.96137

Step 2 Subtract the weight of all the parts from the total weight.

	2.00000
	−1.96137
	0.03863

0.038 63 M kg = 38 630 kg
which is still very heavy!

Weight of shuttle body = 0.038 63 M kg

- You can check your answer to a subtraction (or addition) problem by performing the **inverse operation**.

example

Larry and Grant run the 200 m at the school sports day.

Larry's time is 26.457 secs   Grant's time is 30.2 secs

Steve says that Grant took 4.257 secs longer than Larry.

How do you know Steve's answer is wrong?

Steve can check his answer using addition, because

Difference + Larry's time = Grant's time

4.257 secs + 26.457 secs   = 30.714 secs ≠ 30.2 secs

	30.200
	−26.457
	3.743

Exercise 16b

1 Tron2 is a robot chef.
He measures all his ingredients
very precisely.
Work out the total weight of each
of his recipes.

Risotto Twist	
25.38 g	butter
154.4 g	onions
0.22 g	rice
59 g	water
0.065 g	salt

Spiced Rice Cakes	
13.475 g	ghee
215.07 g	rice
0.4 g	water
0.075 g	salt
6.63 g	tumeric

2 Lee plants a bean in the ground.
At the end of each week he records
the height of the bean
plant as it grows.
Here are his results.

a What was the
height of the plant
after 5 weeks?

b How much did the
plant grow in the
next 3 weeks?

Height (cm)

Height in cm

Week

Week	Height(cm)
1	0
2	0.1
3	1.157
4	3.65
5	8
6	11.305
7	15.07
8	23.258

c How much did the plant grow in each of the 8 weeks?

d Why do you think the plant has grown at different
amounts each week?

3 Verity has measured the perimeter of the
main school building.
Here is a plan showing the
measurements she has made.
The perimeter of the whole
school building is 158.11 m.

a What is the length of the side
marked y?

b What is the length of the side
marked x?

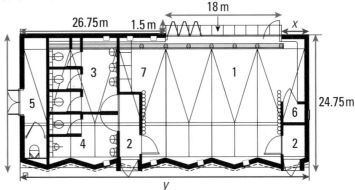

4 Kirsty is delivering
packages to a factory.
At the factory, all the
packages are weighed
on a giant weighing
scale.
Use the information in
these three diagrams to work
out Kirsty's weight.

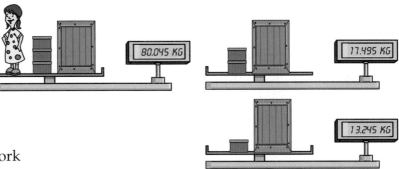

- Consolidate a range of mental strategies for multiplication and division
- Make and justify estimates and approximations
- Break a problem down into smaller steps which can be done as separate calculations

Keywords
Approximation
Estimate

- Some problems can be solved by breaking down the working out into smaller steps which involve just one mathematical operation.

example

Karim pays £36 800 for printing 20 000 holiday guidebooks.
The printing costs are
1.5p per page   16p for the cover
How many pages are there in Karim's guidebook?

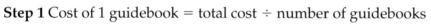

Step 1 Cost of 1 guidebook = total cost ÷ number of guidebooks
                              = £36 800 ÷ 20 000 = £1.84   Use factors ÷ 10 000 and then ÷ 2
Step 2 Cost of all pages   = 184p − 16p = 168p   Convert all quantities to pence.
Step 3 Number of pages   = cost of all pages ÷ cost of
                              one page   Use equivalent calculation
                              = 168 ÷ 1.5 = 112 pages   168 ÷ 1.5 = 336 ÷ 3

- You should always check your working by performing an **approximation** whenever you solve a problem involving multiplication or division.

example

Heath is looking at the cost of tickets for Liverton United football matches.
Adult   £27.99   Child   £18.99
He wants to buy 4 adult tickets and 6 child tickets. He has £230.
Will he have enough money to pay for the tickets?

4 adult tickets = 4 × £27.99 ≈ 4 × £28 = £112
6 child tickets = 6 × £18.99 ≈ 6 × £19 = £114
                        Total cost ≈ £226
Heath will have enough money because he has rounded up the prices of the tickets. His answer is an over-**estimate**.

Exact calculation:
Total cost
= 4 × £27.99 + 6 × £18.99
= £225.90
Change
= £230 − £225.90
= £4.10

Exercise 16c

1 Joachim is trying to improve his fitness levels. Here is how fast
his heart beats per minute for three activities.

cycling 83   running 91   swimming 75

Each day Joachim cycles for 15 mins, runs for 13 mins and swims
for 17 mins.

In which activity does Joachim's heart beat the greatest number
of times in total?

Explain and justify your answer.

2 Derek pays £9750 for printing 15 000 holiday guidebooks.
The printing costs are

2.5p per page   25p for the cover

How many pages are there in Derek's guidebook?

3 'Nut-e-nuts' is an online retailer.

Work out, using an approximation, if each of these people has
enough money for the cost of their orders.

Explain and justify your answers.

Almonds £7.95
Peanuts £4.85
Pecans £14.39
Walnuts £9.99
(Prices per kilogram)

  a Marge orders 3 kg of almonds, 2 kg of peanuts and 4 kg
of walnuts. She has £75.

  b Jameela orders 8 kg of walnuts and 15 kg of pecans. She has £300.

  c Bert orders 17 kg of almonds, 15 kg of peanuts and 12 kg of
pecans. He has £350.

4 Every person is recommended to consume 5 portions of
fruit and vegetables every day. A 150 ml glass of fruit juice
counts as one daily portion. A carton of fruit juice normally
contains 1000 ml (= 1 litre). This week the fruit juice is in
special Xtra packs with 15% extra free.

  a How many recommended daily portions of fruit juice
are there in one Xtra carton?

  b A family of 4 decide to each drink 150 ml of fruit juice
every day.

    i How much fruit juice will they drink in 1 week?

    ii How many Xtra cartons of fruit juice will they need to buy?

  c A carton of Xtra fruit juice costs £1.80. What is the approximate
cost in a year for the family of 4 to each drink 150 ml of fruit
juice a day?

- Consolidate a range of written methods for multiplication and division
- Identify the information necessary to solve a problem
- Check by doing the inverse operation

Keywords
Information
Inverse operation

- Write the **information** you know and the information you are trying to find out when solving a problem.

  This makes it easier to solve the problem by changing it into a calculation.

example

Here are the prices for buying calculators in bulk.

Gary buys 65 DAZIO CX 283P calculators.

Norbet buys 45 SHIP TQ 83SE calculators.

Who spends the most money on calculators?

Number ordered	DAZIO CX 283	DAZIO CX 283P	SHIP TQ 83S	SHIP TQ 83SE
1–10	£3.45	£3.85	£4.85	£5.15
11–30	£3.30	£3.70	£4.49	£4.99
31–50	£3.19	£3.55	£4.30	£4.89
Over 50	£3.09	£3.40	£4.19	£4.79

	Make	Price each	Number
Gary	DAZIO CX 283P	£3.40	65
Norbet	SHIP TQ 83SE	£4.89	45

Gary's total   = £3.40 × 65 = £221.00
Norbet's total = £4.89 × 45 = £220.05

Gary spends £221.00 − £220.05 = £0.95 more than Norbet.

Change the decimal calculation to an equivalent integer calculation by multiplying by 100 and dividing the answer by 100.

- Check answers to a division (or multiplication) problem by taking the answer and performing the **inverse operation**.

example

Mr Barnes wants to take 867 KS3 pupils and teachers from High Class Comprehensive to the theatre. He has ordered 18 coaches, which can each carry 48 people, for the trip. Has he ordered the correct number?

His answer × 48 = total number of pupils and teachers
18 × 48 = 864
This is smaller than the actual number of pupils and teachers, so Mr Bennett has not ordered enough coaches.

Exercise 16d

1 Here are the offers from three phone companies for text messages.

Number ordered	CO2	Yello	Four	Skyte
1–9	4.25p	4.5p	4.25p	4.8p
10–49	4.2p	4.3p	4.15p	4.35p
50–99	4.15p	4.1p	4.05p	3.9p
Over 100	4.1p	3.9p	3.95p	3.45p

a Karl buys 35 text messages from CO2. How much money would he save if he switched to Four to buy his text messages?

b Zak buys 160 text messages a week from Yello.
   i How much money would he save each week if he switched to Skyte?
   ii How much money would he save in a year if he switched?

c Which phone company would you recommend to these people?
   i Pete spends about £1.50 a week on text messages
   ii Josh spends about £3 a week on text messages
   iii Kath spends about £5 a week on text messages
   In each case, explain and justify your choice.

2 Maude is working out the costs of her motoring each week.
Petrol costs £1.18 a litre.
Maude's car travels 9.8 km for each litre of petrol.
Each week Maude travels 343 km in her car.

a How much money does Maude spend on petrol each week?
b How much money would you expect Maude to spend on petrol in a year? Explain your answer.

3 a Roger drives on the motorway at an average speed of 64 mph for 1.2 hours. Sarah completes the same journey in 1.6 hours. At what speed does Sarah drive?
b Isobel travels at 60 mph for 6 hours. Investigate other speeds and the time it would take to complete the same journey.

4 a Miss McCloud wants to take 650 KS3 pupils and teachers to a football match. She orders 11 coaches, which can each carry 58 people. Has she ordered the correct number? Explain your answer.
b Mr Kinsella wants to organise the 250 pupils in Year 8 into nine maths groups. There are supposed to be no more than 28 pupils in any class. Can Mr Kinsella fit the pupils into the 9 groups? Explain your thinking.

- Calculate accurately, selecting mental methods, written methods or using a calculator
- Record working and method, showing all the steps in your thinking
- Estimate, approximate and check working

Keywords
Approximation
Check working
Estimate

- When you are working through a problem you need to systematically write all the steps of your working out.

This makes it much easier to check if you have made any 'silly' or arithmetic errors.

- You should always choose the most appropriate method for working out a mathematical calculation.

example

Double Choc biscuits are sold in three different-sized packets.

Packet A

Packet B

Packet C

Work out which packet is the best value for money.

Packet A cost of 1 g = 192 ÷ 120
= 1.6p

Use a written method:

$$120\overline{)192.0}$$
$$\underline{-120.0} \quad 120 \times 1 = 120$$
$$72.0$$
$$\underline{-72.0} \quad 120 \times 0.6 = 72$$
$$0$$
$$192 \div 120 = 1.6$$

Packet B cost of 1 g = 215 ÷ 150
= 1.433333p
= 1.43p (2 dp)

Use a calculator.
First, **estimate**
≈ 210 ÷ 150 = 1.4

Packet C cost of 1 g = 280 ÷ 200
= 1.4p

Use a mental method.
÷ 2 then ÷ 100

This means that packet C is the best value for money.

- Once you've worked out your answer, you must **check** that it is correct before moving on to the next question.

There are lots of strategies for checking your answer.
– Compare your answer with your **approximation**.
– Check that your answer is sensible.
– Check using inverse operations.
– Make sure your answer is to the appropriate degree of accuracy for the problem.

Exercise 16e

1 Wheat is sold in three different-sized sacks.
Work out which size of sack is the best value for money.
Explain your answer.

Sack A   Sack B   Sack C

2 Solve each problem using the most appropriate method.
Explain your choice of method.

a Marek saves £48 a week for 24 weeks. He takes his money on holiday.
How much money would he have to spend each day if his holiday lasted
i 16 days   **ii** 7 days   **iii** 30 days?
Investigate his daily spending money for other lengths of holiday.

b Otis goes on a sponsored charity walk from Blackburn
to Cardiff dressed as a giant bear. He takes 12 days to
complete the walk. Each day he walks the same distance.
He returns by car along the same route in 3.2 hours at an
average speed of 60 mph. He raises £38.95 for charity for
each mile he walks.

i How far did Otis travel each day on his charity walk?

ii How much money did Otis raise for charity by
completing his walk?

1 mile = 1.6 km

3 Jordan travels 42 miles to work each day. She is trying to
decide whether it is better to travel to work by car or by
train. Here are some ideas she has written down.

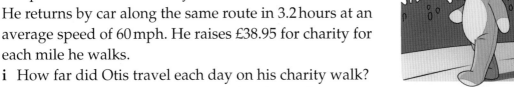

Travelling by car...	
Car insurance	= £480.45 (each year)
Road tax	= £180 (yearly)
Servicing	= £195 (twice a year)
MOT	= £50.63 (each year)
Depreciation	= £1200 (each year)
Petrol	= 118.9p per litre
Consumption	= 13.5 km per litre
Each journey lasts about 1 hour 10 mins	

Travelling by train...	
Monthly season ticket	= £730
Daily return ticket	= £42.50
Home to station	= 18 mins walk
Journey on train	= 31 mins
Station to work	= 19 mins walk

Jordan works for 44 weeks a year.
She has a 4-week holiday in August.
Write a short report recommending which form of transport
Jordan should take. Explain and justify your answer.

Assessment criteria
- Solve a substantial problem by breaking it into simpler tasks, using a range of efficient techniques **Level 6**

1 The labels on two cereal boxes are shown.

Whole Wheat
Salt 0.225 g per 30 g of cereal

Crispy Corn
Salt 0.24 g per 36 g of cereal

a How many grams of salt are contained in 6 grams of Whole Wheat cereal?

b Which cereal has more salt per gram?
Show your working.

c Calculate the ratio of salt in Whole Wheat to Crispy Corn.

Peter's answer ✔

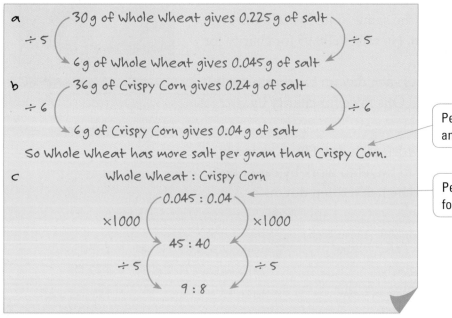

a
$\div 5$ 30 g of Whole Wheat gives 0.225 g of salt $\div 5$
6 g of Whole Wheat gives 0.045 g of salt

b
$\div 6$ 36 g of Crispy Corn gives 0.24 g of salt $\div 6$
6 g of Crispy Corn gives 0.04 g of salt

So Whole Wheat has more salt per gram than Crispy Corn.

c   Whole Wheat : Crispy Corn
$\times 1000$ 0.045 : 0.04 $\times 1000$
45 : 40
$\div 5$ $\div 5$
9 : 8

Peter remembers to give an answer.

Peter uses the information for 6 g of each cereal.

7 One day, each driver entering a car park paid exactly £1.50

Car Park
Pay exactly £1.50 to enter
Machine accepts only £1 coins and 50p coins

Here is what was put into the machine that day.

Number of £1 coins   136   Number of 50 p coins   208

On that day, what percentage of drivers paid with three 50 p coins?

KS3 2007 5–7 Paper 2

17 Functional maths

Real life, functional maths relies on using mathematical processes and applications.

Using mathematical reasoning

Representing

Using mathematical procedures

Interpreting and evaluating

DISTRIBUTION CENTRE

Communicating

Miss Perry is planning a trip for 50 year 8 students.
They will travel from Birmingham to Sarlat in France.

She has to decide whether to travel by coach or train.

Coach	£3560
Ferry berths	£975
Accommodation	£1475
Food	£1450
Insurance	£516
Activities	£1700

Train	£6000
Accommodation	£1550
Food	£1450
Insurance	£500
Activities	£1700

The students would spend 4 days travelling and have 5 days of activities.

The students would spend 3 days travelling and have 6 days of activities.

1 **a** For each possibility work out
   i the total cost of the trips
   ii the costs per student.
    Round the costs to the nearest whole pound (£).

  b Which is the most expensive way to travel and by how much?

2 Miss Perry wants to show parents the difference in cost as a percentage of the total cost of the coach trip.
Do the calculation for her giving your answer to the nearest whole percent.

3 By working out the daily cost for each student say which transport method gives the best value for money.
Include only the number of days spent doing activities, and justify your choice.

The group decide to travel by train.
Their journey starts in Birmingham.

These tables show the train times from
Birmingham to London, and London to Sarlat
(in France)

Depart St Pancras	Arrive Sarlat
04.30	16.50
08.26	18.55
11.05	20.55

Birmingham	23.00	23.00	00.10	05.40	06.40
London	06.50	01.02	07.00	07.00	08.09

When deciding on their schedule they have to take into account
these factors.

- When the group arrive in Sarlat they will have to drive for
  20 minutes to reach the campsite.
- They have to set-up their tents and this will take about
  one hour.
- The sun sets at about 8 p.m.
- To be safe, the party will need at least 1 hour to transfer
  between stations in London.

4 Which trains will the party need to take?

5 What will be their total journey time to the nearest hour?
  Remember that French time is one hour ahead of UK time.

From London to Birmingham is about 120 miles.
From London to Sarlat is about 1300 km.

6 What is the total distance between Birmingham and Sarlat
  stations?
  Write your answer in miles or kilometres to the nearest
  whole unit.

7 Using your answers to questions 5 and 6 to calculate the
  average speed for the whole journey in kilometres per hour
  or in miles per hour.

To convert between
kilometres (k) and
miles (m) use

$$m = \frac{5 \times k}{8}$$

or

$$k = 1.6 \times m$$

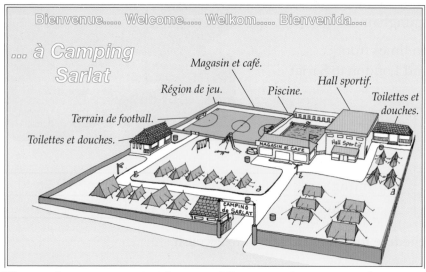

The students are staying in tents. There are three sizes of tent: 2 person, 3 person and 4 person.

1 Working with a partner use the information given to calculate the missing quantity for each tent.

a □ m Area = 3.3 m² ←2.2 m→

b 0.7 m 0.7 m 1.75 m Area = □ m² ←2.1 m →

c 0.8 m Area = 8.03 m² □ m ←2.2 m→

2 The students are shown to their tents. Here are the first five tents – A to E.

A sleeps 4 B sleeps 2 C sleeps 2 D sleeps 4 E sleeps 3

Again with a partner, use these clues to work out which tents Pete, Cherry, John, Kadeja and Magnus are in.

Boys and girls are in separate tents.

- Fifteen pupils are put in these tents: seven girls and eight boys.
- John's tent is at the end of the row.
- Cherry shares a tent with three other girls.
- The four boys in the tent beside Pete's tent make a lot of noise.
- Kadeja likes her tent.
- Pete, Cherry, John, Kadeja and Magnus are in different tents.

The students are given a map of the camp.

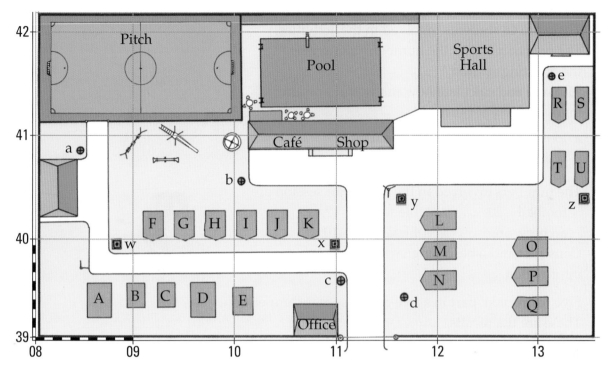

3 a Given their six-figure grid references, which tents are these people in?
   i Kia is at 104, 402   ii Hamad is at 129, 399   iii David is at 132, 413

   b Where would you be if you were standing at these six-figure grid references?
   i 124, 416   ii 108, 393   iii 113, 410

4 a There are five bins around the site, marked ☐. (aw_8B_17b_5)
   Find the bins labeled a – e and give their six-figure grid
   references.

   Bin a is at 084, 408

   b There are four water taps around the site marked ☐. (aw_8B_17b_6)
   Find the taps labeled w – z and give their six-figure grid references.

5 It is dark and Ronnie walks from 107, 408 to 101, 395.
   Which tent does he blunder into?

The next day there is a sports competition.

1 There are 48 students involved in the activities. The pie chart shows the numbers taking part in the morning session.
Measure and calculate how many students are involved in

a football   **b** table tennis

c archery   **d** athletics

2 The numbers involved in the afternoon session are

football   20   table tennis   12
archery   6   athletics   10

Construct and label a pie chart to display this information.

3 Five teams take part in a five-a-side soccer competition. These are the results.

	Games				Goals		Points
	played	won	drawn	lost	for	against	
All Stars	4	0	2	2	6	12	2
Champions	4	2	2	0	7	4	8
Cheetahs	4	1	0	3	10	10	3
High 5	4	1	2	1	7	8	5
Superstars	4	2	2	0	9	5	8

Points scoring system
win = 3 pt
draw = 1 pt
lose = 0 pt

The score boards below show the results of each match.
Using the data in the table above, work out the missing scores from the matches below.

Round 1				
High 5	2	v	Superstars	a
Champions	3	v	Cheetahs	1
High 5	b	v	All Stars	2
Cheetahs	0	v	Superstars	2
Champions	2	v	Stars	1

Round 2				
High 5	3	v	Cheetahs	2
All Stars	1	v	Superstars	1
High 5	0	v	Champions	c
All Stars	2	v	Cheetahs	d
Champions	2	v	Superstars	2

4 Using the results table and score boards.

a What is the range of goals scored in a match?

b What is the modal average number of goals scored by each team?

c What is the mean average number of goals scored in each match?

5 In the archery competition each student gets to fire four arrows.
Their scores are shown below the targets.

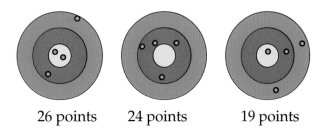

26 points   24 points   19 points

   a Using this information, how many points do you get for a hit in the
     i red circle   **ii** blue circle   **iii** gold bull's eye?

   b What is the mean average of these scores?

6 A running track has to be marked out for
the athletics.
The perimeter must be 400 m. The
radius of the semicircles at each end
is 40 m.

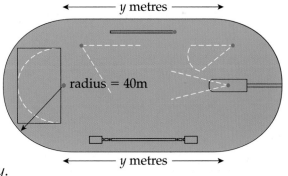

   a What is the total distance around
   the two semicircles?

   b Using your answer to part **a**.
   Calculate the lengths of the straights, y.
   Round your answer to a useful number.

7 Three lanes are marked out.
Each lane is 1 m wide.

The runners run one lap of the track
in lanes.
The runner in the inside lane will
run 400 m.

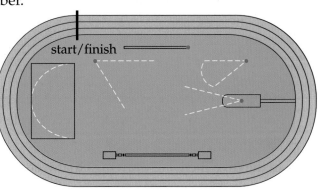

   a After one lap, how far has the
   runner in
     i middle lane run   **ii** outer lane run?

   b How do track markers prevent this when they mark out a real track?

The group is going on an expedition and must pack their own rucksacks. To be comfortable the ratio of your body weight to the weight of the rucksack should be 6 : 1.

Bart 36 kg

Gabby 40 kg

Martia 54 kg

1 a Calculate the weight of each student's rucksack using the above ratio.
Round your answers to the nearest useful number.

b Steve has 7 kg in his rucksack. What is his minimum weight?

Rick 48 kg

Jules 70 kg

Helina 37 kg

c Who is closest to the mean weight of the six students?

This is the route the students will take from Camp Sarlat.

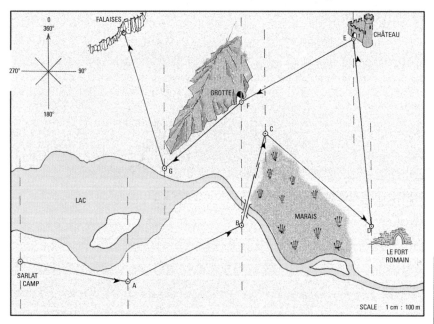

2 Using the scale on the map copy and complete this table of distances and bearings.

3 a In the cave there are drawings that were made in 2150 B.C. How many years ago is this?

b The Roman fort was occupied between 74 B.C. and 48 A.D. How many years is this?

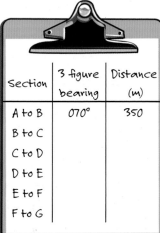

Section	3 figure bearing	Distance (m)
A to B	070°	350
B to C		
C to D		
D to E		
E to F		
F to G		

At the end of the journey the students learn to mountaineer.

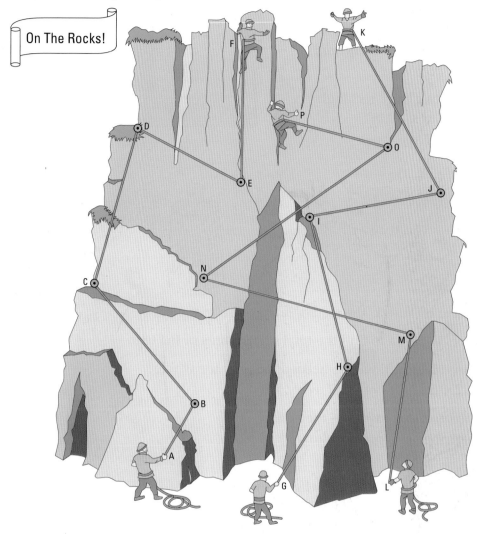

On The Rocks!

4 Measure accurately and record these

a acute angles **b** obtuse angles
  i MN̂O **ii** DÊF **iii** IĴK **i** BĈD **ii** LM̂N **iii** GĤI

c Measure these angles and hence find the reflex angles
  i CD̂E **ii** NÔP **iii** AB̂C

5 Using what you know about angles, show that the sections
of rope MN and OP are parallel.

6 The scene is drawn to a scale of 1 cm : 1 m (1 : 100).
To the nearest 0.1 m give theses distances in real life.

a MN **b** DE **c** HI **d** CD **e** NO

The day started badly for Miss Perry — her tent leaked in the night and she is not pleased. She asks Mr Powell to waterproof the tent for her.

1 The tent is made from a large rectangle and two triangles.

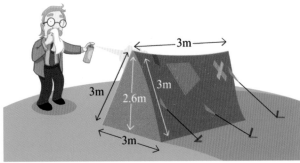

SEAL IT !
WATERPROOF

250ml
will seal
5m²

Content 250ml

50 L

  a Calculate the area of   **i** the rectangle   **ii** a triangle.

  b use you answers to part **a** to find the total surface area of the tent.

  c How many cans of Seal It! will be needed to spray the whole tent if it takes 250 ml to waterproof every 5 m².

Ms. Perry refuses to use the showers — they are just too dirty for her! She has a private shower made for her.

2 The students have to carry the water to her shower in containers. Meg and Leroy use different sized containers. They empty their containers in to the shower and fill it exactly.

      = 50 litres

Leroy empties container A three times and Meg empties container B once. They refill the shower and again fill it exactly.

   = 50 litres

This time they use 1 A container and 7 B containers. Work out how much water each container holds.

While waiting to board the coach to go home, the students gather in the play area.

Sam has placed his sandwich on the roundabout which is rotating slowly in a clockwise direction.

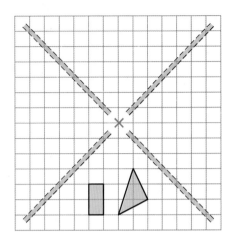

3 On graph paper draw the centre of rotation and the position of the sandwich and chocolate bar.

    a Starting from the start positions, rotate the shapes through
       i 90° in a clockwise direction and draw the image.
      ii 270° in a clockwise direction and draw the image.

    b From the start positions the roundabout spins through a total of 1890° before stopping.
       Draw the final positions of the sandwich and chocolate bar.

4 Claire sits on the see-saw. She weighs 37 kg. Which of the weights shown can be used to balance her?

11.5 kg   19 kg   8.5 kg   15 kg   9.5 kg

Miss Perry calls to the students from a plane. She explains that her best friend Rupert happened to be flying by and offered her a lift. She decided to hurry home and compete all her unfinished marking.

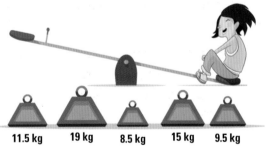

5 The distance from camp Sarlat to Birmingham is 550 miles. The plane's average speed is 130 m.p.h.
There is a 10 m.p.h. wind against the plane all the way back.

How long will it take them to fly home?

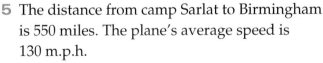

17

Assessment criteria

- Solve demanding problems and check solutions; explore connections between different parts of mathematics; find more general solutions — **Level 7**

- Explain why you chose to solve a given problems in a particular way — **Level 7**

- Justify generalisations, arguments and solutions — **Level 7**

- Recognise the difference between a mathematical explanation and experimental evidence — **Level 7**

- Solve problems by breaking them down into smaller tasks and using a range of methods, including ICT; give solutions to an appropriate degree of accuracy — **Level 6**

- Interpret, discuss and combine information presented in a variety of mathematical forms — **Level 6**

- Give short, reasoned arguments using mathematics and explanatory text — **Level 6**

Check in and Summary answers

Check in

1 a -6   b -25   c 5   d -8

2 a -20   b 15   c 24   d -5
   e 6   f -4

3 a 1, 2, 3, 4, 5, 6, 10, 12, 15, 20, 30, 60
  b 1, 2, 3, 6, 11, 12, 22, 44, 66, 132
  c 1, 3, 5, 9, 15, 25, 45, 75, 225

4 a HCF = 4   LCM = 24
  b HCF = 5   LCM = 60
  c HCF = 9   LCM = 54

5 a 30   b 36   c 350

6 a $2 \times 2 \times 2 \times 3$
  b $2 \times 2 \times 2 \times 5$
  c $2 \times 2 \times 3 \times 7$

7 a 81   b 169   c 1225
  d 125   e 3375

Summary

2

3	6	9	18
5	-3	2	-15
-8	3	-5	-24

Check in

1 a 74   b 0.39   c 60   d 0.25

2 a 15   b 54   c 165   d 12.1

3 a 28   b 0.8   c 300   d 9

4 a 26 m, 40 m²
  b 21 cm, 30 cm²
  c 75 mm, 312.5 mm²

Summary

2 35 cm² (units must be given)

Check in

1 a $\frac{3}{4}$ b $\frac{17}{20}$ c $\frac{2}{3}$ d $\frac{3}{5}$ e $\frac{3}{5}$

2 a $\frac{1}{2}$ b 0.55   c $\frac{1}{2}$ d 70%

3 a $\frac{7}{16}$ b $\frac{11}{16}$ c $\frac{1}{2}$ d $\frac{2}{3}$ e $\frac{71}{105}$

4

	Fraction	Percentage	Decimal
Liquorice	$\frac{1}{4}$	25%	0.25
Chocolate button	$\frac{7}{20}$	35%	0.35
Toffee	$\frac{3}{20}$	11.5%	0.15
Mint	$\frac{1}{8}$	12.5%	0.125
Jelly bean	$\frac{1}{8}$	12.5%	0.125

Summary

2 General solution: n red, $2n$ white,
   $< n$ yellow. For example, 5, 10, 1

Check in

1 a $1\frac{1}{2}$ b $\frac{39}{50}$ c $\frac{1}{8}$

2 a 0.7   b 1.35   c 0.52   d 0.875

3 a $\frac{13}{20}$ b $\frac{4}{21}$

4 a £65   b 350 kg

5 a $5\frac{5}{7}$ b 12

6

Fraction	Decimal	Percentage
$\frac{13}{20}$	0.65	65%
$\frac{1}{8}$	0.125	12.5%

Summary

2 a $1\frac{4}{5}$

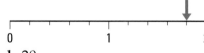

  b 20
  c 4 with correct working

Check in

1 a -5   b -3   c 10   d -9
  e -20   f -7   g 42   h 6

2 a 10   b 8   c 17   d 16
  e 10   f 12   g 25   h 4

3 a $2x$ **b** $3y$ **c** $3a$
d $2b$ **e** $5p + q$ **f** $8k - 3$
g $5x + y$ **h** $4m - 3n$

Summary

2 $2n + 4, n + 2, n$

Check in

1 a 45°, acute **b** 115°, obtuse
c 295°, reflex
2 a $a = 36°$ **b** $b = 18°$ **c** $c = 24°$

Summary

2 $a = 110°, b = 130°, c = 50°, d = 70°$

7

Check in

1 a $x = 5$ **b** $y = 4$ **c** $p = 6$ **d** $k = 3$
2 a $2a + 10$ **b** $3b - 30$
c $x^2 + 2x$ **d** $ab - 3a$
e $3t^2 - 3t$ **f** $6pq + 8p$
g $9k + 2$ **h** $7n + 12$
3 a

x	0	2	3
y	1	3	4

b The y-coordinate is equal to the x-coordinate + 1.
c $y = x + 1$

Summary

2 a Any straight line parallel to the given line
b $(0, 20)$ **c** $y = 5x + 10$

Check in

1 a 6; 6.1 **b** 16; 15.5 **c** 217; 217.4
2 a 12.1 **b** 8.41 **c** 38.16 **d** 3.81
3 a 120 **b** 3.8 **c** 0.037 **d** 480
4 a 58.8 **b** 1645.8
5 a 18.6 **b** 7.7
6 a 28 **b** 17 **c** 104

Summary

2 a 3.1416 **b** $\frac{355}{113}$

Check in

1 a 800 mm **b** 200 m **c** 350 cm
d 0.45 km **e** 0.75 m **f** 1.5 cm
2 a Students' drawings
b (0, 2) (2, 3) (4, 2) (4, -2)
c y-axis

Summary

2 a

b 4 cm, 40°, 12 cm

Check in

1 a 36, 42 **b** 28, 33 **c** 45, 36
d 22.5, 11.25
2 a 4, 9, 14, 19, 24, ...
b 1, 3, 9, 27, 81, ...
c 10, 5, 2.5, 1.25, 0.625, ...
3 a 64 **b** 196 **c** 343 **d** 1728
4 a 16 **b** 21 **c** 12 **d** 18

Summary

2 a $4n$ 4, 8, 12, 16, ...
$(n + 1)^2$ 4, 9, 16, 25, ...
$n^2 + 3$ 4, 7, 12, 19, ...
$n(n + 3)$ 4, 10, 18, 28, ...
b 4, 11, 30, 67

11

Check in

1 Specific responses which cover all options without any overlap, for example
i at least once a week
ii less than once a week but at least once a month
iii sometimes but less than once a month
iv never

---

2 None of these people will answer 'never' and those who go to the cinema regularly will be over-represented in the sample she takes.

Summary

2 a False, with a correct explanation
  b Cannot be certain, with a correct explanation

Check in

1 a 3 : 5 **b** 3 : 2 **c** 4 : 3
2 24 : 36 **3** 435p **4** 48 kg
5 a $\frac{1}{2} = 50\%$ **b** 5 : 2
6 £72

Summary

2 125 g

Check in

1 a $P = 36$ **b** $k = 3.2$ **c** $V = 12$
2 a $\frac{3}{5}$ **b** $\frac{7}{9}$ **c** $\frac{3}{8}$
  d $\frac{11}{15}$ **e** $\frac{8}{9}$ **f** $\frac{7}{12}$
  g $1\frac{3}{20}$ **h** $\frac{23}{24}$
3 a $24a + 16$ **b** $20b - 4$
  c $k^2 - 4k$ **d** $5x - xy$
  e $10p^2 - 15p$ **f** $12 - 24q$
  g $-21 + 3m$ **h** $-10n + n^2$
4 a $x = 2$ **b** $y = 4$ **c** $m = 5$
  d $n = 6$

Summary

2

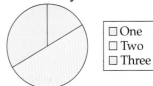

Check in

1 a $a = 40°$ **b** $b = 140°$
2 a 50.24 cm **b** 200.96 cm^2
3 a 72 cm^3 **b** 24 m^3

Summary

2 60.8 cm^2

Check in

1 a 6 **b** 5.5 **c** 5 **d** 5
2 a

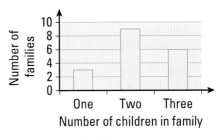

b **Number of children in family**

Summary

2 a N
  b True,
    Coursework range = 40,
    Test range = 30

Check in

1 a 338.32 **b** 204.6 **c** 365.9
  d 554.97
2 a 60.84 **b** 232.65 **c** 262.88
  d 48.705
3 a 148.2 **b** 192.1 **c** 380 **d** 170

Summary

2 15%

Index